ADVANCED MATHS FOR

Core Maths

Robert Smedley   Garry Wiseman

Course consultant: Jeff Searle

C1

C2

OXFORD
UNIVERSITY PRESS

OXFORD
UNIVERSITY PRESS

Great Clarendon Street, Oxford OX2 6DP

Oxford University Press is a department of the University of Oxford.
It furthers the University's objective of excellence in research, scholarship,
and education by publishing worldwide in

Oxford New York

Auckland Bangkok Buenos Aires Cape Town Chennai
Dar es Salaam Delhi Hong Kong Istanbul Karachi Kolkata
Kuala Lumpur Madrid Melbourne Mexico City Mumbai Nairobi
São Paulo Shanghai Taipei Tokyo Toronto

Oxford is a registered trade mark of Oxford University Press
in the UK and in certain other countries

British Library Cataloguing in Publication Data

Data available

ISBN 0 19 914936 4

10 9 8 7 6 5 4 3 2

Typeset by Tech-Set Ltd, Gateshead, Tyne and Wear
Printed and bound in Great Britain by Bell and Bain.

Acknowledgements
The publishers would like to thank AQA for their kind permission to reproduce
past paper questions. AQA accept no responsibility for the answers to the past
paper questions which are the sole responsibility of the publishers.

The publishers would also like to thank James Nicholson for his authoritative
guidance in preparing this book.

The photograph on the cover is reproduced courtesy of Mehan Kulyk/Science
Photo Library.

About this book

This Advanced level book is designed to help you get your best possible grade in the AQA MPC1 and MPC2 modules for first examination in 2005. These two modules can contribute to an award in GCE AS level Mathematics or A level Mathematics.

The book is divided into the two modules, C1 and C2, and you can use the tabs at the edge of the page for quick reference.

Each chapter starts with an overview of what you are going to learn and a list of what you should already know. The 'Before you start' section contains 'Check in' questions, which will help to prepare you for the topics in the chapter.

Key information is highlighted in the text so you can see the facts you need to learn.

> The sum of the first n natural numbers is $S_n = \dfrac{n}{2}(n+1)$.

Worked examples showing the key skills and techniques you need to develop are shown in boxes. Also hint boxes show tips and reminders you may find useful.

Example 22

Find the equation of the normal to the circle
$x^2 + y^2 - 2x - 4y - 20 = 0$ at the point $P(5, 5)$.

The normal is perpendicular to the tangent at P and passes through both P and the centre of the circle.

$$x^2 - 2x + y^2 - 4y - 20 = 0$$
$$(x-1)^2 - 1 + (y-2)^2 - 4 - 20 = 0$$

> To find the centre of the circle, express its equation in the form $(x-a)^2 + (y-b)^2 = r^2$.

The questions are carefully graded, with lots of basic practice provided at the beginning of each exercise.

At the end of an exercise, you will sometimes find underlined questions.

10 The curve with equation $y = ax^2 + bx + c$ passes through the points $P(2, 6)$ and $Q(3, 16)$, and has a gradient of 7 at the point P. Find the values of the constants a, b and c.

These are optional questions that go beyond the requirements of the specification and are provided as a challenge. Furthermore, within the book there are two small sections, prefixed with an asterix, which extend slightly beyond the scope of the specification.

At the end of each chapter there is a summary. The 'You should now know' section is useful as a quick revision guide, and each 'Check out' question identifies important techniques that you should remember.

Following the summary you will find a revision exercise with past paper questions from AQA. These will enable you to become familiar with the style of questions you will see in the exam.

At the end of each module you have a Practice Paper. These will directly help you to prepare for your exams.

The last chapter is entitled 'GCSE Algebra Review'. It is an optional chapter that will be useful for you to revise the algebra that you will have learned at GCSE. Used in conjunction with Chapter 1, it should help to bridge the gap between GCSE and Advanced level.

At the end of the book you will find numerical answers, a list of formulae you need to learn, and a list of useful mathematical notation.

Contents

1 Basic algebra

This chapter will show you how to

- ✦ Manipulate surds
- ✦ Solve quadratic equations
- ✦ Sketch the graphs of quadratic functions
- ✦ Solve quadratic inequalities
- ✦ Solve a pair of simultaneous equations where one is a quadratic and one is linear

Before you start

C1

You should know how to ...	Check in
1 Identify a linear function.	**1** Identify the linear functions. a) $y = 3x - 1$ b) $y = 2x^2 + 1$ c) $xy = 1$ d) $x = 2y + 3$ e) $3(x - 1) = 2y$ f) $y = \sqrt{3x} - 2$
2 Sketch the graph of a linear function.	**2** Sketch the graphs of these linear functions, indicating where the graph crosses the x and y axes. a) $y = 2x + 3$ b) $y = 3x - 5$ c) $x + y = 6$ d) $2y + 3x = 7$
3 Manipulate an algebraic expression.	**3** Expand and simplify these expressions where possible. a) $3(x - 2)$ b) $5 - 2(3 + x)$ c) $4(2x - 3) - 3(2x - 1)$ d) $(x - 1)(x + 1)$ e) $(2x + 3)(3x + 2)$ f) $(1 - 2x)(3x + 4)$
4 Factorise algebraic expressions, including quadratic expressions.	**4** Factorise these expressions. a) $3x - 12$ b) $x^2 + 5x$ c) $3x - 6x^2$ d) $x^2 + x - 6$ e) $4x^2 - 9$ f) $3x^2 + 11x - 4$ *(continued)*

5 Solve a linear equation.

5 Solve these equations.

a) $3x + 2 = 17$

b) $7 - 5x = 21 + 2x$

c) $5 + 2(3 - x) = 4x - 1$

d) $3(x - 1) - 2(3 - x) = 1$

e) $3(2 + 3x) - 2(3x - 2) = 2(2x - 1)$

6 Solve simultaneous linear equations and interpret the solution graphically.

6 Solve these simultaneous equations, illustrating your solution with a sketch graph.

a) $x + y = 6$
$x - y = 2$

b) $3x + y = 5$
$x + y = 1$

c) $x + 2y = 5$
$5x - 3y = 7$

d) $2x - 5y = 3$
$5x - 8y = 3$

7 Solve linear inequalities and interpret the solution graphically.

7 Solve these inequalities and illustrate your solutions by drawing a number line.

a) $3x < 12$

b) $2y + 7 > 4$

c) $3x - 5 < 4$

d) $9 < 5 - 2x$

C1

1.1 Surds

You should know that $\sqrt{16} = 4$ and that $\sqrt{\frac{1}{4}} = \frac{1}{2}$. These are examples of **rational numbers**.

✦ A rational number can be expressed as a fraction of two integers:

$$\frac{p}{q}$$

For example, 1.5 and $\sqrt{9}$ are rational numbers.

$1.5 = \frac{3}{2}$

$\sqrt{9} = 3 = \frac{3}{1}$

However, $\sqrt{2}$ cannot be expressed as a fraction of two integers. $\sqrt{2}$ is an example of an **irrational number**.

Roots such as $\sqrt{2}$, $\sqrt{3}$, $\sqrt{5}$, ... are called **surds**.

The solutions to mathematical problems often contain surds. You could use your calculator to work out a decimal approximation of the surd, but the decimal goes on and on. An answer rounded to, say, three decimal places is not accurate. It is more accurate to leave the answer in surd form as this is exact.

> For example,
> $\sqrt{2} = 1.414\,213\,562\ldots$
> $= 1.414$ (to 3 d.p.)

Here are some properties of surds:

> Note that a, b and c are integers.

- $\sqrt{a} \times \sqrt{b} = \sqrt{ab}$
- $\dfrac{\sqrt{a}}{\sqrt{b}} = \sqrt{\dfrac{a}{b}}$
- $a\sqrt{c} \pm b\sqrt{c} = (a \pm b)\sqrt{c}$

You can use these properties to simplify expressions involving surds.

C1

Example 1

Simplify each of these quantities.
a) $\sqrt{48}$ b) $3\sqrt{50} + 2\sqrt{18} - \sqrt{32}$

a) To simplify $\sqrt{48}$, notice that:

$$48 = \underbrace{16 \times 3}_{\text{largest square factor of 48}} = 4^2 \times 3$$

Therefore,

$$\sqrt{48} = \sqrt{4^2 \times 3} = 4\sqrt{3}$$

b)
$$3\sqrt{50} + 2\sqrt{18} - \sqrt{32} = 3\sqrt{\mathbf{25} \times 2} + 2\sqrt{\mathbf{9} \times 2} - \sqrt{\mathbf{16} \times 2}$$
$$= 15\sqrt{2} + 6\sqrt{2} - 4\sqrt{2}$$
$$= 17\sqrt{2}$$

> 25, 9 and 16 are the largest square factors of 50, 18 and 32 respectively.

When surds appear in the denominator of a fraction, it is usual to eliminate them. This is called **rationalising the denominator**.

For example, to rationalise the fraction $\dfrac{1}{\sqrt{3}}$, multiply both the numerator and denominator by $\sqrt{3}$ giving:

$$\frac{1}{\sqrt{3}} \times \frac{\sqrt{3}}{\sqrt{3}} = \frac{\sqrt{3}}{3}$$

> **Remember:** You can obtain equivalent fractions by multiplying numerator and denominator by the same number.

To rationalise the fraction $\dfrac{1}{1 + \sqrt{3}}$, multiply its numerator and its denominator by $1 - \sqrt{3}$, giving:

$$\frac{1}{(1 + \sqrt{3})} \times \frac{1 - \sqrt{3}}{(1 - \sqrt{3})} = \frac{1 - \sqrt{3}}{1 - \sqrt{3} + \sqrt{3} - 3}$$
$$= \frac{1 - \sqrt{3}}{-2}$$
$$= -\frac{1}{2} + \frac{1}{2}\sqrt{3}$$

> To expand $(1 + \sqrt{3})(1 - \sqrt{3})$ you need to multiply each term in the first bracket by each term in the second bracket.
> $(1 + \sqrt{3})(1 - \sqrt{3})$
> $= 1 + \sqrt{3} - \sqrt{3} - 3 = -2$

In general, to rationalise the fraction $\dfrac{1}{a \pm \sqrt{b}}$, multiply its numerator and its denominator by $a \mp \sqrt{b}$.

Example 2

Express each of these fractions in the form $a + b\sqrt{c}$ where a, b, and c are rational numbers.

a) $\dfrac{3}{\sqrt{5}}$ b) $\dfrac{2 + \sqrt{3}}{1 - \sqrt{3}}$

a) Multiplying numerator and denominator by $\sqrt{5}$ gives:

$$\dfrac{3}{\sqrt{5}} \times \dfrac{\sqrt{5}}{\sqrt{5}} = \dfrac{3\sqrt{5}}{5}$$

This is in the form $a + b\sqrt{c}$, where $a = 0$, $b = \frac{3}{5}$ and $c = 5$.

b) Multiplying numerator and denominator by $1 + \sqrt{3}$ gives:

$$\dfrac{2 + \sqrt{3}}{1 - \sqrt{3}} \times \dfrac{1 + \sqrt{3}}{1 + \sqrt{3}} = \dfrac{2 + 2\sqrt{3} + \sqrt{3} + 3}{1 - 3}$$

$$= \dfrac{5 + 3\sqrt{3}}{-2} = -\dfrac{5}{2} - \dfrac{3}{2}\sqrt{3}$$

This is in the form $a + b\sqrt{c}$, where $a = -\frac{5}{2}$, $b = -\frac{3}{2}$ and $c = 3$.

Exercise 1A

1 Simplify each of these expressions involving surds.
   a) $\sqrt{12}$ b) $\sqrt{50}$ c) $\sqrt{112}$
   d) $\sqrt{75} + 2\sqrt{27}$ e) $5\sqrt{20} + 2\sqrt{45}$ f) $2\sqrt{8} + \sqrt{200} - 4\sqrt{18}$
   g) $\sqrt{32} + \sqrt{128} - \sqrt{200}$ h) $7\sqrt{5} + 3\sqrt{20} - \sqrt{80}$

2 Express each of these fractions in the form $\dfrac{a\sqrt{c}}{b}$, where a, b and c are integers.

   a) $\dfrac{3}{\sqrt{2}}$ b) $\dfrac{5}{\sqrt{3}}$ c) $\dfrac{2}{\sqrt{6}}$ d) $\dfrac{\sqrt{7}}{\sqrt{2}}$
   e) $\dfrac{10\sqrt{7}}{\sqrt{5}}$ f) $\dfrac{3\sqrt{5}}{2\sqrt{6}}$ g) $\dfrac{3\sqrt{50}}{5\sqrt{27}}$ h) $\dfrac{4\sqrt{45}}{5\sqrt{8}}$

3 Express each of these fractions in the form $\dfrac{a + b\sqrt{c}}{d}$, where a, b, c and d are integers.

   a) $\dfrac{1}{2 - \sqrt{3}}$ b) $\dfrac{1}{3 + \sqrt{5}}$ c) $\dfrac{2}{5 - \sqrt{7}}$ d) $\dfrac{3}{6 + \sqrt{3}}$
   e) $\dfrac{2 + \sqrt{2}}{2 - \sqrt{2}}$ f) $\dfrac{3 + \sqrt{2}}{5 + \sqrt{2}}$ g) $\dfrac{6 + \sqrt{5}}{2 - \sqrt{5}}$ h) $\dfrac{3 + \sqrt{24}}{2 + \sqrt{6}}$

4 Simplify $\dfrac{(2 + \sqrt{2})(3 + \sqrt{5})(\sqrt{5} - 2)}{(\sqrt{5} - 1)(1 + \sqrt{2})}$

1.2 Quadratic functions and their graphs

The simplest quadratic function is $y = x^2$. If y is plotted against x then the resulting graph would be as shown in the diagram.

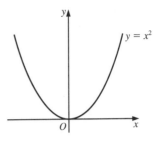

Important features of the graph to note are:

✦ It is ∪ shaped
✦ It has a line of symmetry, which is the y-axis
✦ It has a vertex at $(0, 0)$.

Consider these quadratic functions and their graphs.

The graph of $y = x^2 - 2$ can be obtained by translating the graph of $y = x^2$ two units in the negative y direction.

The graph of $y = (x + 3)^2$ can be obtained by translating $y = x^2$ three units in the negative x direction.

The graph of $y = (x + 3)^2 - 2$ can be obtained by translating $y = x^2$

✦ three units in the negative x direction,
✦ two units in the negative y direction.

C1

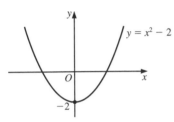

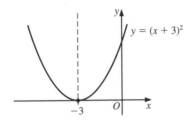

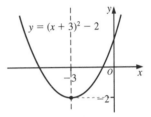

The vertex is $(0, -2)$ and the line of symmetry is the line $x = 0$ (the y-axis).

The vertex is $(-3, 0)$ and the line of symmetry is the line $x = -3$.

The vertex is $(-3, -2)$ and the line of symmetry is the line $x = -3$.

Expanding and simplifying $y = (x + 3)^2 - 2$ gives:

$$y = x^2 + 3x + 3x + 9 - 2$$
$$= x^2 + 6x + 7$$

This is the standard form for a quadratic function.

> In general, y is a quadratic function of x if it can be expressed in the form $y = ax^2 + bx + c$, with $a \neq 0$.

> $y = x^2 - 2$ is a quadratic function with $a = 1$, $b = 0$ and $c = -2$.

Example 3

By expanding and simplifying, determine which of these are quadratic functions.

a) $y = 5 + (x - 3)^2$ b) $y = (x + 2)^2 - (x - 1)^2 + 3$
c) $y = 2(x + 5)^2 - 2$

··

a) Expanding and simplifying gives:

$$y = 5 + (x^2 - 3x - 3x + 9)$$
$$= 5 + x^2 - 6x + 9$$
$$= x^2 - 6x + 14$$

This is in the form $ax^2 + bx + c$ and hence is a quadratic function.

b) Expanding and simplifying gives:

$$y = (x^2 + 2x + 2x + 4) - (x^2 - x - x + 1) + 3$$
$$= (x^2 + 4x + 4) - (x^2 - 2x + 1) + 3$$
$$= 6x + 6$$

> Take care of negatives within brackets: $4x - (-2x) = 6x$

This is not in the form $ax^2 + bx + c$ with $a \neq 0$, so it is not a quadratic function.

> A quadratic function must have a term in x^2 as its highest power.

c) Expanding and simplifying gives:

$$y = 2(x^2 + 5x + 5x + 25) - 2$$
$$= 2(x^2 + 10x + 25) - 2$$
$$= 2x^2 + 20x + 50 - 2$$
$$= 2x^2 + 20x + 48$$

C1

This is in the form $ax^2 + bx + c$ and hence is a quadratic function.

You can draw the graph of a quadratic function by plotting it accurately on graph paper.

Example 4

Draw the graph of $y = x^2 + 2x - 2$, taking values of x from -4 to 2. Describe the shape of the curve and state the coordinates of the vertex.
....

First construct a table of values:

x	-4	-3	-2	-1	0	1	2
x^2	16	9	4	1	0	1	4
$2x$	-8	-6	-4	-2	0	2	4
-2	-2	-2	-2	-2	-2	-2	-2
y	6	1	-2	-3	-2	1	6

> You may find it helps to use a separate row for each single term of the function.

Plotting y against x gives the graph shown in the diagram.

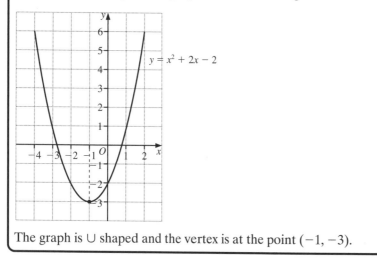

The graph is $\cup$ shaped and the vertex is at the point $(-1, -3)$.

In a quadratic function, the coefficient of x^2 can be negative.

Example 5

Draw the graph of $y = -2x^2 + 4x - 3$, taking values of x from -1 to 3.
Describe the shape of the curve and state the coordinates of the vertex.

First construct a table of values:

x	-1	0	1	2	3
$-2x^2$	-2	0	-2	-8	-18
$4x$	-4	0	4	8	12
-3	-3	-3	-3	-3	-3
$-y$	-9	-3	-1	-3	-9

Plotting y against x gives the graph shown in the diagram.

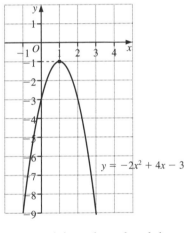

The graph is ∩ shaped and the vertex is at the point $(1, -1)$.

Sketching graphs

y is a quadratic function of x if it can be expressed in the form $y = ax^2 + bx + c$, with $a \neq 0$.

♦ When $a > 0$ the graph of y is ∪ shaped and y has a minimum value.
♦ When $a < 0$ the graph of y is ∩ shaped and y has a maximum value.

You can use this information to sketch a quadratic graph without plotting it accurately.

C1

Example 6

Sketch the graphs of these quadratic functions.

a) $y = -x^2 + 2$

b) $y = (x - 1)^2$

c) $y = -(x + 2)^2 + 4$

In each case state (i) the coordinates of the vertex, and hence the maximum or minimum value of the function, (ii) the equation of the line of symmetry.

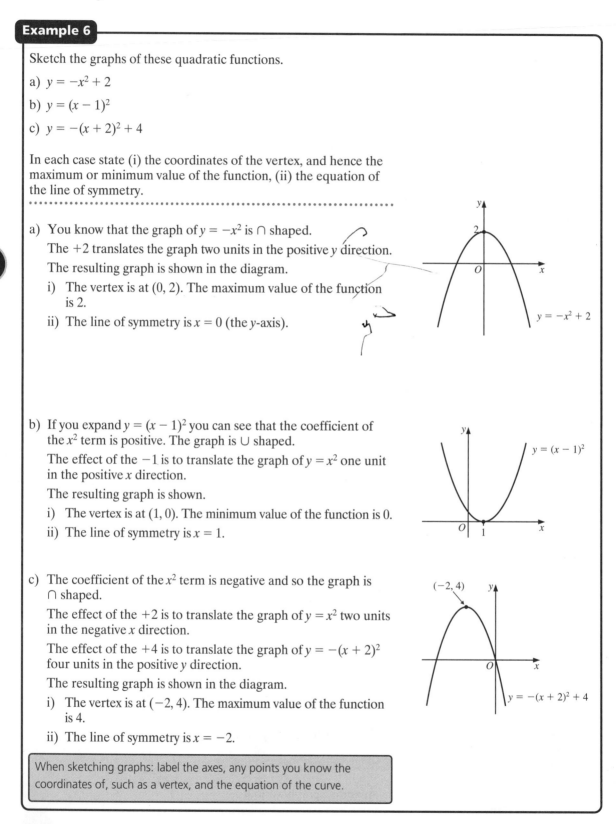

a) You know that the graph of $y = -x^2$ is $\cap$ shaped.

The $+2$ translates the graph two units in the positive y direction.

The resulting graph is shown in the diagram.

   i) The vertex is at $(0, 2)$. The maximum value of the function is 2.

   ii) The line of symmetry is $x = 0$ (the y-axis).

b) If you expand $y = (x - 1)^2$ you can see that the coefficient of the x^2 term is positive. The graph is $\cup$ shaped.

The effect of the -1 is to translate the graph of $y = x^2$ one unit in the positive x direction.

The resulting graph is shown.

   i) The vertex is at $(1, 0)$. The minimum value of the function is 0.

   ii) The line of symmetry is $x = 1$.

c) The coefficient of the x^2 term is negative and so the graph is $\cap$ shaped.

The effect of the $+2$ is to translate the graph of $y = x^2$ two units in the negative x direction.

The effect of the $+4$ is to translate the graph of $y = -(x + 2)^2$ four units in the positive y direction.

The resulting graph is shown in the diagram.

   i) The vertex is at $(-2, 4)$. The maximum value of the function is 4.

   ii) The line of symmetry is $x = -2$.

> When sketching graphs: label the axes, any points you know the coordinates of, such as a vertex, and the equation of the curve.

Exercise 1B

1 Expand and simplify each of these functions.

a) $y = 3 + (x - 2)^2$ b) $y = 5 + (2x + 1)^2$

c) $y = 7 - (x + 2)^2$ d) $y = (x - 3)^2 + (x + 4)^2$

e) $y = (x - 5)^2 - (x - 1)^2$ f) $y = (2x + 3)^2 + (3x - 2)^2$

g) $y = 2(x + 1)^2 + 5$ h) $y = 3(x - 1)^2 + 2x + 7$

i) $y = 4(x - 3)^2 + 5(x + 2)^2 - 12$

2 Sketch the graphs of these quadratic functions, in each case stating the vertex and the equation of the line of symmetry.

a) $y = x^2 + 5$ b) $y = x^2 - 1$

c) $y = 3x^2 - 12$ d) $y = -x^2 + 9$

e) $y = (x - 2)^2$ f) $y = 2(x + 3)^2$

g) $y = -(x - 5)^2$ h) $y = (x - 1)^2 + 3$

i) $y = 2(x - 3)^2 + 5$

3 Given that a and b are both positive, sketch the graph of $y = (x - a)^2 + b$, labelling the vertex and the point at which the curve crosses the y-axis.

C1

1.3   Quadratic factors

Consider the quadratic function $y = x^2 - 4x$. Factorising the RHS gives:

$$y = x(x - 4)$$

RHS = right-hand side.

The factorised form gives information about the graph of the quadratic function.

Notice that when $x = 0$, $y = 0$ and when $x = 4$, $y = 0$.
Two points on the graph are therefore $(0, 0)$ and $(4, 0)$.

The graph of $y = x^2 - 4x$ is shown with these two points marked.

The line of symmetry is the line $x = 2$, which bisects the x-axis between the two points $(0, 0)$ and $(4, 0)$.

You can also use the factorised form of the quadratic function $y = x^2 - 4x$ to solve the quadratic equation:

$$x^2 - 4x = 0$$

Factorising and solving gives:

$$x(x - 4) = 0$$

Either or both of these factors must equal zero. Hence:

$$x = 0 \text{ or } x - 4 = 0$$
$$\therefore x = 0 \text{ or } x = 4$$

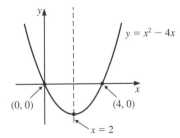

Notice that 0 and 4 are the x-coordinates of the x-axis intercepts.

C1

Example 7

By factorising $y = x^2 - 6x$:

a) sketch the graph of $y = x^2 - 6x$ and state the coordinates of the vertex,

b) solve the associated quadratic equation $x^2 - 6x = 0$.

a) Factorising the RHS gives:

$$y = x(x - 6)$$

When $x = 0, y = 0$

When $x = 6, y = 0$

This gives the points $(0, 0)$ and $(6, 0)$ on the graph.

The coefficient of x^2 is positive so the graph is $\cup$ shaped.

The line of symmetry bisects the x-axis between $x = 0$ and $x = 6$ $\therefore$ $x = 3$ is the equation of the line of symmetry.

The vertex occurs at $x = 3$.

When $x = 3, y = (3)^2 - 6(3) = -9$.

The vertex is at $(3, -9)$.

From this information you can complete the sketch.

b) $x^2 - 6x = 0$

Factorising and solving gives:

$$x(x - 6) = 0$$

$$\therefore x = 0 \text{ or } x = 6$$

Example 8

Sketch the graph of $y = 3x^2 + 5x$. State the coordinates of the vertex.

Factorising the RHS gives:

$$y = x(3x + 5)$$

When $x = 0, y = 0$

When $x = -\frac{5}{3}, y = 0$

So $(0, 0)$ and $\left(-\frac{5}{3}, 0\right)$ are points on the graph.

The coefficient of x^2 is positive so the graph is $\cup$ shaped.

The line of symmetry bisects the x-axis between $x = 0$ and

$x = -\frac{5}{3}$, so $x = \dfrac{0 + \left(-\frac{5}{3}\right)}{2} = -\frac{5}{6}$ is the equation of the line of symmetry.

The vertex occurs when $x = -\frac{5}{6}$.

When $x = -\frac{5}{6}, y = 3\left(-\frac{5}{6}\right)^2 + 5\left(-\frac{5}{6}\right) = -\frac{25}{12}$.

The vertex is at $\left(-\frac{5}{6}, -\frac{25}{12}\right)$.

From this information you can complete the sketch.

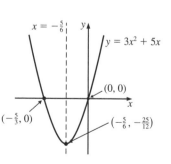

It often helps if you can identify the **difference of two squares**.

In general, $a^2 - b^2 = (a - b)(a + b)$ for any two values a and b.

Example 9

a) Sketch the graph of $y = x^2 - 25$.
b) Solve the quadratic equation $x^2 - 25 = 0$.

$$x^2 - 25 = x^2 - 5^2$$
$$= (x - 5)(x + 5)$$

a) Factorising the RHS gives:
$$y = (x - 5)(x + 5)$$
By inspection you can see that $(5, 0)$ and $(-5, 0)$ are the points where the graph intersects the x-axis. The coefficent of x^2 is positive so the graph is $\cup$ shaped. This gives the sketch shown.

b)
$$x^2 - 25 = 0$$
$$(x - 5)(x + 5) = 0$$
$$x - 5 = 0 \text{ or } x + 5 = 0$$
$$\therefore \qquad x = 5 \text{ or } x = -5$$

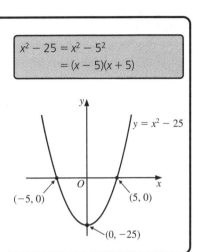

Take care when factorising a quadratic with a negative x^2 term.

Example 10

Sketch the graph of $y = -x^2 + 5x + 6$.

Factorising the RHS gives:
$$y = -(x^2 - 5x - 6)$$
$$= -(x + 1)(x - 6)$$
By inspection you can see that $(-1, 0)$ and $(6, 0)$ are the points where the graph intersects the x-axis.

The coefficient of x^2 is negative so the graph is $\cap$ shaped.

The line of symmetry bisects the x-axis between $x = -1$ and $x = 6$.
$$\therefore \quad x = \frac{-1 + 6}{2} = \frac{5}{2}$$

$x = \frac{5}{2}$ is the equation of the line of symmetry. This gives the sketch shown.

Example 11

Sketch the graph of $y = 2x^2 - 13x - 24$.

Factorising the RHS gives:
$$y = (2x + 3)(x - 8)$$
By inspection you can see that $(-\frac{3}{2}, 0)$ and $(8, 0)$ are the points where the graph intersects the x-axis.

The coefficient of x^2 is positive so the graph is $\cup$ shaped.

The line of symmetry bisects the x-axis between $x = -\frac{3}{2}$ and $x = 8$.
$$\therefore \quad x = \frac{-\frac{3}{2} + 8}{2} = \frac{13}{4}$$

The equation of the line of symmetry is $x = \frac{13}{4}$. This gives the sketch shown.

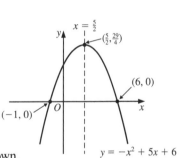

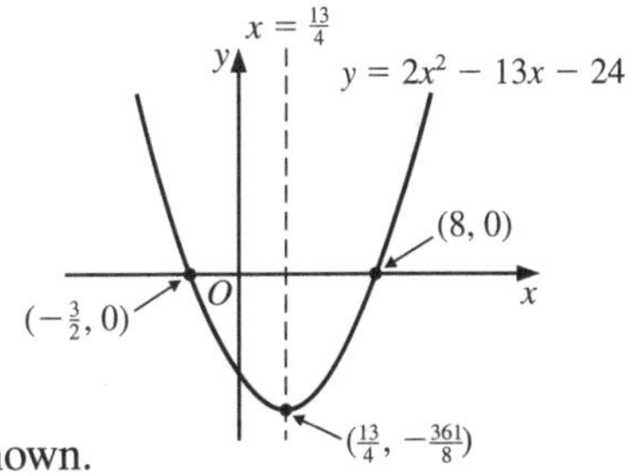

Exercise 1C

1 Sketch the graph of each of these quadratic functions. Remember to label all axis intercepts and find the vertex.

a) $y = (x - 3)(x + 3)$ b) $y = (x - 5)(x - 9)$

c) $y = (2x - 3)(x + 2)$ d) $y = x^2 - 4$

e) $y = 25 - x^2$ f) $y = x^2 - 3x - 4$

g) $y = x^2 + 7x + 12$ h) $y = 2x^2 - 3x - 2$

i) $y = -2x^2 - 5x + 7$

2 a) Sketch the graph of $y = x^2 - 16$.

b) Hence solve the equation $x^2 - 16 = 0$.

3 a) Sketch the graph of $y = x^2 - 5x + 6$.

b) Hence solve the equation $x^2 - 5x + 6 = 0$.

C1

4 a) Sketch the graph of $y = x^2 - 6x - 7$.

b) Hence solve the equation $x^2 - 6x - 7 = 0$.

5 a) Sketch the graph of $y = 3x^2 - 5x - 8$.

b) Hence solve the equation $3x^2 - 5x - 8 = 0$.

Solving problems with quadratic equations

You can often apply quadratic equations to real-life situations.

> Practical applications of quadratics are not assessed in the C1 module. This brief section is included here to illustrate the usefulness of quadratic equations.

Example 12

a) A garden is in the shape of a rectangle, 20 metres by 8 metres. Around the outside is a border of uniform width, and in the middle is a square pond. The width of the border is the same as the width of the pond. The size of the area which is not occupied by either border or pond is 124 m².

Letting the width of the border be x metres, show that

$$3x^2 - 56x + 36 = 0$$

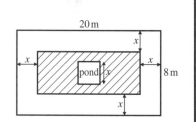

b) Solve this equation to find the value of x.

a) The area of the shaded region is given by:

$$(20 - 2x)(8 - 2x) - x^2$$
$$= 160 - 56x + 4x^2 - x^2$$
$$= 160 - 56x + 3x^2$$

The area of the shaded region is 124 m².

$$160 - 56x + 3x^2 = 124$$
$$\therefore \quad 3x^2 - 56x + 36 = 0, \text{ as required}$$

b) Factorising this quadratic gives:

$$(3x - 2)(x - 18) = 0$$
$$3x - 2 = 0 \text{ or } x - 18 = 0$$
$$\therefore \quad x = \tfrac{2}{3} \text{ or } x = 18$$

x cannot be 18, because the width of the garden is only 8 metres.
So $x = \tfrac{2}{3}$ and the width of the border is $\tfrac{2}{3}$ metre.

> You should always assess whether the solutions are sensible in the context of the problem.

Exercise 1D

1 Solve these quadratic equations. You may need to rearrange them first.

   a) $x^2 - 5x + 6 = 0$ b) $x^2 - 3x - 4 = 0$ c) $x^2 - 7x + 10 = 0$

   d) $x^2 + 5x + 6 = 0$ e) $x^2 - 6x + 8 = 0$ f) $x^2 - 5x - 6 = 0$

   g) $x^2 = 9$ h) $x^2 + 2x = 8$ i) $x^2 = x + 12$

   j) $x^2 + 20 = 9x$ k) $x^2 = 4x$ l) $x^2 - 8 = 7x$

2 Solve these quadratic equations. You may need to rearrange them first.

   a) $2x^2 + 5x + 2 = 0$ b) $3x^2 - 7x + 2 = 0$ c) $2x^2 - 3x - 5 = 0$

   d) $5x^2 + 14x - 3 = 0$ e) $4x^2 + 5x + 1 = 0$ f) $6x^2 - 5x + 1 = 0$

   g) $3x^2 = 10x + 8$ h) $2x^2 + x = 15$ i) $16x^2 = 9$

   j) $3x^2 - x = 10$ k) $5x^2 + 13x = 6$ l) $8x^2 + 3 = 14x$

3 The perimeter of a rectangle is 34 cm. Given that the diagonal is of length 13 cm, and that the width is x cm, derive the equation $x^2 - 17x + 60 = 0$. Hence find the dimensions of the rectangle.

> Questions 3 to 7 involve practical applications, which will not be assessed in the C1 module.

4 A metal sleeve of length 20 cm has rectangular cross-section 10 cm by 8 cm. The metal has uniform thickness, x cm, along the sleeve, and the total volume of metal in the sleeve is 495 cm³.

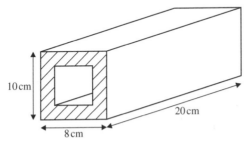

Derive the equation $16x^2 - 144x + 99 = 0$, and solve it to find the value of x.

5 A strand of wire of length 32 cm is cut into two pieces. One piece is bent to form a rectangle of width x cm and length $(x + 2)$ cm, and the other piece is bent to form a square.

   a) Show that the square has sides of length $(7 - x)$ cm.

   b) Given that the total of the areas enclosed by both the rectangle and the square is 31 cm², form an equation for x and solve it to find the value of x.

6 A train usually covers a journey of 240 km at a steady speed of v km h^{-1}. One day, due to adverse weather conditions, it reduces its speed by 40 km h^{-1} and the journey takes one hour longer.

Derive the equation $v^2 - 40v - 9600 = 0$, and solve it to find the value of v.

7 As part of his training an athlete usually runs 80 km at a steady speed of v km h^{-1}. One day, he decides to reduce his speed by 2.5 km h^{-1} and his run takes him an extra 2 h 40 min.

Derive the equation $\dfrac{80}{v} + \dfrac{8}{3} = \dfrac{160}{2v - 5}$, and solve it to find the value of v.

1.4 Completing the square

Factorising a quadratic function makes it easy to sketch its graph.

For example:

$y = x^2 + 6x + 9$

Factorise: $y = (x + 3)^2$

> $y = (x + 3)^2$ is a perfect square.

$\therefore \quad y = x^2 + 6x + 11$

can be written as $y = (x + 3)^2 + 2$

You can use your knowledge of functions to sketch the graph.

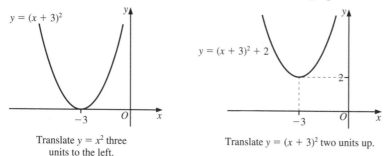

$y = (x + 3)^2$ $y = (x + 3)^2 + 2$

Translate $y = x^2$ three units to the left.   Translate $y = (x + 3)^2$ two units up.

> You will learn more about translating graphs in Chapter 6.

Expressing a quadratic function in the form $y = (x + p)^2 + q$ is called **completing the square**.

You can use this technique to sketch quadratic graphs and to solve quadratic equations.

Consider the function $y = x^2 + 8x$. To express this in the form $(x + p)^2 + q$ you can first see that $8x = 4x + 4x$.

So the first part is $(x + 4)^2$. Expanding this gives a constant which is not required:

$(x + 4)^2 = x^2 + 8x + 16$

> The constant $+16$ is not required.

Therefore the requested form is $(x + 4)^2 - 16$

In summary, to complete the square:

✦ Halve the coefficient of x to obtain p.

✦ Subtract the square of the constant to obtain q.

Example 13

Express each of these quadratic functions in the form
$y = (x + p)^2 + q$:
a) $y = x^2 - 10x$
b) $y = x^2 + 4x + 7$
c) $y = x^2 - 3x - 4$

In each case use the form $(x + p)^2 + q$ to sketch the graph of the
quadratic function.

a) Completing the square gives:

$$x^2 - 10x = \left(x - \frac{10}{2}\right)^2 - \left(\frac{10}{2}\right)^2$$

$$= (x - 5)^2 - 25$$

The x^2 term is positive and hence the graph is ∪ shaped. The
vertex of the graph is at $(5, -25)$.

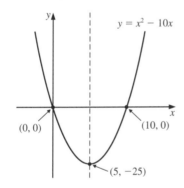

b) Completing the square gives:

$$x^2 + 4x + 7 = \left(x + \frac{4}{2}\right)^2 - \left(\frac{4}{2}\right)^2 + 7$$

$$= (x + 2)^2 - 4 + 7$$

$$= (x + 2)^2 + 3$$

The x^2 term is positive and hence the graph is ∪ shaped. The
vertex of the graph is at $(-2, 3)$.

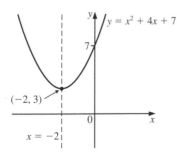

The coefficient of x is -10.

C1

See page 5.

When $x = -2$
$$y = (-2 + 2)^2 + 3$$
$$= 0 + 3$$
$$= 3$$

c) Completing the square gives:

$$x^2 - 3x - 4 = \left(x - \frac{3}{2}\right)^2 - \left(-\frac{3}{2}\right)^2 - 4$$

$$= \left(x - \frac{3}{2}\right)^2 - \frac{9}{4} - 4$$

$$= \left(x - \frac{3}{2}\right)^2 - \frac{25}{4}$$

The x^2 term is positive and hence the graph is $\cup$ shaped. The vertex of the graph is at $(\frac{3}{2}, -\frac{25}{4})$ and the graph is given below.

> Note that the vertex of the graph is always at the point which makes the squared bracket zero.

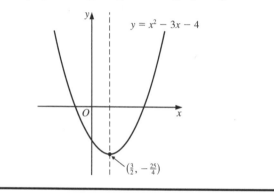

$y = x^2 - 3x - 4$

$(\frac{3}{2}, -\frac{25}{4})$

Writing a quadratic function in the form $(x + p)^2 + q$ also allows you to solve the associated quadratic equation.

Example 14

Express the function $y = x^2 + 2x - 15$ in the form $(x + p)^2 + q$ and hence solve the equation $x^2 + 2x - 15 = 0$.
....

Completing the square gives:

$$x^2 + 2x - 15 = (x + 1)^2 - 1^2 - 15$$
$$= (x + 1)^2 - 16, \text{ as required.}$$

So: $(x + 1)^2 - 16 = 0$

$$(x + 1)^2 = 16$$
$$x + 1 = \pm\sqrt{16}$$
$$x + 1 = \pm 4$$
$$x = -1 \pm 4$$
$$x = 3 \text{ or } x = -5$$

> **Remember:** Square roots can be positive or negative.

You could have solved the equation by factorising:

$$(x - 3)(x + 5) = 0$$
$$\therefore x = 3 \text{ or } x = -5$$

which agrees with the method of completing the square.

Completing the square is particularly useful if a quadratic function does not factorise.

Example 15

Solve the equation $x^2 + 3x + 1 = 0$.

Completing the square gives:

$$x^2 + 3x + 1 = \left(x + \frac{3}{2}\right)^2 - \left(\frac{3}{2}\right)^2 + 1$$

$$= \left(x + \frac{3}{2}\right)^2 - \frac{9}{4} + 1$$

$$= \left(x + \frac{3}{2}\right)^2 - \frac{5}{4}$$

The equation becomes:

$$\left(x + \frac{3}{2}\right)^2 - \frac{5}{4} = 0$$

$$\left(x + \frac{3}{2}\right)^2 = \frac{5}{4}$$

$$\left(x + \frac{3}{2}\right) = \pm\sqrt{\frac{5}{4}} = \pm\frac{\sqrt{5}}{2}$$

$$x = -\frac{3}{2} \pm \frac{\sqrt{5}}{2}$$

$$\therefore \quad x = -\frac{3}{2} + \frac{\sqrt{5}}{2} \quad \text{or} \quad x = -\frac{3}{2} - \frac{\sqrt{5}}{2}$$

These solutions are exact, so you can leave them in this form.

> $\sqrt{5}$ is a surd. If you work it out using a calculator you will get an inexact decimal.

Exercise 1E

1 Express each of these functions in the form $(x + p)^2 + q$.

a) $y = x^2 + 4x + 6$ b) $y = x^2 - 6x + 13$ c) $y = x^2 - 10x + 40$

d) $y = x^2 - x - 5$ e) $y = x^2 - 5x + 9$ f) $y = x^2 - 20x + 3$

2 Use the method of completing the square to solve these quadratic equations. Give your answers in the form $a \pm b\sqrt{n}$. where a and b are rational, and n is an integer.

a) $x^2 + 4x - 1 = 0$ b) $x^2 + 6x + 2 = 0$ c) $x^2 - 2x - 1 = 0$

d) $x^2 - 8x - 3 = 0$ e) $x^2 + x - 1 = 0$ f) $x^2 + 3x + 1 = 0$

g) $x^2 - 5x - 2 = 0$ h) $x^2 - x - 3 = 0$ i) $x^2 + 5x + 1 = 0$

j) $x^2 + 12x + 5 = 0$ k) $x^2 - 9x + 10 = 0$ l) $x^2 - \frac{1}{2}x - \frac{1}{4} = 0$

3 Use the method of completing the square to sketch the graphs of these quadratic functions.

a) $y = x^2 + 2x - 5$ b) $y = x^2 + 8x + 3$ c) $y = x^2 + 3x + 5$

d) $y = x^2 + 10x + 23$ e) $y = x^2 - 3x - 6$ f) $y = x^2 - 5x + 4$

You can use the technique of completing the square to find a maximum or minimum value.

Example 16

Complete the square for the quadratic expression $2x^2 - 12x + 3$, and hence:

a) find the minimum value of the function $y = 2x^2 - 12x + 3$

b) solve the equation $2x^2 - 12x + 3 = 0$

c) sketch the graph of the quadratic function $y = -2x^2 + 12x - 3$.

Calling the expression y and factorising out 2 gives

$$y = 2\left(x^2 - 6x + \frac{3}{2}\right)$$

> You need to take care when the coefficient of x^2 is not 1.

Now complete the square:

$$y = 2\left((x - 3)^2 - 9 + \frac{3}{2}\right)$$

$$= 2\left((x - 3)^2 - \frac{15}{2}\right)$$

$$= 2(x - 3)^2 - 15$$

a) Minimum value occurs when $2(x - 3)^2$ is zero.

$2(x-3)^2 = 0 \qquad \therefore \quad x = 3$

When $x = 3, y = 2(3)^2 - 12\,(3) + 3 = -15$

The minimum value of the function is -15.

> $2(x - 3)^2$ cannot be negative.

b) $2x^2 - 12x + 3 = 0$

$$2(x - 3)^2 - 15 = 0$$

$$2(x - 3)^2 = 15$$

$$(x - 3)^2 = \frac{15}{2}$$

$$x - 3 = \pm \sqrt{\frac{15}{2}}$$

$$x = 3 \pm \sqrt{\frac{15}{2}}$$

c) Notice that $y = -2x^2 + 12x - 3$

$$y = -(2x^2 - 12x + 3)$$

$$= -2(x - 3)^2 + 15$$

The graph has line of symmetry $x = 3$ and vertex $(3, 15)$. In this case the coefficient of the x^2 term is negative and hence the graph is $\cap$ shaped.

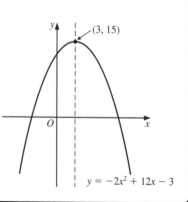

$y = -2x^2 + 12x - 3$

Exercise 1F

1 Complete the square for each of these quadratic expressions.

a) $2x^2 + 8x - 13$

b) $3x^2 - 6x + 2$

c) $5 - 4x - x^2$

d) $5 + 4x - 2x^2$

e) $2x^2 - 6x + 5$

f) $23 - 10x - 5x^2$

2 Use the method of completing the square to solve each of these quadratic equations. Express your solutions in the form $a \pm b\sqrt{n}$. where a, b and n are rational.

a) $2x^2 - 3x - 3 = 0$

b) $3x^2 - 6x + 1 = 0$

c) $4x^2 + 4x - 5 = 0$

d) $3x^2 + 5x - 1 = 0$

e) $5x^2 + x - 3 = 0$

f) $2x^2 - 3x - 1 = 0$

g) $2x^2 - x - 2 = 0$

h) $4x^2 + 3x - 2 = 0$

i) $7x^2 - 14x + 5 = 0$

j) $6x^2 + 4x - 3 = 0$

k) $5x^2 - 20x + 17 = 0$

l) $2x^2 + 18x + 21 = 0$

3 Use the method of completing the square to sketch the graphs of these quadratic functions.

a) $y = 2x^2 - 4x - 4$

b) $y = 3x^2 + 6x - 15$

c) $y = 8 + 2x - x^2$

d) $y = 4 + 8x - 2x^2$

e) $y = 2x^2 - 4x + 5$

f) $y = 6 - 6x - 3x^2$

4 A farmer has 40 m of fencing with which to enclose a rectangular pen. Given the pen is x m wide,

a) show that its area is $(20x - x^2)\,\text{m}^2$

b) deduce the maximum area that he can enclose.

5 Another farmer also has 40 m of fencing, and he also wishes to enclose a rectangular pen of maximum area, but one side of his pen will consist of part of a wall which is already in place.

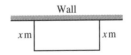

Given that the two sides of his pen touching the wall each have length x m, find an expression, in terms of x, for the area that he can enclose. Deduce that the maximum area is 200 m².

6 A third farmer has 40 m of fencing but he decides to use a right-angled corner of a building, as in the diagram.

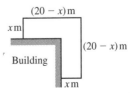

Show that the area which he can enclose is given by the expression $(40x - 3x^2)\,\text{m}^2$, and deduce the maximum value of this area.

C1

1.5 The quadratic formula and discriminant

The general quadratic equation has the form $ax^2 + bx + c = 0$, where
a, b, c are constants with $a \neq 0$. You can use the technique of
completing the square to solve this equation. This will give the formula:

$$x = \frac{-b \pm \sqrt{b^2 - 4ac}}{2a}$$

known as the **quadratic formula**. You can use the quadratic formula
to solve quadratic equations.

> As a challenge, you could try to obtain this formula. Treat a, b and c as if they were ordinary numbers.

Example 17

Solve the equation $x^2 + 5x + 6 = 0$ using the quadratic formula.

In this case $a = 1, b = 5, c = 6$ which gives:

$$x = \frac{-5 \pm \sqrt{5^2 - 4(1)(6)}}{2(1)}$$

$$= \frac{-5 \pm 1}{2}$$

$$\therefore \quad x = -3 \text{ or } x = -2$$

Notice that the solutions could be obtained by factorising.
Factorising and solving gives:

$$\therefore \quad (x + 3)(x + 2) = 0$$
$$\therefore \quad x + 3 = 0 \text{ or } x + 2 = 0$$
$$\therefore \quad x = -3 \text{ or } x = -2$$

In the next example, the quadratic function does not factorise. You
can use the quadratic formula to solve the equation.

Example 18

Solve the equation $2x^2 + 2x - 1 = 0$.

In this case $a = 2, b = 2, c = -1$ which gives:

$$x = \frac{-2 \pm \sqrt{2^2 - 4(2)(-1)}}{2(2)}$$

$$= \frac{-2 \pm \sqrt{12}}{4}$$

$$= \frac{-2 \pm 2\sqrt{3}}{4}$$

$$= \frac{-1 \pm \sqrt{3}}{2}$$

$$\therefore \quad x = \frac{-1 + \sqrt{3}}{2} \text{ or } \frac{-1 - \sqrt{3}}{2}$$

These are the exact solutions and are left in this form.

> You could get the same solutions by completing the square. Using the formula is generally quicker.

Discriminant of a quadratic equation

The quantity

$$D = b^2 - 4ac$$

is called the **discriminant** of the quadratic equation $ax^2 + bx + c = 0$.

The type of **root** which arises from a quadratic equation depends on the value of the discriminant.

> A **root** is the solution of an equation in the form $f(x) = 0$. Graphically, roots are the x-coordinates where the graph crosses the x-axis.

Consider the general quadratic equation

$$ax^2 + bx + c = 0$$

✦ When $b^2 - 4ac > 0$, the equation has two distinct real roots.
✦ When $b^2 - 4ac < 0$, the equation has no real roots.
✦ When $b^2 - 4ac = 0$, the equation has one repeated root.

> A quadratic equation may have roots that are not real. These are beyond the scope of this module.

C1

The discriminant of a quadratic equation indicates whether the associated graph cuts the x-axis at two different points, does not cut the x-axis at all or touches the x-axis at one point. Each case is illustrated here, for $a > 0$.

> You can think of one repeated root as being the same as two equal roots.

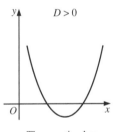

$D > 0$

The equation has two distinct roots.

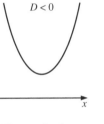

$D < 0$

The equation has no real roots.

$D = 0$

The equation has one repeated root.

Example 19

Use the discriminant to determine whether each of these quadratic equations has two distinct real roots, equal roots or no real roots.

a) $3x^2 - x + 2 = 0$

b) $x^2 - 3x - 28 = 0$

c) $4x^2 - 4x + 1 = 0$

. . . .

a) $a = 3, b = -1, c = 2$. The discriminant is given by:

$$D = b^2 - 4ac$$
$$= (-1)^2 - 4(3)(2)$$
$$= -23$$

Since $D < 0$ the equation has no real roots.

b) $a = 1, b = -3, c = -28$. The discriminant is given by:

$$D = (-3)^2 - 4(1)(-28)$$
$$= 9 + 112$$
$$= 121$$

Since $D > 0$ the equation has two distinct roots.

c) $a = 4, b = -4, c = 1$. The discriminant is given by:

$$D = (-4)^2 - 4(4)(1)$$
$$= 0$$

Since $D = 0$ the equation has equal (repeated) roots.

> D is a perfect square ($\sqrt{121} = 11$), so the quadratic function will factorise.

C1

Example 20

Calculate the discriminant of the quadratic equation $2x^2 + 7x + 7 = 0$.
Hence show that $2x^2 + 7x + 7$ is always positive.

Calculating the discriminant with $a = 2, b = 7$ and $c = 7$ gives:

$$D = b^2 - 4ac$$
$$= (7)^2 - 4(2)(7)$$
$$= -7$$

The discriminant is -7.

Since $D = -7$ which is negative, the equation $2x^2 + 7x + 7 = 0$ has no real roots. Therefore, $y = 2x^2 + 7x + 7$ is never zero and the graph of $y = 2x^2 + 7x + 7$ does not cut the x-axis.

Since the coefficient of the x^2 term is positive, the curve is $\cup$ shaped. Therefore, the entire curve lies above the x-axis and is always positive.

$y = 2x^2 + 7x + 7$

Exercise 1G

1 Use the quadratic formula to solve each of these quadratic equations.
a) $x^2 + 7x + 6 = 0$
b) $x^2 + 3x - 10 = 0$
c) $x^2 - 7x + 12 = 0$
d) $x^2 + x - 20 = 0$
e) $x^2 - 9x + 18 = 0$
f) $x^2 + 5x - 6 = 0$
g) $2x^2 - 5x + 2 = 0$
h) $3x^2 - 11x - 4 = 0$
i) $4x^2 + 4x - 3 = 0$
j) $3x^2 + 5x + 2 = 0$
k) $2x^2 - 9x + 10 = 0$
l) $5x^2 - 9x - 2 = 0$

2 Use the quadratic formula to solve each of these quadratic equations, leaving your answers in surd form.
a) $x^2 + 3x - 1 = 0$
b) $x^2 + x - 3 = 0$
c) $x^2 - 5x + 3 = 0$
d) $x^2 - x - 4 = 0$
e) $x^2 + 5x + 3 = 0$
f) $x^2 - 3x - 5 = 0$
g) $2x^2 + 3x - 4 = 0$
h) $3x^2 + x - 3 = 0$
i) $4x^2 + 5x - 7 = 0$
j) $2x^2 - 7x + 4 = 0$
k) $6x^2 - 9x - 2 = 0$
l) $5x^2 + x - 3 = 0$

3 Use the discriminant to determine the number of real roots of
each of these quadratic equations.

a) $5x^2 - 3x + 7 = 0$ b) $6x^2 - 5x - 3 = 0$

c) $9x^2 - 12x + 4 = 0$ d) $2x^2 + 6x + 3 = 0$

e) $4x^2 + 20x + 25 = 0$ f) $3x^2 + 2x + 1 = 0$

4 Calculate the discriminant of the quadratic $3x^2 + 5x + 8$.
Hence show that $3x^2 + 5x + 8 > 0$, for all values of x.

5 Calculate the discriminant of the quadratic $5x^2 + 2x + 1$.
Hence show that $5x^2 + 2x + 1 > 0$, for all values of x.

6 Show that $x^2 + 3x + 5 > 0$, for all values of x.

7 Show that $x^2 + 6x > 3x - 4$, for all values of x.

8 Show that $2x^2 + 6 > 4x + 1$, for all values of x.

9 Prove that the inequality $3x^2 + 13 < 12x$ has no real solution.

10 Find the possible values of the constant a given that the equation
$ax^2 + (8 - a)x + 1 = 0$ has a repeated root.

11 Given that the equation $x^2 - 3bx + (4b + 1) = 0$ has a repeated
root, find the possible values of the constant b.

C1

....

1.6 Methods of solving $ax^2 + bx + c = 0$

You now have a number of ways of solving quadratic equations:

✦ Factorise
✦ Complete the square
✦ Use the quadratic formula.

Example 21

Decide on an appropriate method to solve each quadratic equation.

a) $x^2 + 3x = 0$

b) $(x - 2)^2 - 16 = 0$

c) $x^2 + 6x + 1 = 0$

d) $2x^2 + x - 1 = 0$

e) $5x^2 - 2x - 1 = 0$

....

a) Factorising and solving gives:

$$x(x + 3) = 0$$

$$x = 0 \text{ or } x + 3 = 0$$

∴ $x = 0 \text{ or } x = -3$

b) Rearranging and solving gives:

$$(x - 2)^2 = 16$$
$$x - 2 = \pm 4$$
$$x = 2 \pm 4$$
$$\therefore \quad x = 6 \text{ or } x = -2$$

c) This will not factorise. Use the method of completing the square which gives:

$$(x + 3)^2 - 9 + 1 = 0$$
$$(x + 3)^2 = 8$$
$$x + 3 = \pm \sqrt{8}$$
$$x = -3 \pm \sqrt{8} = -3 \pm 2\sqrt{2}$$
$$\therefore \quad x = -3 + 2\sqrt{2} \text{ or } x = -3 - 2\sqrt{2}$$

> You could also use the quadratic formula in this case.

C1

d) Factorising and solving gives:

$$(2x - 1)(x + 1) = 0$$
$$2x - 1 = 0 \text{ or } x + 1 = 0$$
$$\therefore \quad x = \tfrac{1}{2} \text{ or } x = -1$$

> Always check whether a quadratic will factorise before deciding to use another method.

e) This will not factorise. Using the quadratic formula with $a = 5, b = -2, c = -1$ gives:

$$x = \frac{-(-2) \pm \sqrt{(-2)^2 - 4(5)(-1)}}{2(5)}$$
$$= \frac{2 \pm \sqrt{24}}{10}$$
$$= \frac{2 \pm 2\sqrt{6}}{10}$$
$$\therefore \quad x = \frac{1 + \sqrt{6}}{5} \text{ or } x = \frac{1 - \sqrt{6}}{5}$$

Exercise 1H

In each part of questions 1 and 2 decide on an appropriate method and solve the quadratic equation.

1
a) $x^2 + 5x = 0$
b) $x^2 - 8x + 12 = 0$
c) $(x - 3)^2 - 25 = 0$
d) $x^2 - 4x + 2 = 0$
e) $3x^2 + 5x - 2 = 0$
f) $2x^2 - 3x - 8 = 0$

2
a) $3x^2 = 2x$
b) $x^2 = 2x + 15$
c) $x^2 + 2x + 1 = 16$
d) $x^2 + 4x = 1$
e) $6x^2 = x + 2$
f) $3 + 6x = 5x^2$

3 Solve the quadratic equation $\dfrac{3x + 2}{2x - 1} = \dfrac{5x + 6}{x + 4}$.

4 Solve the quadratic equation $\dfrac{6}{x-1} + \dfrac{1}{x-4} = 2$.

5 Find the equation of the quadratic function whose graph is sketched below, expressing your answer in the form $y = ax^2 + bx + c$.

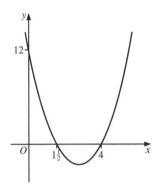

6 Express $x^2 + 4x + 7$ in the form $(x + p)^2 + q$. Hence show that the equation $x^2 + 4x + 7 = 0$ has no real root.

7 Show that the equation $\dfrac{x+2}{x-3} = \dfrac{x+4}{2x+3}$ has no real root.

1.7 Quadratic inequalities

To solve a quadratic inequality you should sketch a graph of the quadratic function involved.

Example 22

Solve the inequality $x^2 + 3x - 4 < 0$.

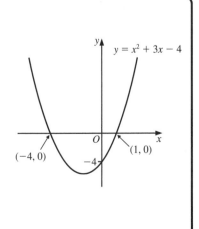

The graph of $y = x^2 + 3x - 4$ is ∪ shaped because the coefficient of the x^2 term is positive.

Factorising gives:

$$y = (x + 4)(x - 1)$$

$(-4, 0)$ and $(1, 0)$ are the points where the graph intersects the x-axis. When $x = 0$, $y = -4$. So the graph cuts the y-axis at $(0, -4)$. The sketch graph is shown.

You can see that the graph is below the x-axis when $-4 < x < 1$.

So $x^2 + 3x - 4 < 0$ when $-4 < x < 1$.

Note that if the inequality had been $x^2 + 3x - 4 > 0$, the solutions would be $x < -4, x > 1$.

C1

Example 23

Solve the inequality $-x^2 + x + 6 \geqslant 0$.

The graph of $y = -x^2 + x + 6$ is $\cap$ shaped because the coefficient of the x^2 term is negative.

Factorising gives:

$$y = -(x^2 - x - 6) = -(x - 3)(x + 2)$$

$(3, 0)$ and $(-2, 0)$ are the points where the graph intersects the x-axis. Also, when $x = 0$, $y = -(-3)(2) = 6$. The sketch graph is shown.

The graph is on or above the x-axis when $-2 \leqslant x \leqslant 3$.

So $x^2 + x + 6 \geqslant 0$ when $-2 \leqslant x \leqslant 3$.

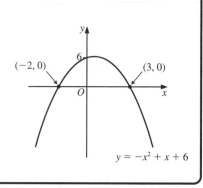

Exercise 1I

C1

Solve each of these inequalities for x.
In each case you should sketch a graph.

1 a) $(x - 3)(x - 5) > 0$ b) $(x + 4)(x - 3) < 0$
    c) $(x + 3)(x + 1) \leqslant 0$ d) $(2x + 3)(x - 1) < 0$
    e) $(3x + 2)(2x - 1) \geqslant 0$ f) $(3 + x)(1 - x) < 0$

2 a) $x^2 - 2x - 8 > 0$ b) $x^2 - 2x - 15 \leqslant 0$
    c) $x^2 + 7x + 12 < 0$ d) $2x^2 + 3x - 5 \geqslant 0$
    e) $5x^2 + 11x + 6 \leqslant 0$ f) $x^2 - 8x + 16 \leqslant 0$

3 a) $x^2 + 3x \geqslant 10$ b) $x^2 + 21 < 10x$
    c) $x^2 + 4 > 5x$ d) $54 - 11x \leqslant 30 - x^2$
    e) $5x > 3 - 2x^2$ f) $x(10x - 13) + 4 < 0$

4 $\dfrac{2}{x - 3} \leqslant 1$

1.8 Simultaneous equations

You can solve simultaneous equations where one is linear and the other is quadratic. The way to do this is to substitute the linear expression into the quadratic equation.

There are three possibilities, which you can show graphically.

◆ Two distinct roots   ◆ One repeated root   ◆ No real roots

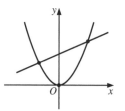

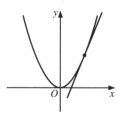

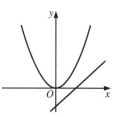

The straight line intersects the quadratic curve at two distinct points.

The straight line touches the quadratic curve at one point.

The straight line does not intersect the quadratic curve.

Example 24

Solve the simultaneous equations $y = x^2 + 3x + 2$ and $y = 2x + 8$.
Interpret your result graphically.

Substituting $y = 2x + 8$ into the quadratic function gives:

$$2x + 8 = x^2 + 3x + 2$$
$$x^2 + x - 6 = 0$$
$$(x + 3)(x - 2) = 0$$
$$\therefore \qquad x = -3 \text{ or } x = 2$$

> **Remember:** You need to find the y value as well.

There are two real roots, which means that the line $y = 2x + 8$ intersects the curve $y = x^2 + 3x + 2$ at two distinct points.

When $x = -3$: $\quad y = 2(-3) + 8 = 2$.
When $x = 2$: $\qquad y = 2(2) + 8 = 12$.

The solutions are $x = -3, y = 2$ and $x = 2, y = 12$.

So the line intersects the curve at the points $(-3, 2)$ and $(2, 12)$.

You can see this from the sketch graph.

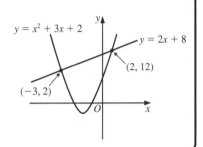

C1

Example 25

Solve the simultaneous equations $y = x^2 - 2x + 2$ and $y = 4x - 7$.
Interpret your result graphically.

Substituting $y = 4x - 7$ into the quadratic function gives:

$$4x - 7 = x^2 - 2x + 2$$
$$x^2 - 6x + 9 = 0$$
$$(x - 3)(x - 3) = 0$$
$$\therefore \qquad x = 3 \text{ (repeated root)}$$

There is a repeated root, so the line $y = 4x - 7$ touches the curve $y = x^2 - 2x + 2$ at one point.

When $x = 3, y = 4(3) - 7 = 5$.

The solution is $x = 3, y = 5$.

> You can substitute $x = 3$ into the linear or the quadratic function.

The line intersects the curve at only one point. Therefore, the line $y = 4x - 7$ is a **tangent** to the curve $y = x^2 - 2x + 2$ at the point $(3, 5)$.

You can see this from the sketch graph.

> A **tangent** is a straight line that touches a curve at a single point.

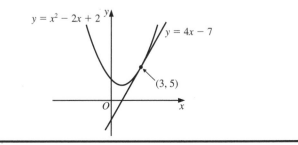

Example 26

Show that the line $y = x - 1$ does not intersect the curve $y = x^2 - 2x + 3$.

....

Substituting $y = x - 1$ into the quadratic function gives:

$$x - 1 = x^2 - 2x + 3$$

$$\therefore \quad x^2 - 3x + 4 = 0$$

Using the discriminant with $a = 1, b = -3, c = 4$ gives:

$$D = (-3)^2 - 4(1)(4)$$
$$= 9 - 16$$
$$= -7$$

Since the discriminant is negative, the quadratic has no real roots. Therefore, the line $y = x - 1$ does not intersect the curve with equation $y = x^2 - 2x + 3$.

C1

Example 27

Solve the simultaneous equations $y = x^2 + xy + 11$ and $y = 2x + 9$.

....

Substituting $y = 2x + 9$ gives:

$$2x + 9 = x^2 + x(2x + 9) + 11$$
$$2x + 9 = x^2 + 2x^2 + 9x + 11$$
$$\therefore \quad 3x^2 + 7x + 2 = 0$$

> $y = x^2 + xy + 11$ is not actually a quadratic function as it contains an xy term.

Factorising and solving gives:

$$(3x + 1)(x + 2) = 0$$
$$3x + 1 = 0 \text{ or } x + 2 = 0$$
$$\therefore \qquad x = -\tfrac{1}{3} \text{ or } x = -2$$

When $x = -\tfrac{1}{3}, y = 2\left(-\tfrac{1}{3}\right) + 9 = -\tfrac{2}{3} + 9 = \tfrac{25}{3}$.

When $x = -2, y = 2(-2) + 9 = 5$.

> You should **check** your solutions; for example
> $$5 = (-2)^2 + -2(5) + 11$$
> $$= 4 - 10 + 11 = 5$$

Exercise 1J

....

1 Solve each of these pairs of simultaneous equations.

a) $y = 3x - 4$
   $y = x^2 - 4x + 6$

b) $y = 4x + 1$
   $y = 2x^2 - 3x + 4$

c) $y = 3x + 4$
   $y = 3x^2 - 8x$

d) $y = 4 - 11x$
   $y = 2x^2 + 19$

e) $y = x - 3$
   $y^2 + xy + 4x = 7$

f) $y + 2x = 3$
   $y^2 + xy = 13 - 16x$

g) $x + y = 5$
   $xy = 6$

h) $xy = 2$
   $3y - 2x = 11$

2 a) Solve the simultaneous equations $x + y + 3 = 0, y = 2x^2 + 3x - 1$.

b) Interpret your solution graphically.

Simultaneous equations can help you to solve real-life problems.

Example 28

The diagram shows the plan of a room *ABCDEF*.

The length of *BC* is half the length of *AB*, and the length of *EF* is half the length of *AF*. Given that the room has an area of 113 m^2 and a perimeter of 48 m, find the length of CD.

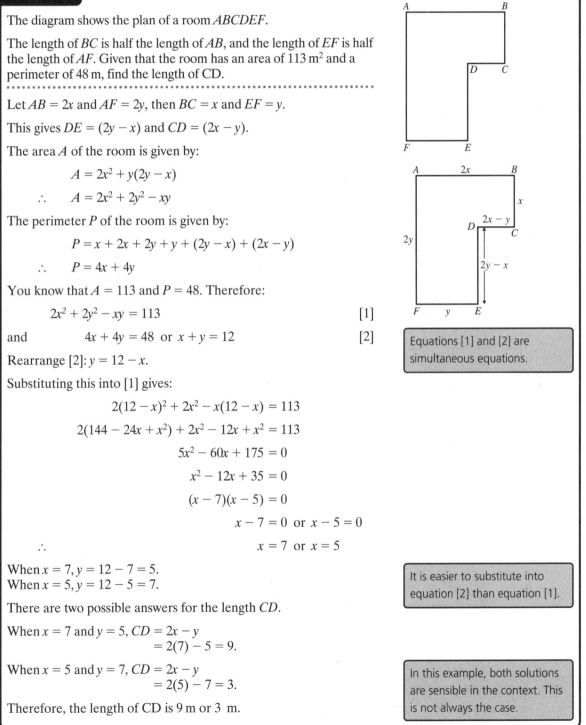

Let $AB = 2x$ and $AF = 2y$, then $BC = x$ and $EF = y$.

This gives $DE = (2y - x)$ and $CD = (2x - y)$.

The area A of the room is given by:

$$A = 2x^2 + y(2y - x)$$
$$\therefore \quad A = 2x^2 + 2y^2 - xy$$

The perimeter P of the room is given by:

$$P = x + 2x + 2y + y + (2y - x) + (2x - y)$$
$$\therefore \quad P = 4x + 4y$$

You know that $A = 113$ and $P = 48$. Therefore:

$$2x^2 + 2y^2 - xy = 113 \qquad [1]$$

and $\qquad 4x + 4y = 48$ or $x + y = 12 \qquad [2]$

> Equations [1] and [2] are simultaneous equations.

Rearrange [2]: $y = 12 - x$.

Substituting this into [1] gives:

$$2(12 - x)^2 + 2x^2 - x(12 - x) = 113$$
$$2(144 - 24x + x^2) + 2x^2 - 12x + x^2 = 113$$
$$5x^2 - 60x + 175 = 0$$
$$x^2 - 12x + 35 = 0$$
$$(x - 7)(x - 5) = 0$$
$$x - 7 = 0 \text{ or } x - 5 = 0$$
$$\therefore \qquad x = 7 \text{ or } x = 5$$

When $x = 7$, $y = 12 - 7 = 5$.
When $x = 5$, $y = 12 - 5 = 7$.

> It is easier to substitute into equation [2] than equation [1].

There are two possible answers for the length *CD*.

When $x = 7$ and $y = 5$, $CD = 2x - y$
$$= 2(7) - 5 = 9.$$

When $x = 5$ and $y = 7$, $CD = 2x - y$
$$= 2(5) - 7 = 3.$$

> In this example, both solutions are sensible in the context. This is not always the case.

Therefore, the length of CD is 9 m or 3 m.

C1

Exercise 1K

1 In order to make a new type of beer, a brewer decides to mix x kg of malt with y kg of hops, in such a way that x and y satisfy the following equations:

$$x + y = 8 \qquad x^2 - xy = 24$$

Find the pairs of values of x and y which satisfy these equations. Which of these answers can the brewer use in practice?

2 A rectangle, which is x cm long by y cm wide, has an area of 48 cm^2 and a perimeter of 32 cm. Derive the equations

$$xy = 48$$
$$x + y = 16$$

Hence deduce the dimensions of the rectangle.

3 A right-angled triangle has sides of length x cm, y cm and $(y - 2)$ cm, as shown in the diagram.

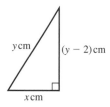

Given that the perimeter of the triangle is 60 cm and its area is 120 cm^2, derive the equations

$$x + 2y = 62$$
$$xy - 2x = 240$$

Find the pairs of values of x and y which satisfy these equations. Which of the answers works in practice?

4 A box is in the shape of a cuboid, x cm wide by y cm long by 5 cm high.

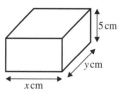

It has a volume of 40 cm^3 and an external surface area of 76 cm^2. Derive the equations

$$xy = 8$$
$$xy + 5x + 5y = 38$$

Find the pairs of values of x and y which satisfy these equations.

Summary

You should know how to ...	Check out
1 Manipulate surds.	**1** a) Find k if $2\sqrt{18} - \sqrt{72} + 3\sqrt{50} = k\sqrt{2}$. b) Rationalise i) $\dfrac{3}{\sqrt{5}}$ ii) $\dfrac{2}{\sqrt{5} - \sqrt{3}}$.
2 Sketch the graphs of linear and quadratic functions.	**2** Sketch the graphs of a) $y = 2x - 3$ b) $y = 5 - 3x$ c) $y = x^2 + 3x - 10$ d) $y = 2x^2 - 9x + 4$
3 Use the technique of completing the square.	**3** a) Write $x^2 - 6x + 11$ in the form $(x + a)^2 + b$. Find the least value of $x^2 - 6x + 11$, and the value of x where it occurs. b) If $y = 2x^2 + 12x + 13$, write y as $k(x + a)^2 + b$. Find the least value of y, and state the value of x where it occurs.
4 Use the discriminant of a quadratic expression to determine the nature of the roots of a quadratic equation.	**4** State, giving reasons, how many solutions there are to each of these quadratic equations. a) $2x^2 - x - 15 = 0$ b) $4x^2 - 12x + 15 = 0$ c) $2 + x - x^2 = 0$ d) $9x^2 + 6x + 2 = 0$
5 Solve quadratic equations by selecting an appropriate technique.	**5** Solve these quadratic equations by an appropriate method. a) $2x^2 + 7x - 15 = 0$ b) $4 - 3x + 2x^2 = 0$ c) $4x^2 - 12x - 5 = 0$

6 Solve simultaneous equations when one of the equations is quadratic.	**6** Solve these simultaneous equations.
	 a) $y = 2x^2 - x - 3$
	   $2x - y = 1$
	 b) $x^2 - y^2 = 3$
	   $x + y = 2$

7 Solve quadratic inequalities.	**7** Solve these inequalities. a) $2x^2 - 3x - 1 > 4$ b) $5x^2 - 8 \leqslant x^2 + 1$

C1

Revision exercise 1

1 a) Express $x^2 + 4x - 5$ in the form $(x + a)^2 + b$, finding the values of a and b.

b) Find the values of x for which $x^2 + 4x - 5 > 0$. *(AQA, 2001)*

2 Solve the simultaneous equations
$$y = 2 - x \qquad x^2 + 2xy = 3.$$
(AQA, 2002)

3 a) Solve the equation $2x^2 + 32x + 119 = 0$.
Write your answers in the form $p + q\sqrt{2}$ where p and q are rational numbers.

b) i) Express $2x^2 + 32x + 119$ in the form $2(x + m)^2 + n$ where n and m are integers.

ii) Hence write down the minimum value of $2x^2 + 32x + 119$. *(AQA, 2002)*

4 Express each of the following in the form $p + q\sqrt{3}$.

a) $(2 + \sqrt{3})(5 + 2\sqrt{3})$ b) $\dfrac{26}{4 - \sqrt{3}}$ *(AQA, 2002)*

5 a) Express each of the following in the form $k\sqrt{5}$.

i) $\sqrt{45}$ ii) $\dfrac{20}{\sqrt{5}}$

b) Hence write $\sqrt{45} + \dfrac{20}{\sqrt{5}}$ in the form $n\sqrt{5}$, where n is an integer. *(AQA, 2003)*

6 a) Express $x^2 + 8x + 11$ in the form $(x + p)^2 + q$.

b) Hence, or otherwise, find the coordinates of the minimum point of the curve with the equation $y = x^2 + 8x + 11$. *(AQA, 2003)*

7 a) i) Solve $2x^2 + 8x + 7 = 0$, giving your answer in surd form.

ii) Hence solve $2x^2 + 8x + 7 > 0$.

b) Express $2x^2 + 8x + 7$ in the form $A(x + B)^2 + C$ where A, B and C are constants.

c) i) State the minimum value of $2x^2 + 8x + 7$.

ii) State the value of x which gives this minimum value. *(AQA, 2002)*

8 Solve the following inequalities.

a) $5(y + 5) < 7 - 3(y + 2)$

b) $x^2 + 4x - 12 > 0$ *(AQA, 2002)*

9 Find the values of x and y that satisfy the simultaneous equations
$$y = 2 - x^2 \qquad x + 2y = 1$$
(AQA, 2002)

10 a) Sketch the graph of $y = 2x\,(7x - 3)$. Indicate clearly the exact values of the coordinates of the points where the curves crosses the x-axis.

b) Find the exact values of the solutions of the equation $2x(7x - 3) = 2x + 4$.

c) Solve the inequalities   i) $2x(7x - 3) > 0$ ii) $2x(7x - 3) < 2x + 4$. *(AQA/NEAB, 1998)*

C1

2 Polynomials

This chapter will show you how to

- Manipulate polynomial expressions
- Factorise polynomial expressions
- Sketch graphs of polynomial functions
- Sketch graphs of translations of curves and circles

Before you start

You should know how to ...	Check in
1 Sketch graphs of linear and quadratic functions.	**1** Sketch graphs of these functions. a) $y = 3x - 2$ b) $y = x^2 - 9$ c) $y = x^2 - 3x + 1$
2 Use the technique of completing the square.	**2** Complete the square for each of these quadratic expressions. a) $x^2 + 3x - 2$ b) $2x^2 + 7x - 11$ c) $20 - 8x - 4x^2$
3 Solve quadratic equations.	**3** Solve these quadratic equations using an appropriate method. a) $x^2 - x - 12 = 0$ b) $x^2 - 3x + 1 = 0$ c) $2x^2 - 6x + 1 = 0$
4 Solve simultaneous equations.	**4** Solve these simultaneous equations. a) $y = 3x - 4, y = x^2 - 4x + 6$ b) $y = 4x + 1, y = 2x^2 - 3x + 4$ c) $y = 3x + 4, y = 3x^2 - 8x$

C1

◆ An expression of the form

$$a_n x^n + a_{n-1} x^{n-1} + a_{n-2} x^{n-2} + \ldots + a_0$$

where $a_n, a_{n-1}, \ldots a_0$ are real numbers with $a_n \neq 0$ and n is a positive integer, is called a **polynomial** of degree n.

> You can say:
> 'A quadratic is a polynomial of degree 2'.

◆ When $n = 2$, the polynomial is called a **quadratic**.
  For example, $3x^2 - 4x + 5$
◆ When $n = 3$, the polynomial is called a **cubic**.
  For example, $2x^3 + x^2 - 1$
◆ When $n = 4$, the polynomial is called a **quartic**.
  For example, $x^4 - 3x^3 + x^2 - 7x + 1$

Example 1

C1

State the degree of each of these polynomials.

a) $4x^6 + 3x^5 + x^3 - x^2 + 5x$ b) $x^4 - 3x^3 + 2x^9 - 7$

a) The highest power of x is 6. The degree of the polynomial is 6.

b) Rearranging the terms in descending order gives:

$$2x^9 + x^4 - 3x^3 - 7$$

The highest power of x is 9. The degree of the polynomial is 9.

An alternative way of writing $y = x^2 + x - 20$ is to write
$f(x) = x^2 + x - 20$.

> $f(x)$ means 'function of x'.

Then: $f(2) = (2)^2 + 2 - 20$
$$= -14$$

2.1 Adding and subtracting polynomials

You can add or subtract polynomials by collecting together terms of the same degree.

> Terms of the same degree are **'like terms'**.

Example 2

Given the two polynomials $f(x) = 3x^3 + 2x^2 - x + 4$ and
$g(x) = x^3 - x^2 + 7$, find:

a) $f(x) + g(x)$ b) $f(x) - g(x)$

a) $f(x) + g(x) = (3x^3 + 2x^2 - x + 4) + (x^3 - x^2 + 7)$
$$= (3x^3 + x^3) + (2x^2 - x^2) + (-x) + (4 + 7)$$

> Collect the like terms and simplify.

Therefore,

$$f(x) + g(x) = 4x^3 + x^2 - x + 11$$

b) $f(x) - g(x) = (3x^3 + 2x^2 - x + 4) - (x^3 - x^2 + 7)$
$$= (3x^3 - x^3) + (2x^2 - -x^2) + (-x) + (4 - 7)$$

Therefore,

$$f(x) - g(x) = 2x^3 + 3x^2 - x - 3$$

> In general, the result of adding and subtracting any number of polynomials is also a polynomial.

2.2 Multiplying polynomials

When two polynomials are multiplied together, each term of one polynomial is multiplied by each term of the other polynomial.

Example 3

Given the two polynomials $f(x) = x^2 + 3x - 2$ and $g(x) = 3x - 1$, find in its simplest form each of the polynomials:

a) $f(x)g(x)$　　b) $2f(x) + xg(x)$

a)　　$\begin{aligned} f(x)g(x) &= (x^2 + 3x - 2)(3x - 1) \\ &= x^2(3x - 1) + 3x(3x - 1) - 2(3x - 1) \\ &= 3x^3 - x^2 + 9x^2 - 3x - 6x + 2 \\ &= 3x^3 + 8x^2 - 9x + 2 \end{aligned}$

> Multiply each term in the first bracket by the second bracket.

b)　　$\begin{aligned} 2f(x) + xg(x) &= 2(x^2 + 3x - 2) + x(3x - 1) \\ &= 2x^2 + 6x - 4 + 3x^2 - x \\ &= 5x^2 + 5x - 4 \end{aligned}$

> In general, the product of any number of polynomials is also a polynomial.

C1

Sometimes you just need to know the coefficient of a single term.

Example 4

Find the coefficient of the x^3 term in the expansion of:

a) $(x^3 + 4x^2 - 7x + 1)(x + 2)$

b) $(2x + 1)(x^4 + x^3 + 3x^2 - 2) + x(x^2 + 3x - 4)$

a) The terms contributing to the x^3 term are:

$$(x^3 + 4x^2 - 7x + 1)(x + 2)$$

The x^3 term is $2x^3 + 4x^3 = 6x^3$. Therefore, the coefficient of the x^3 term is 6.

b) The terms contributing to the x^3 term are:

$$(2x + 1)(x^4 + x^3 + 3x^2 - 2) + x(x^2 + 3x - 4)$$

The x^3 term is $6x^3 + x^3 + x^3 = 8x^3$. Therefore, the coefficient of the x^3 term is 8.

Exercise 2A

1 Find the degree of each of these polynomials.

a) $2x^3 + 3x^2 - 2x + 4$　　　b) $x^2 + 3x - 2$

c) $5x + 7$　　　d) $x^{12} - 4$

e) $4 + x^2$　　　f) $4x - 3x^4$

2   Evaluate each function as indicated.

a) $f(x) = x^2 + 3x + 4$, evaluate f(2).

b) $f(x) = x^3 - 2x^2 + 5x + 1$, evaluate f(3).

c) $f(x) = 2x^2 + 5x - 1$, evaluate f(-1).

d) $f(x) = 3x^2 - 5x + 2$, evaluate f(-4).

e) $f(x) = 5x^4 + 2x - 1$, evaluate f(0).

f) $f(x) = 6x^2 - 3x + 2$, evaluate f(3).

3   Simplify each function as indicated.

a) $f(x) = x^3 + 2x^2 - 3x + 2$ and $g(x) = 2x^3 - x^2 + 5x - 4$, find f(x) + g(x).

b) $f(x) = 5x^3 - 4x^2 + 3x + 2$ and $g(x) = x^3 - 2x^2 + 4x + 7$, find f(x) - g(x).

c) $f(x) = 2x^3 - 5x^2 + 6x$ and $g(x) = x^3 - 6x^2 + 5x + 1$, find f(x) - g(x).

d) $f(x) = 2x^3 + 3x^2 + 7x - 5$ and $g(x) = x^2 + 3x - 5$, find 2f(x) + g(x).

e) $f(x) = 3x^4 + 2x^2 + 6x - 8$ and $g(x) = 2x^3 + 7x^2 + 5x - 4$, find 3f(x) - g(x).

f) $f(x) = 3x^5 + 7x^2 - 2$ and $g(x) = x^4 + x^2 - 7$, find 3f(x) + 2g(x).

4   Expand and simplify each of these products.

a) $(x + 3)(2x^2 - 3x + 1)$ b) $(x - 2)(x^2 - 3x + 5)$

c) $(x - 4)(5x^2 - 2x - 3)$ d) $(2x + 1)(x^2 - x + 3)$

e) $(3x - 2)(2x^2 + 5x - 1)$ f) $(4x - 1)(2x^2 - 5x + 6)$

5   Expand and simplify $(3x^2 - 5x + 6)(2x^2 + 3x - 5)$.

6   Expand and simplify $(2a + 3b)^3$.

2.3 The Factor Theorem

Consider the function $f(x) = x^2 + 3x - 10$.

Factorise it:

$$f(x) = (x + 5)(x - 2)$$

Then

$$f(-5) = 0 \quad \text{and} \quad f(2) = 0$$

You can now sketch the graph of f(x).

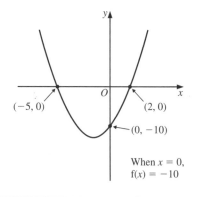

When $x = 0$,
$f(x) = -10$

> The **Factor Theorem** states that if $f(a) = 0$ for a polynomial f(x) then $(x - a)$ is a factor of the polynomial f(x).

This theorem is particularly useful for factorising cubic polynomials.

Example 5

Factorise the cubic polynomial $f(x) = x^3 - 2x^2 - x + 2$ and hence sketch the graph of the function.

Start by checking some values of x:

$\quad$ $f(1) = 1 - 2 - 1 + 2 = 0 \therefore (x - 1)$ is a factor

$\quad$ $f(2) = 8 - 8 - 2 + 2 = 0 \therefore (x - 2)$ is a factor

So $x^3 - 2x^2 - x + 2 \equiv (x - 1)(x - 2)(ax + b)$

$\quad$ $a = 1$, since $x \times x \times ax$ must equal x^3.

$\quad$ $b = 1$, since $-1 \times -2 \times b$ must equal 2.

$\quad$ So the missing factor is $(x + 1)$.

$\quad\quad\therefore$ $f(x) = (x - 1)(x - 2)(x + 1)$

So $(1, 0)$, $(2, 0)$ and $(-1, 0)$ are all points on the graph where the graph intersects the x-axis.

Also, the graph intersects the y-axis at $(0, 2)$.

You can now sketch the cubic function.

> $x^3 - 2x^2 - x + 2$
> $= (x - a)$ (a function of x)
> a must be a factor of 2
> $\therefore$ a must be ±1 or ±2.

> The missing factor must be linear, so you can write it as $ax + b$.

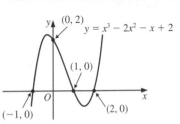

C1

Example 6

Express $f(x) = x^3 + x^2 - 5x + 3$ as the product of three linear factors. Hence:

a) Sketch the graph of the function.

b) Solve the equation $x^3 + x^2 - 5x + 3 = 0$.

If $(x - a)$ is a factor, the constant a will be a factor of 3 and $f(a) = 0$.

So a must be one of ±1, ±3.

$\quad$ $f(1) = 1 + 1 - 5 + 3 = 0$ $\quad\quad\therefore (x - 1)$ is a factor

$\quad$ $f(3) = 27 + 9 - 15 + 3 \neq 0$ $\quad\therefore (x - 3)$ is not a factor

$\quad$ $f(-1) = -1 + 1 + 5 + 3 \neq 0$ $\quad\therefore (x + 1)$ is not a factor

$\quad$ $f(-3) = -27 + 9 + 15 + 3 = 0 \therefore (x + 3)$ is a factor

This now gives:

$\quad\quad f(x) = (x - 1)(x + 3)(ax + b)$

The missing factor is linear, and by inspection you can see that it is $(x - 1)$.

$\quad\quad\therefore$ $f(x) = (x - 1)^2(x + 3)$

> $a = 1$, since $x \times x \times ax = x^3$
> $b = -1$, since $-1 \times 3 \times b = 3$

a) $f(0) = 1 \times 3 = 3$ ∴ the curve cuts the y-axis at $(0, 3)$.

When $f(x) = 0$, $x = 1$ or -3 ∴ the curve cuts the x-axis at $(1, 0)$ and $(-3, 0)$.

You can now sketch the curve.

b) $(x - 1)^2 (x + 3) = 0$

∴ $x = 1$ or $x = -3$

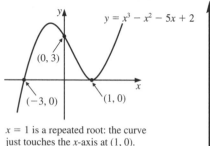

$y = x^3 - x^2 - 5x + 2$

$(0, 3)$

$(-3, 0)$ $(1, 0)$

$x = 1$ is a repeated root: the curve just touches the x-axis at $(1, 0)$.

Sometimes you may find a quadratic factor that cannot be factorised.

Example 7

C1

Factorise the cubic polynomial $f(x) = x^3 + 3x^2 - 12x - 14$.

$f(1) = -24$, and $f(-1) = 0$

Since $f(-1) = 0$, $(x + 1)$ is a factor of $f(x)$.

$x^3 + 3x^2 - 12x - 14 \equiv (x + 1)(ax^2 + bx + c)$

Expand and compare coefficients:

$x^3 + 3x^2 - 12x - 14 \equiv ax^3 + ax^2 + bx^2 + bx + cx + c$

$\equiv ax^3 + (a + b)x^2 + (b + c)x + c$

So $a = 1$, $a + b = 3$, $b + c = -12$ and $c = -14$

Then $a = 1$, $b = 2$ and $c = -14$

∴ $f(x) = (x - 1)(x^2 + 2x - 14)$

> Since $(x + 1)$ is linear, the remaining factor must be quadratic.

> Expanding and comparing is an effective way of finding unknown coefficients.

> $x^2 + 2x - 14$ cannot be factorised further.

Exercise 2B

1 Factorise each of these expressions.

a) $x^3 - x^2 - 9x + 9$
b) $x^3 + 6x^2 + 11x + 6$
c) $x^3 - 2x^2 + 2x - 4$
d) $x^3 - 4x^2 - x + 4$
e) $x^3 - 2x^2 - 5x + 6$
f) $x^3 - 4x^2 - 21x$
g) $x^3 - 5x^2 + 8x - 4$
h) $x^3 - 9x^2 + 27x - 27$
i) $x^3 + 6x^2 - x - 30$
j) $x^3 + x^2 + 4x + 4$
k) $x^3 - x^2 - 5x - 3$
l) $x^3 + 7x^2 - x - 7$

2 a) Factorise the expression $x^3 - 3x^2 - 4x + 12$.
b) Sketch the graph of the function $y = x^3 - 3x^2 - 4x + 12$.
c) Solve the equation $x^3 - 3x^2 - 4x + 12 = 0$.

3 a) Factorise the expression $x^3 - 5x^2 - 2x + 24$.
b) Sketch the graph of the function $y = x^3 - 5x^2 - 2x + 24$.
c) Solve the equation $x^3 - 5x^2 - 2x + 24 = 0$.

4 a) Factorise the expression $x^3 - x^2 - x - 2$.
b) Sketch the graph of the function $y = x^3 - x^2 - x - 2$.
c) Solve the equation $x^3 - x^2 - x - 2 = 0$.

5 Find all of the solutions to each of these equations.

a) $x^3 + x^2 - 10x + 8 = 0$ b) $x^3 - 6x^2 + 12x - 8 = 0$

c) $x^3 - 7x - 6 = 0$ d) $x^3 - 3x = 2$

e) $x^3 + 7x^2 = 15 - 7x$ f) $x^3 + 5 = 8x - 2x^2$

6 Given $p(x) \equiv x(x^2 - 13) + 12$, express $p(x)$ as a product of linear factors. Hence solve the equation $p(x) = 0$.

7 Express the function $(x - 1)(x^2 - 2x - 11) - 16$ as the product of linear factors. Hence solve the equation $(x - 1)(x^2 - 2x - 11) = 16$.

8 a) Factorise the expression $2x^3 - x^2 - 5x - 2$.

b) Sketch the graph of the function $f(x) = 2x^3 - x^2 - 5x - 2$.

c) Solve the equation $2x^3 - x^2 - 5x - 2 = 0$.

9 a) Factorise the expression $5x^3 + 14x^2 + 7x - 2$.

b) Sketch the graph of the function $f(x) = 5x^3 + 14x^2 + 7x - 2$.

c) Solve the inequality $5x^3 + 14x^2 + 7x - 2 < 0$.

C1

2.4 The Remainder Theorem

Many quadratic expressions will factorise. For example:

$$x^2 + 3x + 2 = (x + 1)(x + 2)$$

$(x + 1)$ and $(x + 2)$ are **factors** of $x^2 + 3x + 2$ $\therefore$ $(x + 1)$ and $(x + 2)$ divide $x^2 + 3x + 2$ exactly.

You can write:

$$\frac{x^2 + 3x + 2}{x + 1} = \frac{(x + 1)(x + 2)}{x + 1} = x + 2$$

However, as a numerical example, 5 is not a factor of 19 as 5 does not divide exactly into 19. There is a **remainder**:

$$\frac{19}{5} = 3 \text{ remainder } 4$$

$$\text{or } 19 = 5 \times \underset{\text{the quotient}}{3} + \underset{\text{the remainder}}{4}$$

Example 8

Find the quotient and the remainder when the polynomial $x^2 + 4x - 5$ is divided by $x + 3$.

Write $x^2 + 4x - 5$ in terms of a quotient and a remainder:

$$x^2 + 4x - 5 \equiv (x + 3)\,(\text{quotient}) + (\text{remainder})$$

To obtain a quadratic, the quotient must be linear. Therefore:

$$x^2 + 4x - 5 \equiv (x + 3)\,(ax + b) + r$$

Expanding and collecting like terms gives:

$$x^2 + 4x - 5 \equiv ax^2 + bx + 3ax + 3b + r$$
$$\equiv ax^2 + (3a + b)x + 3b + r$$

$\equiv$ means 'is identical to'. For example, $x + x \equiv 2x$

You can write a linear expression generally as $ax + b$.

Comparing the coefficients of the x^2 terms gives:

$a = 1$ [1]

Comparing the coefficients of the x terms gives:

$3a + b = 4$ [2]

Comparing the constant terms gives:

$3b + r = -5$ [3]

Substituting $a = 1$ into [2] gives $b = 1$. Substituting $b = 1$ into [3] gives $r = -8$.

Therefore, when you divide $x^2 + 4x - 5$ by $x + 3$ the quotient is $x + 1$ and the remainder is -8.

> Since the two expressions are identical, you can match the coefficients.

> Note that $f(-3) = -8$ for $f(x) = x^2 + 4x - 5$.

C1

Example 9

Find the remainder when the polynomial $x^3 + x^2 - 14x - 24$ is divided by $x + 1$.

$x^3 + x^2 - 14x - 24 \equiv (x + 1)(\text{quotient}) + (\text{remainder})$

To make a cubic, the quotient must be quadratic. Therefore,

$x^3 + x^2 - 14x - 24 \equiv (x + 1)(ax^2 + bx + c) + r$

Expanding and collecting like terms gives:

$x^3 + x^2 - 14x - 24 \equiv ax^3 + bx^2 + cx + ax^2 + bx + c + r$
$\equiv ax^3 + (a + b)x^2 + (b + c)x + c + r$

Comparing the coefficients of the x^3 terms gives:

$a = 1$ [1]

Comparing the coefficients of the x^2 terms gives:

$a + b = 1$ [2]

Comparing the coefficients of the x terms gives:

$b + c = -14$ [3]

Comparing the constant terms gives:

$c + r = -24$ [4]

Substituting $a = 1$ into [2] gives $b = 0$. Substituting $b = 0$ into [3] gives $c = -14$ and substituting $c = -14$ into [4] gives $r = -10$.

When $x^3 + x^2 - 14x - 24$ is divided by $x + 1$, the remainder is -10.

> You can write a quadratic expression generally as $ax^2 + bx + c$.

> Note that $f(-1) = -10$ for $f(x) = x^3 + x^2 - 14x - 24$.

Exercise 2C

1 Find the quotient and the remainder when
  a) $x^2 + 6x + 5$ is divided by $x + 2$.
  b) $x^2 - 4x + 3$ is divided by $x + 1$.
  c) $2x^2 + 5x - 4$ is divided by $x + 2$.
  d) $2x^2 - 5x + 8$ is divided by x.
  e) $6x^2 - x + 2$ is divided by $x + 1$.
  f) $6x^2 - 7x + 5$ is divided by $x - 3$.

2 Find the quotient and the remainder when
  a) $x^3 + 3x^2 - 2x + 1$ is divided by $x - 2$.
  b) $x^3 + 5x^2 - 6x + 3$ is divided by $x + 3$.
  c) $2x^3 - 3x^2 - 4x + 1$ is divided by $x - 4$.
  d) $2x^3 + x^2 - 3x - 14$ is divided by $x - 2$.
  e) $2x^3 + x^2 + 5x - 4$ is divided by $x - 1$.
  f) $4x^3 - 3x^2 + x + 2$ is divided by $x + 3$.

Examples 8 and 9 illustrate what is known as the **Remainder Theorem**.

> When a polynomial f(x) is divided by ($x - a$), the remainder is f(a).

You can use the Remainder Theorem as a quick way to find remainders.

C1

Note that this is consistent with the Factor Theorem:
if f(a) = 0, then the remainder is zero
$\therefore$ ($x - a$) is a factor.

Example 10

Find each of the remainders when the polynomial
$x^3 + 5x^2 - 17x - 21$ is divided by
a) $x + 1$ b) $x - 4$

Let f(x) = $x^3 + 5x^2 - 17x - 21$.

a) By the Remainder Theorem, the remainder when f(x) is divided by $x + 1$ is given by f(-1). Now:
$$f(-1) = (-1)^3 + 5(-1)^2 - 17(-1) - 21$$
$$= -1 + 5 + 17 - 21$$
$$= 0$$

Therefore, the remainder is 0 and ($x + 1$) is a factor.

b) By the Remainder Theorem, the remainder when f(x) is divided by $x - 4$ is given by f(4). Now:
$$f(4) = (4)^3 + 5(4)^2 - 17(4) - 21$$
$$= 64 + 80 - 68 - 21$$
$$= 55$$

Therefore, the remainder is 55.

Example 11

Find the remainder when the polynomial

$$f(x) = 2x^3 + 5x^2 - 39x + 18$$

is divided by $x + 6$. Hence solve the equation
$2x^3 + 5x^2 - 39x + 18 = 0$.

By the Remainder Theorem, the remainder when $f(x)$ is divided by $x + 6$ is $f(-6)$. Now:

$$f(-6) = 2(-6)^3 + 5(-6)^2 - 39(-6) + 18$$
$$= -432 + 180 + 234 + 18$$
$$= 0$$

Since the remainder is 0, $x + 6$ is a factor of $f(x)$ and

$$2x^3 + 5x^2 - 39x + 18 \equiv (x + 6)(ax^2 + bx + c).$$

Expanding and comparing coefficients (or by inspection) gives $a = 2, b = -7$ and $c = 3$. Therefore,

$$2x^3 + 5x^2 - 39x + 18 \equiv (x + 6)(2x^2 - 7x + 3)$$
$$\equiv (x + 6)(2x - 1)(x - 3)$$

The equation $2x^3 + 5x^2 - 39x + 18 = 0$ can be written as

$$(x + 6)(2x - 1)(x - 3) = 0$$

Solving gives $x = -6, x = \frac{1}{2}$ or $x = 3$.

> Refer back to page 40 to remind yourself how to compare coefficients.

C1

Example 12

When the polynomial $f(x) = x^3 + ax^2 + bx + 2$ is divided by $x - 1$ the remainder is 4, and when it is divided by $x + 2$ the remainder is also 4. Find the values of the constants a and b.

By the Remainder Theorem, $f(1) = 4$.

$$\therefore (1)^3 + a(1)^2 + b(1) + 2 = 4$$
$$\therefore a + b = 1 \qquad [1]$$

Also by the Remainder Theorem, $f(-2) = 4$.

$$\therefore (-2)^3 + a(-2)^2 + b(-2) + 2 = 4$$
$$\therefore 4a - 2b = 10 \qquad [2]$$

Dividing [2] by 2 gives

$$2a - b = 5 \qquad [3]$$

Solving [1] and [3] simultaneously gives $a = 2$ and $b = -1$.

Exercise 2D

1 Use the Remainder Theorem to find the remainder when:

a) $6x^2 + 5x - 1$ is divided by $x - 1$.

b) $3x^3 + 2x - 4$ is divided by $x - 2$.

c) $3x^2 + 6x - 8$ is divided by $x + 3$.

d) $2x^3 + 4x^2 - 6x + 5$ is divided by $x - 1$.

e) $6x^3 - 2x^2 + 5x - 4$ is divided by x.

f) $8x^3 + 4x + 3$ is divided by $x + 2$.

2 The expression $2x^3 - 3x^2 + ax - 5$ gives a remainder of 7 when divided by $x - 2$. Find the value of the constant a.

3 The cubic $3x^3 + bx^2 - 7x + 5$ gives a remainder of 17 when divided by $x + 3$. Find the value of the constant b.

4 The remainder when $x^3 - 2x^2 + ax + 5$ is divided by $x - 3$ is twice the remainder when the same expression is divided by $x + 1$. Find the value of the constant a.

5 The remainder when $cx^3 + 2x^2 - 5x + 7$ is divided by $x - 2$ is equal to the remainder when the same expression is divided by $x + 1$. Find the value of the constant c.

6 Given that $x - 2$ is a factor of $x^3 + 4x^2 - 2x + k$, find the value of the constant k.

7 The expression $x^3 - 5x^2 + ax + 9$, where a is a constant, gives a remainder of 6 when divided by $x - 3$. Find the remainder when the same expression is divided by $x - 4$.

8 Given that $x - 4$ is a factor of $2x^3 - 3x^2 - 7x + b$, where b is a constant, find the remainder when the same expression is divided by $2x - 1$.

9 The expression $2x^3 + 3x^2 + ax + b$ leaves a remainder of 7 when divided by $x - 2$ and a remainder of -3 when divided by $x - 1$. Find the values of the constants a and b.

10 The cubic $cx^3 + dx^2 + 3x + 8$ leaves a remainder of -6 when divided by $x - 2$ and a remainder of -34 when divided by $x + 2$. Find the values of the constants c and d.

C1

2.5 Algebraic division

You can apply 'long division' to algebra.

For example:
$$\frac{x^2 + 4x + 3}{x + 1}$$

which may be written as

$x + 1\overline{)x^2 + 4x + 3}$

◆ Divide the terms with the greatest degree.
$x^2 \div x = x$

$$x + 1\overline{)\begin{array}{l} x \\ x^2 + 4x + 3 \end{array}}$$

◆ Perform the multiplication $x(x + 1) = x^2 + x$ and calculate the remainder.

$$x + 1\overline{)\begin{array}{l} x \\ x^2 + 4x + 3 \\ \underline{x^2 + x} \\ +3x \end{array}}$$

◆ Divide the terms with the greatest degree.
$3x \div x = 3$

$$x + 1\overline{)\begin{array}{l} x +3 \\ x^2 + 4x + 3 \\ \underline{x^2 + x + 3} \\ +3x \end{array}}$$

◆ Perform the multiplication $3(x + 1) = 3x + 3$ and calculate the remainder.

$$x + 1\overline{)\begin{array}{l} x +3 \\ x^2 + 4x + 3 \\ \underline{x^2 + x} \\ +3x + 3 \\ \underline{3x + 3} \\ 0 \end{array}}$$

The remainder is 0 and hence $x + 1$ is a factor of $x^2 + 4x + 3$.

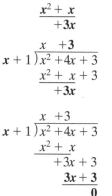

To work out $197 \div 12$ using long division:

```
      16  ← quotient
12)197
    12
    ──
    77
    72
    ──
     5  ← remainder
```

Example 13

Use the method of long division to find the remainder when $x^2 - 3x + 6$ is divided by $x + 2$.

....

Following the stages of algebraic division gives:

$$x + 2\overline{)\begin{array}{l} x -5 \\ x^2 - 3x + 6 \\ \underline{x^2 + 2x} \\ -5x + 6 \\ \underline{-5x - 10} \\ 16 \end{array}}$$

The remainder is 16.

You can check this using the Remainder Theorem. Let $f(x) = x^2 - 3x + 6$. Then
$$f(-2) = 4 + 6 + 6 = 6,$$
as expected.

Example 14

Given that
$$\frac{x^3 + 2x - 5}{x - 1} \equiv ax^2 + bx + c + \frac{d}{x - 1}$$
find the values of the constants a, b, c and d.

....

Performing the long division gives

$$
\begin{array}{r}
x^2 + x +3 \\
x - 1 \overline{)\,x^3 + 0x^2 +2x - 5} \\
\underline{x^3 - x^2} \\
x^2 + 2x \\
\underline{x^2 - x} \\
3x - 5 \\
\underline{3x - 3} \\
-2
\end{array}
$$

The remainder is -2. This result can be written as

$$
\frac{x^3 + 2x - 5}{x - 1} = x^2 + x + 3 + \frac{-2}{x - 1}
$$

Therefore $a = 1, b = 1, c = 3$ and $d = -2$.

Write $x^3 + 2x - 5$ as
$x^3 + 0x^2 + 2x - 5$ so that the x^2
terms are not forgotten.

C1

Exercise 2E

1 Use the method of long division to find the quotient and remainder when:

a) $x^2 - 5x + 7$ is divided by $x - 2$

b) $x^2 + 6x - 8$ is divided by $x + 1$

c) $x^3 - 2x^2 + 4x - 7$ is divided by $x - 3$

d) $x^3 - 5x^2 + 9$ is divided by $x - 6$

e) $x^3 + 7x^2 + 9x + 20$ is divided by $x + 5$

f) $x^3 + x^2 + 10$ is divided by $x + 3$.

2 Given that $\dfrac{x^3 + 3x^2 - 2x - 4}{x + 2} \equiv ax^2 + bx + c + \dfrac{d}{x + 2}$, use the

method of long division to find the values of the constants a, b, c and d.

3 Given that $\dfrac{x^3 - 5x + 8}{x + 1} \equiv ax^2 + bx + c + \dfrac{d}{x + 1}$, use the method of

long division to find the values of the constants a, b, c and d.

4 Find the quotient and remainder when $4x^4 - 3x^2 + x + 2$ is divided by $2x + 3$.

5 The remainder when the expression $x^3 - 2x^2 + ax + b$ is divided by $x - 2$ is five times the remainder when the same expression is divided by $x - 1$, and 12 less than the remainder when the same expression is divided by $x - 3$. Find the values of the constants a and b.

2.6 Sketching graphs of functions

When you sketch the graph of a function you should consider:

✦ the degree of the polynomial function

If the degree is 1 then the function is linear graph is a straight line	If the degree is 2 then the function is quadratic and the graph is a curve (either U shaped or ∩ shaped)	If the degree is 3 then the function is cubic and the graph is a curve (with a maximum of two vertices, one U and one ∩)
╱ or ╲	∪ or ∧	╱ or ╲ / ∿ or ∿

✦ the intersection points with the axes, when $x = 0$ (intersection with the y-axis) and when $y = 0$ (intersection with the x-axis).

C1

Example 15

Sketch the graphs of each of these functions.
a) $2y + 3x - 2 = 0$
b) $y = x^2 - 6x - 7$
c) $y = x^3 - 2x^2 - 5x + 6$

....

a) This is a linear function and hence a straight line graph.
Writing the equation in the form $y = mx + c$ gives:

$$y = -\tfrac{3}{2}x + 1$$

∴ the line intersects the y-axis at $y = 1$.
The line intersects the x-axis when $y = 0$

$$\therefore \quad -\tfrac{3}{2}x + 1 = 0$$
$$\therefore \quad x = \tfrac{2}{3}$$

You can now sketch the graph.

> The y-intercept is $c = 1$.

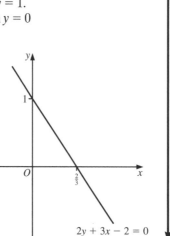

$2y + 3x - 2 = 0$

b) The degree of the polynomial function is 2 and hence this is a quadratic. The x^2 term is positive so the graph is $\cup$ shaped.

When $x = 0, y = -7$ so the graph crosses the y-axis at $y = -7$.

Factorising gives

$$y = (x - 7)(x + 1)$$

$\therefore$ the curve intersects the x-axis at $x = -1$ and $x = 7$

$\therefore$ the line of symmetry of the quadratic curve is $x = 3$.

When $x = 3, y = -16$ and therefore the vertex is at $(3, -16)$. You can now sketch the graph.

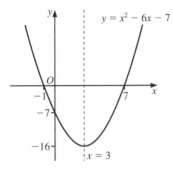

> The line of symmetry is halfway between the two points where the curve crosses the x-axis.
> $$\frac{7 + -1}{2} = 3$$

C1

c) The degree of the polynomial function is 3 and hence this is a cubic.

Any factor $(x + a)$ must be such that a divides the constant 6. In other words, $a = \pm 1, \pm 2, \pm 3$.

When $x = 1, y = 0$ $\therefore (x - 1)$ is a factor

When $x = -2, y = 0$ $\therefore (x + 2)$ is a factor

When $x = 3, y = 0$ $\therefore (x - 3)$ is a factor

So: $y = x^3 - 2x^2 - 5x + 6 = (x - 1)(x + 2)(x - 3)$

This tells you the curve intersects the x-axis at $x = -2, x = 1$ and $x = 3$.

The curve intersects the y-axis when $x = 0$ $\therefore y = 6$.

You can now use all this information to draw the sketch graph of the function.

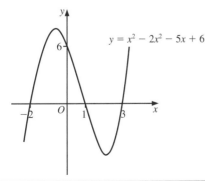

> The cubic shape $\bigwedge$ fits the points that you have deduced.

Exercise 2F

1 Sketch the graphs of each of these linear functions.

a) $y = 2x + 3$

b) $y = 4 - 5x$

c) $y - 4x + 2 = 0$

d) $2y + 3x = 6$

e) $5x - 2y = 4$

f) $3x + 4y + 5 = 0$

2 Sketch the graphs of each of these quadratic functions.

a) $y = (x - 1)(x - 4)$

b) $y = (2x + 1)(x - 2)$

c) $y = (x + 5)^2$

d) $y = x^2 - x - 6$

e) $y = -x^2 - 3x + 4$

f) $y = -3x^2 + 17x - 10$

3 Sketch the graphs of each of these cubic functions.

a) $y = (x - 1)(x - 2)(x - 3)$

b) $y = (2x + 1)(2x - 1)(x - 2)$

c) $y = -(x + 3)(x + 1)(x - 2)$

d) $y = -(3x + 2)(x - 1)(x - 2)$

e) $y = x^3 - 4x^2 - x + 4$

f) $y = 2x^3 + x^2 - 7x - 6$

<u>4</u> Find the equation of the cubic function whose graph is sketched.

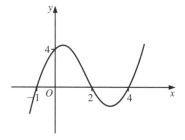

2.7 Translations of curves

The equation of the simplest quadratic function is $y = x^2$.
By modifying the equation, you can transform the graph.

> A translation is a movement in a direction parallel to one or both axes.

Adding a constant produces this effect:

Subtracting a constant produces this effect:

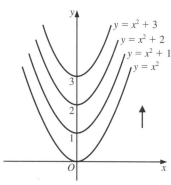

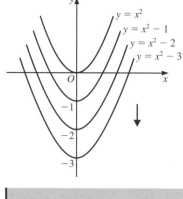

> You can describe these translations by the vectors $\begin{pmatrix} 0 \\ a \end{pmatrix}$ and $\begin{pmatrix} 0 \\ -a \end{pmatrix}$ where a is a constant.

The graph of $y = x^2 + a$ is a translation of $y = x^2$ by $+a$ units parallel to the y-axis.

The graph of $y = x^2 - a$ is a translation of $y = x^2$ by $-a$ units parallel to the y-axis.

You can also add or subtract a constant *before* squaring.

Adding a constant to x produces this effect:

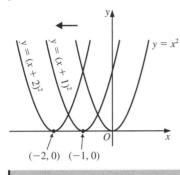

Subtracting a constant from x produces this effect:

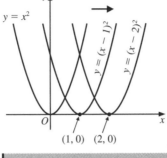

> You can describe these translations by the vectors $\begin{pmatrix} -a \\ 0 \end{pmatrix}$ and $\begin{pmatrix} a \\ 0 \end{pmatrix}$.

The graph of $y = (x + a)^2$ is a translation of $y = x^2$ by $-a$ units parallel to the x-axis.

The graph of $y = (x - a)^2$ is a translation of $y = x^2$ by $+a$ units parallel to the x-axis.

C1

Example 16

By first sketching the graph of $y = x^2$, sketch the graph of each of these quadratic functions.

a) $y = (x - 4)^2$ b) $y = (x + 3)^2 - 2$

a) This is a translation of $y = x^2$ by $\begin{pmatrix} 4 \\ 0 \end{pmatrix}$.

b) This comprises two translations:

firstly, a translation of $\begin{pmatrix} -3 \\ 0 \end{pmatrix}$;

second, a translation of $\begin{pmatrix} 0 \\ -2 \end{pmatrix}$.

This two-stage transformation can be represented by the vector $\begin{pmatrix} -3 \\ -2 \end{pmatrix}$.

The transformed curve is shown in the lower diagram.

Example 17

Express the quadratic function $y = x^2 + 8x + 11$ in the form $(x + p)^2 + q$ and hence

a) determine each of the translations of the graph of $y = x^2$ necessary to obtain the graph of $y = x^2 + 8x + 11$

b) sketch the graph of $y = x^2 + 8x + 11$.

Completing the square gives:

$$y = (x + 4)^2 - 16 + 11$$
$$= (x + 4)^2 - 5$$

a) The translations are:

first, a translation of -4 units parallel to the x-axis, or $\begin{pmatrix} -4 \\ 0 \end{pmatrix}$

second, a translation of -5 units parallel to the y-axis, or $\begin{pmatrix} 0 \\ -5 \end{pmatrix}$

This two-stage transformation can be represented by the vector $\begin{pmatrix} -4 \\ -5 \end{pmatrix}$

Note that you can think of the two translations as combining to make a single translation.

b) The diagram shows the graph of $y = x^2 + 8x + 11$.

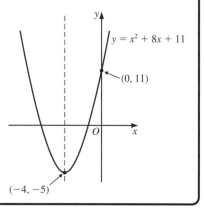

C1

Exercise 2G

1 a) Express the quadratic function $y = x^2 - 6x + 13$ in the form $y = (x + p)^2 + q$.

   b) Hence determine each of the translations of the graph of $y = x^2$ necessary to obtain the graph of $y = x^2 - 6x + 13$.

   c) Sketch the graph of $y = x^2 - 6x + 13$.

2 a) Express the quadratic function $y = x^2 - 8x + 20$ in the form $y = (x + p)^2 + q$.

   b) Hence determine each of the translations of the graph of $y = x^2$ necessary to obtain the graph of $y = x^2 - 8x + 20$.

   c) Sketch the graph of $y = x^2 - 8x + 20$.

3 a) Express the quadratic function $y = x^2 + 4x + 12$ in the form $y = (x + p)^2 + q$.

   b) Hence determine each of the translations of the graph of $y = x^2$ necessary to obtain the graph of $y = x^2 + 4x + 12$.

   c) Sketch the graph of $y = x^2 + 4x + 12$.

Translating the circle

The diagram shows a circle, centre the origin, with radius r.

A point P on the circle has coordinates (x, y).

By Pythagoras' theorem:

$$x^2 + y^2 = r^2$$

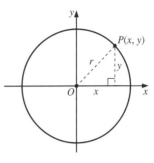

> The equation of a circle with radius r and centre $(0, 0)$ is given by
> $$x^2 + y^2 = r^2$$

You can transform this basic equation in a similar way to quadratics.

> The graph of $(x - a)^2 + (y - b)^2 = r^2$ is a translation of $x^2 + y^2 = r^2$ by the vector $\begin{pmatrix} a \\ b \end{pmatrix}$.
>
> The centre of the circle is obtained by coordinates (a, b).

C1

Example 18

Sketch the circle given by $(x - 3)^2 + y^2 = 4$.

Translate $x^2 + y^2 = 2^2$ by the vector $\begin{pmatrix} 3 \\ 0 \end{pmatrix}$, or a translation parallel to the x-axis by 3 units.

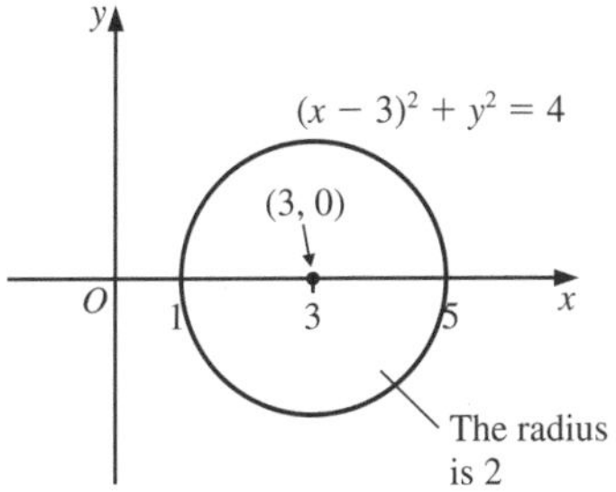

$(x - 3)^2 + y^2 = 4$

$(3, 0)$

The radius is 2

Example 19

Sketch the circle given by $(x + 2)^2 + (y - 1)^2 = 9$.

Translate $x^2 + y^2 = 3^2$ by the vector $\begin{pmatrix} -2 \\ 1 \end{pmatrix}$. This is a two-stage transformation:

◆ a translation of -2 units parallel to the x-axis
◆ a translation of 1 unit parallel to the y-axis.

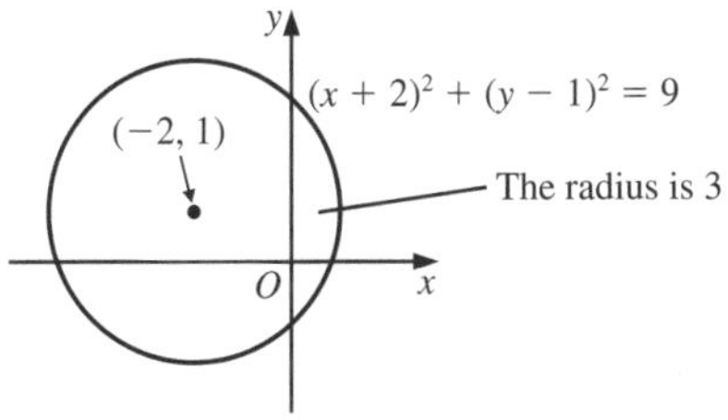

$(x + 2)^2 + (y - 1)^2 = 9$

$(-2, 1)$

The radius is 3

Exercise 2H

1 Sketch the circle described by each equation.

a) $(x - 4)^2 + (y - 3)^2 = 4$ b) $(x - 5)^2 + (y - 3)^2 = 9$

c) $(x + 6)^2 + (y - 5)^2 = 16$ d) $x^2 + (y - 4)^2 = 25$

e) $(x + 2)^2 + y^2 = 4$ f) $(x + 4)^2 + (y + 4)^2 = 32$

2 Find the equations of each of these circles, expressing your answers in the form $(x - a)^2 + (y - b)^2 = r^2$.

a) centre $(4, 5)$, radius 3   b) centre $(6, 7)$, radius 8

c) centre $(2, -1)$, radius 4   d) centre $(-3, 4)$, radius 2

e) centre $(5, 0)$, radius 3   f) centre $(-6, -9)$, radius 11

C1

3 Show that the equation $x^2 + y^2 - 4x + 6y = 12$ represents a circle, and find its centre and radius.

Summary

You should know how to ...	Check out
1 Recognise the graphs of cubic and other polynomial functions.	**1** Identify each of these graphs as linear, quadratic, cubic or other. 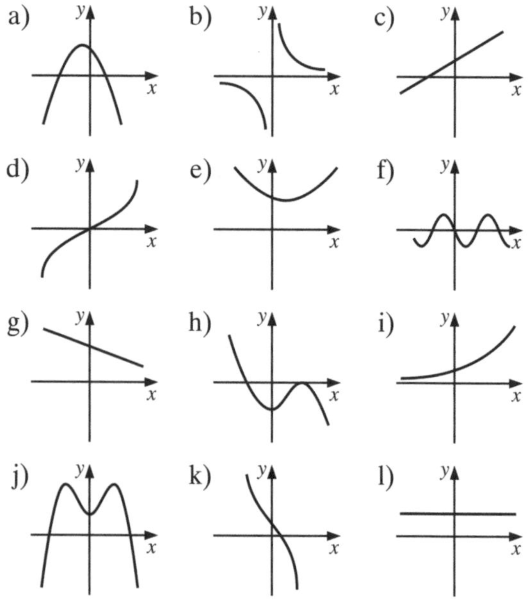

2 Use the Factor Theorem to find a factor of a polynomial expression.

2 a) $f(x) = x^3 - 4x^2 + x + 6$
   i) Show that $f(2) = 0$
   ii) Hence factorise $f(x)$ into three linear factors.

 b) $p(x) = x^3 + 2x^2 + 2x + 1$
   Show that $p(x)$ can be written as
   $$p(x) = (x + 1)(x^2 + ax + b)$$
   and give the values of a and b.

3 Use the Remainder Theorem to find the remainder when a polynomial expression is divided by a linear expression.

3 a) Find the remainder when $x^3 + 2x^2 - 3x - 4$ is divided by $x + 4$.

 b) Find the value of k if $x^3 + x^2 + kx + 3$ gives a remainder of 7 when divided by $x - 2$.

C1

4 Recognise the general equation of a circle and find the radius and the coordinates of the centre.

4 A curve has equation $x^2 + y^2 - 4x + 6y + 1 = 0$.

 a) Explain why this curve must be a circle.

 b) Find the coordinates of the centre, and also the radius.

5 Recognise graphs of quadratic functions and circles as translations of the graphs $y = x^2$ and $x^2 + y^2 = r^2$.

5 a)

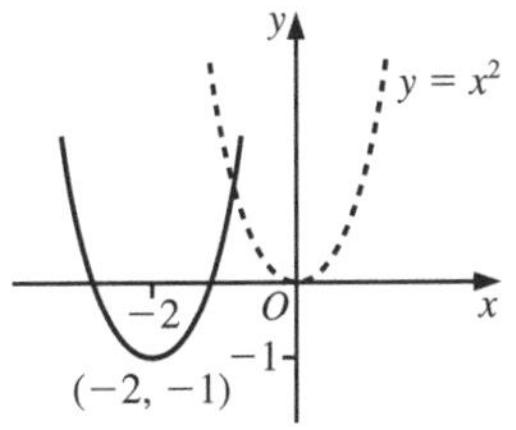

   i) Find the equation of the graph shown by the unbroken line.
   ii) Explain how this graph is related to $y = x^2$ by a translation.

 b)

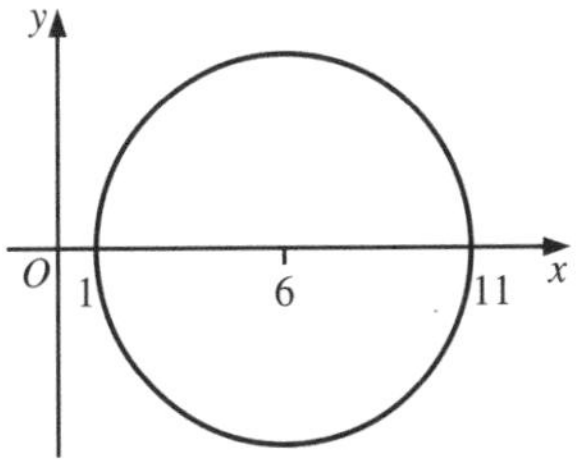

   i) Find the equation of this circle.
   ii) Explain how you can obtain this graph using a translation of $x^2 + y^2 = 25$.

Revision exercise 2

1 A polynomial is given by $p(x) = x^3 - 3x + 2$.

  a) Use the Factor Theorem to show that $(x + 2)$ is a factor of $p(x)$.

  b) Express $p(x)$ as a product of linear factors.

  c) i) Hence sketch the graph of $y = p(x)$.
        Indicate the coordinates of the points where the graph
        intersects the coordinate axes.

   ii) Hence, or otherwise, solve the inequality $x^3 - 3x + 2 < 0$.   *(AQA, 2003)*

2 The cubic polynomial $x^3 + ax^2 + bx + 4$, where a and b are constants,
  has factors $x - 2$ and $x + 1$. Use the Factor Theorem to find the values
  of a and b.   *(AQA, 2001)*

3 a) Prove that, if the polynomial $f(x)$ has a factor $(x - a)$, then
       $f(a) = 0$.

  b) The polynomial $f(x) = x^3 + px^2 + qx + 6$ has a factor $(x - 1)$.
     When $f(x)$ is divided by $x + 1$ there is a remainder of 8.
     Find the values of p and q.   *(AQA, 2001)*

4 The function f is defined for all real values of x by
  $f(x) = x^2 + 6x + 11$.

  a) i) Express $f(x)$ in the form $(x + p)^2 + q$, where p and q are integers.
   ii) State the value of x for which $f(x)$ is least.

  b) Solve the inequality $f(x) > 3$.   *(AQA, 2002)*

5 a) Express $x^2 - 8x - 3$ in completed square form.

     Hence, or otherwise, find the exact solutions of the equation
     $x^2 - 8x - 3 = 0$.

  b) Sketch the graph of $y = (2x - 17)(x^2 - 8x - 3)$ clearly marking
     where the graph crosses both axes.

  c) Solve the inequality $(2x - 17)(x^2 - 8x - 3) \leq 0$.   *(AQA/NEAB, 1996)*

6 Given that $f(x) = x^3 + 4x^2 + x - 6$,

  a) Find $f(1)$ and $f(-1)$.

  b) Factorise $f(x)$ into the product of three linear factors.   *(AQA, 2002)*

7 A polynomial is given by $p(x) = 2x^3 - x^2 - 7x + 6$.

  a) By finding the value of $p(1)$ show that $(x - 1)$ is a factor of $p(x)$.

  b) Express $p(x)$ as a product of three linear factors.   *(AQA, 2002)*

C1

8 $f(x) = 5x^3 + 24x^2 + 29x + 2.$

    a) Use the Factor Theorem to find one factor of $f(x)$.

    b) Hence write $f(x)$ in the form $(x + k)(ax^2 + bx + c)$, giving the value of each of the constants a, b and c.

    c) Hence find the exact solutions to the equation $f(x) = 0$.   *(AQA/NEAB, 1997)*

9 The polynomial $f(x)$ is given by $f(x) = x^3 + px^2 + x + 54$, where p is a real number.

    When $f(x)$ is divided by $x + 3$ the remainder is -3.
    Use the Remainder Theorem to find the value of p.   *(AQA, 2003)*

C1

3 Coordinate geometry

This chapter will show you how to

- ✦ Calculate the distance between two points
- ✦ Calculate the coordinates of the mid-point of a straight line
- ✦ Find the gradient of a straight line
- ✦ Find the equation of a straight line
- ✦ Find the equation of a circle
- ✦ Use the properties of circles
- ✦ Find the equations of tangents and normals to a circle

C1

Before you start

You should know how to ...	Check in
1 Recognise that scaling coordinate axes can affect the geometry.	**1** On a piece of graph paper draw axes for $-4 \leqslant x \leqslant 4$ and $-4 \leqslant y \leqslant 4$, using 1 cm to 1 unit on both Ox and Oy. Plot the points $A(4, 2)$, $B(-1, -3)$, $C(-2, 3)$ and $D(3, -2)$. Draw the lines AB and CD. What is the angle between lines AB and CD? On another piece of graph paper draw axes for $-4 \leqslant x \leqslant 4$ using 1 cm to 1 unit, and for $-4 \leqslant y \leqslant 4$ using 2 cm for 1 unit. Plot the points A, B, C and D as above. What is the angle between lines AB and CD?
2 Use the gradient to measure the steepness of a line.	**2** Find the gradient of the line PQ in the following cases. a) b) c) d) e) f) *(continued)*

3 Use Pythagoras' theorem.

3 Find the length of the side indicated in these right-angled triangles.

a)

p
6
8

b)

7
q
3

c)

5
8
r

d)

d
4
7

4 Use these facts of circle geometry:
   i) The angle in a semi-circle is a right angle.
   ii) The perpendicular bisector of a chord passes through the centre of the circle.
   iii) The radius is perpendicular to the tangent at the point of contact.

4 Draw a circle, radius 4 cm, and mark the centre as point O. Draw a line through O to form diameter AB.

   a) Pick a point P on the circumference. What is the size of angle APB? Explain your answer.

   b) Mark the point M, the mid-point of AP. Join O to M and extend the line to form the radius OC. What is the size of angle OMA? Explain your answer.

   c) At point C, draw a line at 90° to radius OC. What is the geometrical relationship between this line and the circle?

5 Use the rules of signs.

5 Calculate:

   a) $2 + -3$

   b) $-5 + 3$

   c) $2 - -5$

   d) $-7 - -3$

6 Manipulate linear equations.

6 Write each of these equations in the form $ax + by + c = 0$, where a, b and c are integers.

   a) $y = 2x - 7$

   b) $\dfrac{x}{3} + 2y = 4$

   c) $\dfrac{y}{3} - \dfrac{x}{5} = 1$

   Write each of these equations in the form $y = mx + c$, where m and c are rational numbers.

   d) $\dfrac{y}{2 - x} = 3$

   e) $\dfrac{y - 2}{x + 3} = \dfrac{2}{5}$

   f) $\dfrac{y - 1}{x - -2} = -\dfrac{1}{2}$

C1

You can describe the geometry of straight lines and curves in terms of algebra. If you draw two axes in a plane at right angles to each other, you can define any point in the plane in terms of its distance from these two axes.

This kind of geometry is called **coordinate geometry**, and the x and y axes are **coordinate axes**.

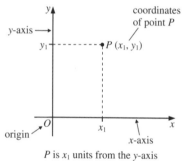

P is x_1 units from the y-axis and y_1 units from the x-axis.

3.1 Distance between two points

If you know the coordinates of any two points in the xy plane you can calculate the distance between them.

Example 1

Find the distance between the points $A(1, 3)$ and $B(6, 15)$.

Construct a right-angled triangle ABC, with AB as the hypotenuse:

   Length $AC = 6 - 1 = 5$ units

   Length $BC = 15 - 3 = 12$ units

Using Pythagoras' theorem gives:

$$AB^2 = 5^2 + 12^2$$
$$= 169$$
$$\therefore \quad AB = \sqrt{169} = 13 \text{ units}$$

The distance between points A and B is 13 units.

Example 2

Find the distance between the points $A(-2, 3)$ and $B(6, -3)$.

Sketching the points and using the right-angled triangle ABC with AB as hypotenuse gives:

   Length $AC = 3 + 3 = 6$ units

   Length $BC = 2 + 6 = 8$ units

Using Pythagoras' theorem gives:

$$AB^2 = 6^2 + 8^2$$
$$= 100$$
$$\therefore \quad AB = 10 \text{ units}$$

The distance between the points A and B is 10 units.

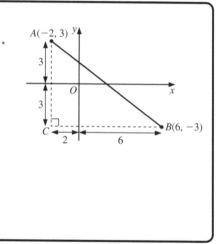

General formula for the distance between two points

If you have two points $A(x_1, y_1)$ and $B(x_2, y_2)$ you can use a general formula to find the distance AB.

In the diagram, the lengths AC and BC are given by

$$AC = x_2 - x_1 \qquad BC = y_2 - y_1$$

Using Pythagoras' theorem gives:

$$AB^2 = (x_2 - x_1)^2 + (y_2 - y_1)^2$$
$$\therefore \quad AB = \sqrt{(x_2 - x_1)^2 + (y_2 - y_1)^2}$$

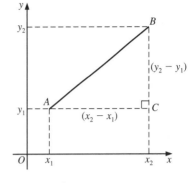

> The distance between the two points $A(x_1, y_1)$ and $B(x_2, y_2)$ is given by
> $$\sqrt{(x_2 - x_1)^2 + (y_2 - y_1)^2}$$

C1

Example 3

Prove that the points $A(-3, 4)$, $B(1, 1)$ and $C(7, 9)$ are the vertices of a right-angled triangle.

. . . .

Using the right-angled triangle shown in the diagram, the distance AB is given by:

$$AB^2 = 4^2 + 3^2$$
$$= 25$$
$$\therefore AB = \sqrt{25} = 5 \text{ units}$$

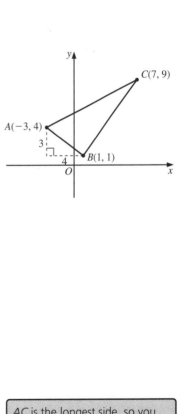

You could also calculate this directly using the general formula:

$$AB^2 = (-3 - 1)^2 + (4 - 1)^2$$
$$= 4^2 + 3^2$$
$$\therefore \quad AB = \sqrt{25} = 5 \text{ units}$$

The distance BC is given by:

$$BC^2 = (7 - 1)^2 + (9 - 1)^2 = 6^2 + 8^2$$
$$= 100$$
$$\therefore \quad BC = \sqrt{100} = 10 \text{ units}$$

The distance AC is given by:

$$AC^2 = (7 - -3)^2 + (9 - 4)^2 = 10^2 + 5^2$$
$$= 125$$
$$\therefore \quad AC = \sqrt{125} \text{ units}$$

When the lengths of the sides of triangle ABC satisfy Pythagoras' theorem, then triangle ABC is right-angled.

$$AC^2 = 125 \quad \text{and} \quad AB^2 + BC^2 = 25 + 100 = 125$$
$$\therefore \quad AC^2 = AB^2 + BC^2$$

Therefore, the triangle ABC is right-angled.

> AC is the longest side, so you need to check that $AC^2 = AB^2 + BC^2$.

Example 4

The points A, B and C have coordinates $(3, 2)$, $(1, -2)$ and $(0, k)$ respectively, where k is a constant. Given that $AC = 5BC$, find the possible values of k.

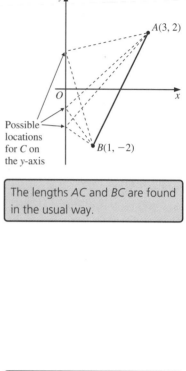

If $AC = 5BC$ then squaring both sides gives:

$$AC^2 = 25BC^2 \qquad [1]$$

Using the formula:

$$AC^2 = (3 - 0)^2 + (2 - k)^2$$
$$= 9 + 4 - 4k + k^2$$
$$= k^2 - 4k + 13 \qquad [2]$$

The lengths AC and BC are found in the usual way.

Similarly,

$$BC^2 = (1 - 0)^2 + (-2 - k)^2$$
$$= 1 + 4 + 4k + k^2$$
$$= k^2 + 4k + 5 \qquad [3]$$

Substituting [2] and [3] into [1] gives:

$$k^2 - 4k + 13 = 25(k^2 + 4k + 5)$$
$$k^2 - 4k + 13 = 25k^2 + 100k + 125$$
$$24k^2 + 104k + 112 = 0$$
$$3k^2 + 13k + 14 = 0$$
$$(3k + 7)(k + 2) = 0$$
$$\therefore \qquad k = -\tfrac{7}{3} \quad \text{or} \quad k = -2$$

Divide through by 8 to simplify.

Factorise and solve the equation.

The possible values of k are $-\tfrac{7}{3}$ and -2.

Exercise 3A

1 Find the distance between each of these pairs of points.
a) $(2, 1)$ and $(5, 5)$
b) $(3, 6)$ and $(8, 18)$
c) $(-3, 2)$ and $(5, 8)$
d) $(0, -2)$ and $(8, 13)$
e) $(-3, -4)$ and $(-15, 12)$
f) $(2, 5)$ and $(6, 1)$
g) $(-7, 3)$ and $(-2, 5)$
h) $(6, 0)$ and $(-4, 0)$
i) $(2, -3)$ and $(7, 7)$
j) $(-7, 4)$ and $(-1, 1)$
k) $(4, -1)$ and $(-2, 1)$
l) $(5, 8)$ and $(8, 5)$

2 The three points A, B and C have coordinates $(-1, 3)$, $(6, 4)$ and $(1, -1)$ respectively. Show that the distance AB is equal to the distance BC.

3 $P(-2, -6)$, $Q(6, 9)$ and $R(1, -3)$ are the vertices of a triangle. Find the number of units by which the length of PQ exceeds the length of QR.

4 Prove that the points $A(2, 3)$, $B(5, 6)$ and $C(8, 3)$ are the vertices of a right-angled triangle.

5 A triangle has vertices at $(1, 2)$, $(13, 7)$ and $(6, 14)$. Prove that the triangle is isosceles.

6 Prove that the triangle with vertices $P(2, 1)$, $Q(5, -1)$ and $R(9, 5)$ is not right-angled.

7 Point C has coordinates $(1, 3)$, point D has coordinates $(5, -1)$, and point E has coordinates $(-1, -3)$. Prove that the triangle CDE is isosceles.

8 By first showing that the triangle with vertices $A(-3, -1)$, $B(1, -4)$ and $C(7, 4)$ is right-angled, deduce that the area of the triangle ABC is 25 units^2.

9 Given that the distance between $P(p, 4)$ and $Q(2, 3)$ is equal to the distance between $R(3, -1)$ and $S(-2, 4)$, calculate the possible values of p.

10 A triangle has vertices $A(6, 2)$, $B(b, 6)$ and $C(-2, 6)$. Given that the triangle is isosceles with $AB = BC$, calculate the value of b.

C1

3.2 Mid-point of a straight line

If you know the coordinates of two points, you can work out the coordinates of the mid-point of the line joining them.

Example 5

Find the coordinates of the mid-point M of the straight line joining $A(1, 3)$ and $B(5, 11)$.

In the diagram, $M(X, Y)$ is the mid-point of the straight line joining $A(1, 3)$ and $B(5, 11)$. Since M is the mid-point of AB, E is the mid-point of AC. Therefore:

$$AE = \tfrac{1}{2}(5 - 1) = 2$$
$$\therefore \quad X = 1 + 2 = 3$$

Similarly, D is the mid-point of BC. Therefore

$$CD = \tfrac{1}{2}(11 - 3) = 4$$
$$\therefore \quad Y = 3 + 4 = 7$$

The coordinates of M are therefore $(3, 7)$.

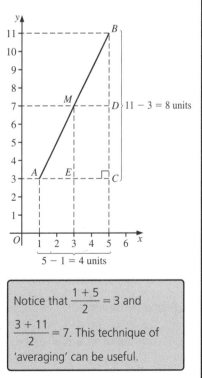

Notice that $\dfrac{1+5}{2} = 3$ and $\dfrac{3+11}{2} = 7$. This technique of 'averaging' can be useful.

General formula for the coordinates of the mid-point of a line

In the diagram, let the mid-point M of AB have coordinates (X, Y). Since M is the mid-point of AB, E is the mid-point of AC. Therefore:

$$AE = \tfrac{1}{2}(x_2 - x_1)$$
$$\therefore \quad X = x_1 + \tfrac{1}{2}(x_2 - x_1) = \frac{x_1 + x_2}{2}$$

Similarly, D is the mid-point of BC. Therefore:

$$DC = \tfrac{1}{2}(y_2 - y_1)$$
$$\therefore \quad Y = y_1 + \tfrac{1}{2}(y_2 - y_1) = \frac{y_1 + y_2}{2}$$

The coordinates of M are therefore $\left(\dfrac{x_1 + x_2}{2}, \dfrac{y_1 + y_2}{2}\right)$.

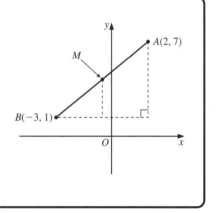

C1

> The coordinates of the mid-point of the straight line joining
> $A(x_1, y_1)$ and $B(x_2, y_2)$ are
> $$\left(\frac{x_1 + x_2}{2}, \frac{y_1 + y_2}{2}\right)$$

Example 6

Find the coordinates of the mid-point M of the straight line joining
$A(2, 7)$ and $B(-3, 1)$.

....

The x-coordinate of M is given by:

$$X = \frac{2 + (-3)}{2} = -\frac{1}{2}$$

The y-coordinate of M is given by:

$$Y = \frac{7 + 1}{2} = 4$$

The coordinates of M are $\left(-\tfrac{1}{2}, 4\right)$.

Example 7

Find the coordinates of the mid-point M of the straight line joining
$A(4, -2)$ and $B(-3, -1)$. Verify that the distance AM is equal to
the distance BM.

....

The x-coordinate of M is given by:

$$X = \frac{4 - 3}{2} = \frac{1}{2}$$

The y-coordinate of M is given by:

$$Y = \frac{-2 - 1}{2} = -\frac{3}{2}$$

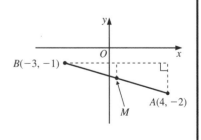

The coordinates of M are $\left(\dfrac{1}{2}, -\dfrac{3}{2}\right)$

The diagrams show the right-angled triangles you need to calculate the distances AM and BM.

Using Pythagoras' theorem gives:

$$AM^2 = \left(4 - \frac{1}{2}\right)^2 + \left(-2 - -\frac{3}{2}\right)^2$$

$$= \left(\frac{7}{2}\right)^2 + \left(-\frac{1}{2}\right)^2$$

$$= \frac{49}{4} + \frac{1}{4} = \frac{50}{4}$$

$$\therefore \quad AM = \sqrt{\frac{50}{4}} = \frac{5\sqrt{2}}{2}$$

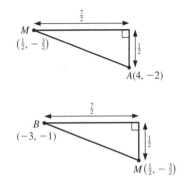

Similarly,

$$BM^2 = \left(-3 - \frac{1}{2}\right)^2 + \left(-1 - -\frac{3}{2}\right)^2$$

$$= \left(-\frac{7}{2}\right)^2 + \left(\frac{1}{2}\right)^2$$

$$= \frac{49}{4} + \frac{1}{4} = \frac{50}{4}$$

$$\therefore \quad BM = \sqrt{\frac{50}{4}} = \frac{5\sqrt{2}}{2}$$

Therefore, the distance AM is equal to the distance BM.

C1

Exercise 3B

1 Find the coordinates of the mid-point of the straight line joining each of these pairs of points.

a) $(3, 2)$ and $(7, 4)$ b) $(3, 5)$ and $(7, 7)$

c) $(-2, 3)$ and $(4, 1)$ d) $(6, 8)$ and $(2, -4)$

e) $(7, -5)$ and $(-2, -3)$ f) $(-6, -7)$ and $(-4, -3)$

g) $(7, 0)$ and $(3, 0)$ h) $(5, -2)$ and $(6, 3)$

i) $(-7, 2)$ and $(7, -2)$ j) $(3, -6)$ and $(5, -4)$

k) $(3, -5)$ and $(4, 9)$ l) $(-2, 5)$ and $(9, -4)$

2 $M(6, 5)$ is the mid-point of the straight line joining the point $A(2, 3)$ to the point B. Find the coordinates of B.

3 P is the mid-point of the straight line joining the point $C(-5, 3)$ to the point D. Given that P has coordinates $(2, 1)$, find the coordinates of D.

4 Find the coordinates of the point S given that $M(3, -2)$ is the mid-point of the straight line joining S to $T(9, -2)$.

5 Prove that the points $A(1, -1)$, $B(2, -5)$ and $C(-2, -4)$ are the vertices of an isosceles triangle. Given that M is the mid-point of the longest side of the triangle ABC, calculate the coordinates of M.

6 A triangle has vertices $A(4, 4)$, $B(7, 6)$ and $C(5, 3)$. Prove that the triangle ABC is isosceles. Given that P is the mid-point of AB, Q is the mid-point of BC and R is the mid-point of CA, prove that the triangle PQR is also isosceles.

7 A quadrilateral has vertices $A(2, 5)$, $B(6, 9)$, $C(10, 3)$ and $D(4, -5)$. The points E, F, G and H are the mid-points of AB, BC, CD and DA, respectively. Prove that
   a) the length EF is equal to the length GH
   b) the length EH is equal to the length FG.

8 $C(2, 1)$, $D(6, 5)$, $E(10, 3)$ and $F(8, 3)$ are the vertices of the quadrilateral $CDEF$. The points P, Q, R and S are the mid-points of CD, DE, EF and FC respectively.
   a) Calculate the coordinates of P, Q, R and S.
   b) Prove that the length of PQ is equal to the length of RS.
   c) Prove that the length of PS is equal to the length of QR.

3.3 Gradient of a straight line

The **gradient** of a straight line is given by

$$\frac{\text{change in } y}{\text{change in } x}$$

> Gradient measures the steepness of a line.

as you move from one point on the line to another point on the line. The gradient is usually denoted by m.

Example 8

Find the gradient of the straight line joining $A(-4, 1)$ and $B(6, 6)$.

As you move from A to B:

   the change in y is 5
   the change in x is 10
   $\therefore$ Gradient $= \frac{5}{10} = \frac{1}{2}$

The gradient of the line AB is $\frac{1}{2}$.

The gradient is independent of which points on the line you choose. To see this, consider point $C(0, 3)$, which lies on the line AB. In moving from A to C,

   the change in y is 2
   the change in x is 4

   $\therefore$ Gradient $= \dfrac{2}{4} = \dfrac{1}{2}$

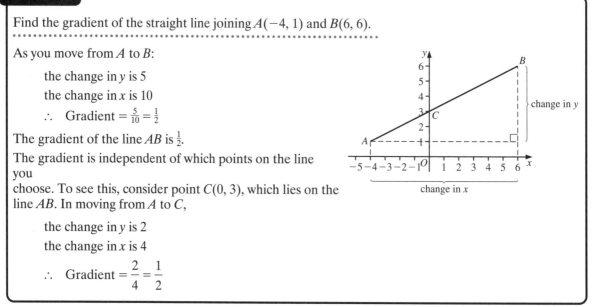

Gradients can be positive or negative.

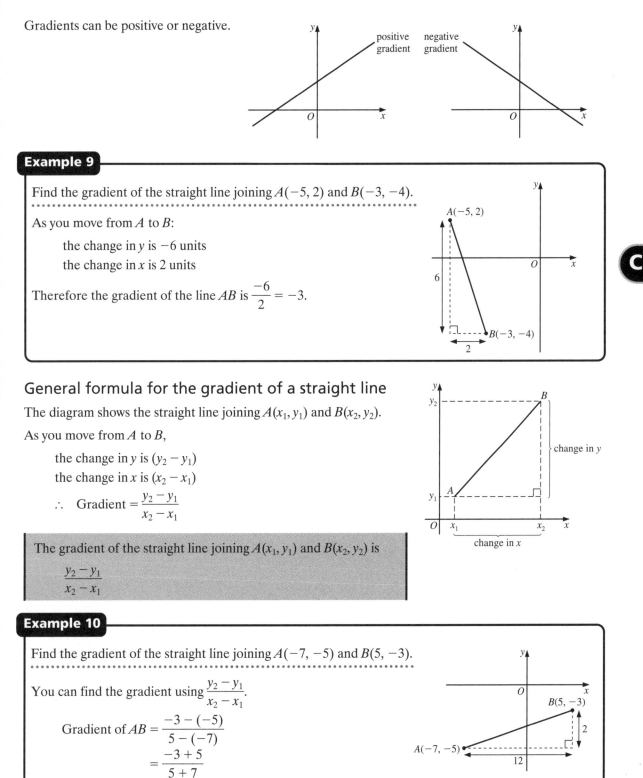

Example 9

Find the gradient of the straight line joining $A(-5, 2)$ and $B(-3, -4)$.

As you move from A to B:

the change in y is -6 units

the change in x is 2 units

Therefore the gradient of the line AB is $\dfrac{-6}{2} = -3$.

General formula for the gradient of a straight line

The diagram shows the straight line joining $A(x_1, y_1)$ and $B(x_2, y_2)$.

As you move from A to B,

the change in y is $(y_2 - y_1)$

the change in x is $(x_2 - x_1)$

$\therefore$ Gradient $= \dfrac{y_2 - y_1}{x_2 - x_1}$

The gradient of the straight line joining $A(x_1, y_1)$ and $B(x_2, y_2)$ is

$$\dfrac{y_2 - y_1}{x_2 - x_1}$$

Example 10

Find the gradient of the straight line joining $A(-7, -5)$ and $B(5, -3)$.

You can find the gradient using $\dfrac{y_2 - y_1}{x_2 - x_1}$.

Gradient of $AB = \dfrac{-3 - (-5)}{5 - (-7)}$

$= \dfrac{-3 + 5}{5 + 7}$

$= \dfrac{2}{12} = \dfrac{1}{6}$

C1

Alternatively, as you move from A to B,

    the change in y is 2 units

    the change in x is 12 units

Therefore, the gradient of the line AB is $\dfrac{2}{12} = \dfrac{1}{6}$.

Exercise 3C

1 Find the gradient of the straight line joining each of these pairs of points.

   a) $(2, 3)$ and $(4, 7)$ b) $(-1, 2)$ and $(1, 8)$

   c) $(5, 4)$ and $(3, 3)$ d) $(7, 4)$ and $(-1, -2)$

   e) $(3, 2)$ and $(-5, 4)$ f) $(-2, -1)$ and $(5, 3)$

   g) $(7, 4)$ and $(-3, 2)$ h) $(3, 8)$ and $(5, 8)$

   i) $(-3, -2)$ and $(-4, -5)$ j) $(-2, 5)$ and $(5, -3)$

   k) $(3, 7)$ and $(7, -4)$ l) $(6, 3)$ and $(6, 4)$

2 A quadrilateral has vertices $A(2, 3)$, $B(7, 5)$, $C(6, 7)$ and $D(1, 5)$.

   a) Show that the gradient of AB is the same as the gradient of DC.

   b) Show that the gradient of AD is the same as the gradient of BC.

   c) What does this tell you about the quadrilateral $ABCD$?

3 $A(-3, 4)$, $B(2, 2)$, $C(5, x)$, $D(0, 5)$ are the vertices of a parallelogram $ABCD$. Calculate the value of x.

3.4 Parallel and perpendicular lines

> Parallel lines have the same gradient.

This is illustrated by the two parallel lines in the diagram.

The gradient of AB is given by $\dfrac{4}{2} = 2$.

The gradient of CD is given by $\dfrac{4}{2} = 2$.

The gradients are equal.

A second useful result is:

> When two straight lines are perpendicular, the product of their gradients is -1.

This is illustrated by the two perpendicular lines in the diagram.

The gradient of AB is 2.

The gradient of EF is given by $-\dfrac{5}{10} = -\dfrac{1}{2}$.

$2 \times -\dfrac{1}{2} = -1$.

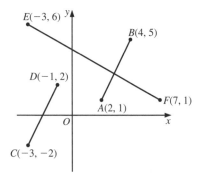

> There is an exception to this rule, when the two lines are parallel to the coordinate axes.

Example 11

A triangle has vertices $A(-2, 4)$, $B(0, 0)$ and $C(-2, -1)$. Show that the triangle ABC is a right-angled triangle.

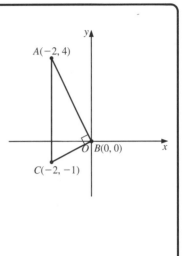

The gradient of AB is:

$$m_{AB} = \frac{0-4}{0-(-2)} = \frac{-4}{2} = -2$$

The gradient of BC is:

$$m_{BC} = \frac{-1-0}{-2-0} = \frac{1}{2}$$

Now

$$m_{AB} \times m_{BC} = -2 \times \frac{1}{2} = -1$$

Therefore the lines AB and BC are perpendicular and triangle ABC is right-angled.

C1

Exercise 3D

1 Given the points $A(2, 3)$, $B(5, 5)$, $C(7, 2)$ and $D(4, 0)$,
   a) show that AB is parallel to DC
   b) show that AC is perpendicular to BD.

> A sketch will help in answering the questions.

2 Show that the line joining the point $A(2, 5)$ to the point $B(5, 12)$ is parallel to the line joining the point $C(-2, -6)$ to the point $D(1, 1)$.

3 A triangle has vertices $A(3, -2)$, $B(2, -14)$ and $C(-2, -4)$. Find the gradients of the straight lines AB, BC and CA. Hence prove that the triangle is right-angled.

4 The straight line joining the point $A(a, 3)$ to the point $B(5, 7)$ is parallel to the straight line joining the point B to the point $C(-3, -1)$. Calculate the value of a.

5 The straight line joining the point $P(5, 6)$ to the point $Q(q, 2)$ is perpendicular to the straight line joining the point Q to the point $R(9, -1)$. Calculate the possible values of q.

6 A triangle has vertices $D(x, -1)$, $E(1, 1)$ and $F(2, -7)$. Given that the triangle is right-angled at D, calculate the possible values of x.

7 Show that the quadrilateral $PQRS$ with vertices $P(-1, 3)$, $Q(2, 4)$, $R(4, -2)$ and $S(1, -3)$ is a rectangle and calculate its area.

8 Show that the points $A(2, 3)$, $B(4, 8)$, $C(8, 9)$ and $D(4, -1)$ form a trapezium.

9   Show that the points $W(1, 3)$, $X(3, 4)$, $Y(5, 0)$ and $Z(3, -1)$ form a rectangle.

10   The quadrilateral $ABCD$ has vertices $A(-2, -3)$, $B(1, -1)$, $C(7, -10)$ and $D(2, -9)$.
   a) Show that AD is parallel to BC.
   b) Show that AB is perpendicular to BC.
   c) Show that the area of the quadrilateral $ABCD$ is $32\frac{1}{2}$ units^2.

3.5 General equation of a straight line

Consider the straight line with gradient m, passing through the point $A(0, c)$ on the y-axis. Let point $P(x, y)$ be a general point on the line.

C1

Then $m = \dfrac{y - c}{x - 0}$

   $\therefore$ $y = mx + c$

> The general cartesian form of the equation of a straight line, where m is the gradient of the line and c is the y-intercept, is
>
> $y = mx + c$

Example 12

Find the gradient of each of these straight lines.
a) $y = 5x - 6$ b) $2y + 4x = 3$ c) $5y - 3x + 4 = 0$

The general equation is $y = mx + c$. You need to express each equation in this form so that you can identify m.

a) $y = 5x - 6$

   $\therefore$ $m = 5$

   The gradient of the line $y = 5x - 6$ is 5.

b) $2y + 4x = 3$

            $2y = -4x + 3$

            $y = -2x + \frac{3}{2}$

   $\therefore$ $m = -2$

   The gradient of the line $2y + 4x = 3$ is -2.

c) $5y - 3x + 4 = 0$

            $5y = 3x - 4$

            $y = \frac{3}{5}x - \frac{4}{5}$

   $\therefore$ $m = \frac{3}{5}$

   The gradient of the line $5y - 3x + 4 = 0$ is $\frac{3}{5}$.

> The xy-coordinate system was introduced by the French mathematician René Descartes (1596–1650). So xy-coordinates are called **cartesian** coordinates after him.

An alternative form of the equation of a straight line is

$$y - y_1 = m(x - x_1)$$

This is useful when you know the gradient and the coordinates of one point that the line passes through.

Example 13

Find the equation of the straight line with gradient 3 which passes through the point $P(4, 2)$.

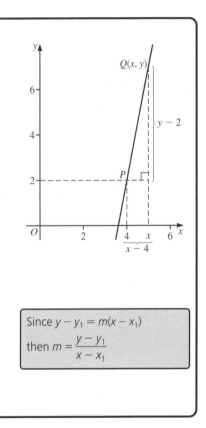

The general equation of the line is $y = mx + c$. You know that the gradient is 3 ($m = 3$). Therefore, the equation of the line is

$$y = 3x + c \qquad [1]$$

Since the line passes through $P(4, 2)$, $x = 4, y = 2$ satisfies [1].
Therefore:

$$2 = 3(4) + c$$
$$\therefore \quad c = -10$$

The equation of the straight line is $y = 3x - 10$.

An alternative method is to let $Q(x, y)$ be a general point on the straight line.

Since the gradient of the line is 3, the gradient of PQ must also be 3. So:

$$\frac{y - 2}{x - 4} = 3$$
$$y - 2 = 3(x - 4)$$
$$\therefore \qquad y = 3x - 10$$

as before.

> Since $y - y_1 = m(x - x_1)$
>
> then $m = \dfrac{y - y_1}{x - x_1}$

C1

Example 14

Find the equation of the straight line joining $A(1, 4)$ and $B(7, 10)$.

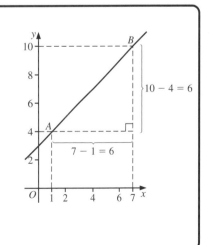

The general equation of the straight line is:

$$y = mx + c \qquad [1]$$

The gradient of the line AB is:

$$m = \frac{10 - 4}{7 - 1} = 1$$

Since the line AB passes through $A(1, 4)$, $x = 1, y = 4$ satisfies [1]. So:

$$4 = 1(1) + c$$
$$\therefore \quad c = 3$$

The equation of the straight line AB is $y = x + 3$.

This is generally used when the gradient is a fraction.

> A third form of the equation of a straight line is
> $$ax + by + c = 0$$

Example 15

Find the equation of the perpendicular bisector of the straight line joining $A(-4, 1)$ and $B(2, 6)$.

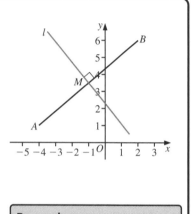

The perpendicular bisector of a line AB is perpendicular to AB and passes through the mid-point of AB.

Let the perpendicular bisector of line AB be line l as in the diagram. To find the equation of line l, you need:

✦   the gradient of l
✦   a point through which line l passes, in this case the mid-point, M, of AB.

The gradient of AB, m_{AB}, is given by:

$$m_{AB} = \frac{6 - 1}{2 - (-4)} = \frac{5}{6}$$

Since line l is perpendicular to AB, the gradient, m_l, is:

$$m_l = -\frac{1}{m_{AB}}$$

$$\therefore \quad m_l = -\frac{1}{\left(\frac{5}{6}\right)} = -\frac{6}{5}$$

> **Remember:**
> When two lines are perpendicular, the product of their gradients is -1.
> $$m_l \times m_{AB} = -1$$

The equation of line l is $y = mx + c$.

$$\therefore \quad y = -\tfrac{6}{5}x + c \qquad\qquad\qquad [1]$$

Line l passes through the mid-point M of AB. The coordinates of M are:

$$\left(\frac{-4 + 2}{2}, \frac{1 + 6}{2}\right) = \left(-1, \tfrac{7}{2}\right)$$

> **Remember:**
> The coordinates of the mid-point of a line joining points (x_1, y_1) and (x_2, y_2) are $\left(\dfrac{x_1 + x_2}{2}, \dfrac{y_1 + y_2}{2}\right)$.

Since line l passes through M, the coordinates of M must satisfy [1]. Substituting $x = -1$, $y = \tfrac{7}{2}$ gives:

$$\frac{7}{2} = -\frac{6}{5}(-1) + c \qquad\qquad \therefore \quad c = \frac{23}{10}$$

Therefore, the equation of line l is:

$$y = -\tfrac{6}{5}x + \tfrac{23}{10} \quad \text{or} \quad 10y + 12x - 23 = 0$$

Exercise 3E

1 Find the gradient of each of these straight lines.

a) $y = 5x - 2$ b) $y = 3x + 5$ c) $y = 8 - 4x$

d) $y = 3 + 7x$ e) $y = 5(x - 2)$ f) $4y = x - 2$

g) $2y = 5x$ h) $7y + 2x = 4$ i) $2y + 5x + 6 = 0$

j) $4y + 5x - 3 = 0$ k) $5 + 3x + 2y = 0$ l) $\dfrac{y}{3} + \dfrac{x}{5} = 4$

2 Find the equation of the straight line that has these properties.

a) Gradient 2 and passes through $(5, 3)$.

b) Gradient -2 and passes through $(6, -3)$.

c) Gradient $\frac{1}{4}$ and passes through $(2, 5)$.

3 Find the equation of the straight line that has these properties.

a) Passes through $(4, 3)$ and is parallel to $y = 3x + 5$.

b) Passes through $(6, -2)$ and is perpendicular to $y = -3x + 4$.

c) Passes through $(3, -5)$ and is parallel to $2y + 5x + 7 = 0$.

4 Find the equations of the straight line joining each of these pairs of points.

a) $(2, 3)$ and $(4, 7)$ b) $(6, 2)$ and $(2, 0)$

c) $(2, -3)$ and $(1, 6)$ d) $(-2, -4)$ and $(-3, -8)$

e) $(3, 7)$ and $(4, -5)$ f) $(3, 9)$ and $(5, 9)$

5 Find the equation of the perpendicular bisector of the straight line joining each of these pairs of points.

a) $(2, 3)$ and $(6, 5)$ b) $(2, 0)$ and $(6, 4)$

c) $(2, -5)$ and $(4, -1)$ d) $(5, 4)$ and $(2, -2)$

e) $(-1, 4)$ and $(3, 3)$ f) $(3, 2)$ and $(-4, 1)$

6 Find the equation of the straight line, p, which is the perpendicular bisector of the straight line joining the points $(1, 2)$ and $(5, 4)$. The line p meets the x-axis at A and the y-axis at B. Calculate the area of the triangle OAB.

7 Find the equation of the straight line, p_1, which is the perpendicular bisector of the points $A(-2, 3)$ and $B(1, -5)$, and the equation of the straight line, p_2, which is the perpendicular bisector of the points $B(1, -5)$ and $C(17, 1)$. Show that p_1 is perpendicular to p_2.

8 The perpendicular bisector of the straight line joining the points $(3, 2)$ and $(5, 6)$ meets the x-axis at A and the y-axis at B. Prove that the distance AB is equal to $6\sqrt{5}$.

9 A is the point $(1, 2)$ and B is the point $(7, 4)$. The straight line l_1 passes through B and is perpendicular to AB; the straight line l_2 passes through A and is also perpendicular to AB. The line l_1 meets the x-axis at P and the y-axis at Q; the line l_2 meets the x-axis at R and the y-axis at S.

a) Find the equations of each of the lines l_1 and l_2.

b) Calculate the area of the triangle OPQ.

c) Calculate the area of the triangle ORS.

d) Deduce that the area of the trapezium $PQSR$ is 100.

C1

3.6 The equation of a circle

The equation of a circle centred at the origin with radius r is given by

$$x^2 + y^2 = r^2$$

In chapter 2 you saw that if this circle is translated by $\begin{pmatrix} a \\ b \end{pmatrix}$ then the equation of the translated circle is:

$$(x - a)^2 + (y - b)^2 = r^2$$

For example, the circle centred at the origin with radius 3 has equation $x^2 + y^2 = 9$. The circle centred at $(2, 3)$ with radius 3 has equation:

$$(x - 2)^2 + (y - 3)^2 = 9$$

This circle is shown in the diagram. $P(x, y)$ is a general point on the circumference.

Using Pythagoras' theorem with the right-angled triangle PCQ gives:

$$(x - 2)^2 + (y - 3)^2 = 3^2 = 9$$

as expected. If you expand the brackets and simplify you get an alternative form of the equation:

$$x^2 - 4x + 4 + y^2 - 6y + 9 = 9$$
$$\therefore \qquad x^2 + y^2 - 4x - 6y + 4 = 0$$

C1

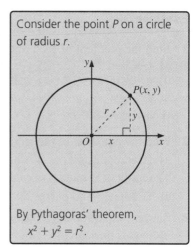

Consider the point P on a circle of radius r.

By Pythagoras' theorem,
$x^2 + y^2 = r^2$.

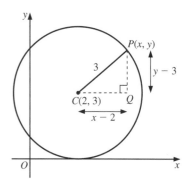

Example 16

Find the equation of the circle with centre $(3, -1)$ and radius 4.

· ·

The equation is

$$(x - 3)^2 + (y - (-1))^2 = 4^2$$
$$\therefore \qquad (x - 3)^2 + (y + 1)^2 = 16$$

Expanding and simplifying give the alternative form:

$$x^2 - 6x + 9 + y^2 + 2y + 1 = 16$$
$$\therefore \qquad x^2 + y^2 - 6x + 2y - 6 = 0$$

The general equation of a circle

The general equation of a circle centred on (a, b) with radius r is given by

$$(x - a)^2 + (y - b)^2 = r^2$$

or, when expanded and simplified,

$$x^2 + y^2 - 2ax - 2by + c = 0$$

where $c = a^2 + b^2 - r^2$.

If the equation of a circle is given in the second of these forms then you can use the technique of completing the square to express it in the form $(x - a)^2 + (y - b)^2 = r^2$.

See section 1.3.

Example 17

Find the centre and radius of the circle with equation
$x^2 + y^2 + 2x - 4y - 4 = 0$.

$$x^2 + y^2 + 2x - 4y - 4 = 0$$
$$\therefore \quad x^2 + 2x + y^2 - 4y - 4 = 0$$

Group x terms together and y terms together.

Complete the square for the x terms and the y terms:

$$(x + 1)^2 - 1 + (y - 2)^2 - 4 - 4 = 0$$
$$\therefore \qquad\qquad (x + 1)^2 + (y - 2)^2 = 9$$

In equation $(x + 1)^2 + (y - 2)^2 = 9$
$a = -1$
$b = 2$
$r^2 = 9$

The centre is $(-1, 2)$ and the radius is $\sqrt{9} = 3$.

C1

Example 18

Find the equation of the circle whose centre is at the point $(1, 3)$ and which passes through the point $(4, 3)$.

Centre is at $(1, 3)$, so: $(x - 1)^2 + (y - 3)^2 = r^2$

For the point $(4, 3)$: $(4 - 1)^2 + (3 - 3)^2 = r^2$
$$9 = r^2, \quad \text{so } r = 3$$
$\therefore$ The equation of the circle is $(x - 1)^2 + (y - 3)^2 = 3$.

Exercise 3F

1 Find the equation of the circles with these centres and radii.
   a) Centre $(1, 2)$, radius 3
   b) Centre $(3, 1)$, radius 4
   c) Centre $(-2, 3)$, radius 1
   d) Centre $(1, -3)$, radius 5
   e) Centre $(-4, 0)$, radius 4
   f) Centre $(2, -4)$, radius 7
   g) Centre $(-3, 5)$, radius 6
   h) Centre $(4, -1)$, radius 3

2 Find the centre and radius of each of these circles.
   a) $x^2 + y^2 = 16$
   b) $x^2 + y^2 = 81$
   c) $x^2 + y^2 + 6x - 4y + 12 = 0$
   d) $x^2 + y^2 - 4x = 0$
   e) $x^2 + y^2 + 6y - 16 = 0$
   f) $x^2 + y^2 - 6x + 8y - 11 = 0$
   g) $x^2 + y^2 + 14x - 10y - 7 = 0$
   h) $x^2 + y^2 - 12x - 12y + 8 = 0$
   i) $x^2 + y^2 + 16x + 12y = 0$
   j) $x^2 + y^2 - 2x + 2y - 2 = 0$
   k) $x^2 + y^2 - 14x + 16y - 31 = 0$
   l) $x^2 + y^2 - 5y + 4 = 0$

3 Find the equation of the circle whose
   a) centre is at the point $(5, 4)$ and which passes through the point $(9, 7)$.
   b) centre is at the point $(1, -7)$ and which passes through the point $(-4, 5)$.
   c) centre is at the point $(5, 7)$ and which touches the x-axis.
   d) centre is at the point $(-2, -3)$ and which touches the y-axis.

4 Find the equation of the circle which has the points $A(2, 5)$ and $B(10, 11)$ as the ends of a diameter.

5 Find the equation of the circle which has the points $P(-2, 3)$ and $Q(4, 5)$ as the ends of a diameter.

6 Find the equations of the circles of radius 5, which touch the x-axis and pass through the point $(3, 1)$.

3.7 Properties of circles

Angle in a semi-circle

One useful property of a circle is that:

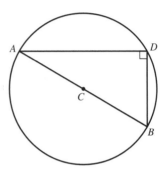

The angle in a semi-circle is a right angle.

In the diagram, if AB is a diameter of the circle then angle ADB is a right angle.

You can use this fact to solve problems in coordinate geometry.

Example 19

a) Show that the three points $A(-2, 3)$, $B(0, 1)$ and $C(4, 5)$ all lie on the circle $x^2 + y^2 - 2x - 8y + 7 = 0$.

b) Show that AC is a diameter of the circle.

a) To show that all three points lie on the circle you need to show that the x and y values of the coordinates satisfy the equation of the circle.

For $A(-2, 3)$:
$$(-2)^2 + 3^2 - 2(-2) - 8(3) + 7 = 0 \therefore A \text{ lies on the circle.}$$

For $B(0, 1)$:
$$0^2 + 1^2 - 2(0) - 8(1) + 7 = 0 \therefore B \text{ lies on the circle.}$$

For $C(4, 5)$:
$$4^2 + 5^2 - 2(4) - 8(5) + 7 = 0 \therefore C \text{ lies on the circle.}$$

b) If you can show that AB is perpendicular to BC then AC must be a diameter by the angle in a semi-circle property.

The gradient of AB is
$$m_{AB} = \frac{3 - 1}{-2 - 0} = -1$$

The gradient of BC is
$$m_{BC} = \frac{5 - 1}{4 - 0} = 1$$

Since $m_{AB} \times m_{BC} = -1$, AB is perpendicular to BC and AC is a diameter.

Perpendicular from centre to a chord

Another useful property of a circle is:

> If a line is drawn from the centre of a circle to a chord, it will bisect the chord.

In the diagram, the radius *CX* bisects the chord *YZ*.

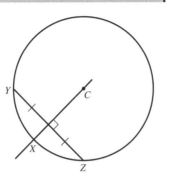

C1

Example 20

The points $A(3, 2)$ and $B(1, 1)$ lie on the circle

$$x^2 + y^2 - 5x - y + 4 = 0$$

Find the equation of a diameter of the circle.

....

AB is a chord of the circle.

The perpendicular from the centre to a chord bisects the chord.

So the perpendicular bisector of *AB* will pass through the centre of the circle and hence is a diameter of the circle.

The mid-point of *AB* has coordinates

$$\left(\frac{3+1}{2}, \frac{2+1}{2}\right) = \left(2, \frac{3}{2}\right)$$

The gradient of *AB* is:

$$m_{AB} = \frac{2-1}{3-1} = \frac{1}{2}$$

Therefore the gradient of the perpendicular bisector is -2.

The equation of the perpendicular bisector is therefore $y = -2x + c$.

Using the mid-point coordinates to find c gives:

$$\frac{3}{2} = -2(2) + c$$

$$\therefore \quad c = \frac{11}{2}$$

The equation of the bisector and hence the diameter is:

$$y = -2x + \tfrac{11}{2} \text{ or } 2y + 4x - 11 = 0.$$

Remember:
The product of the gradients of two perpendicular lines is -1.

You can illustrate this:

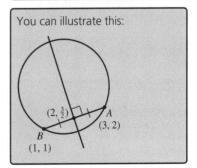

Exercise 3G

1 a) Show that the points $A(1, 2)$, $B(8, 3)$ and $C(7, 10)$ lie on the circle whose equation is

$$x^2 + y^2 - 8x - 12y + 27 = 0$$

b) By calculating the gradients of AB and BC, deduce that AC is a diameter of this circle.

2 a) Show that the points $A(0, 2)$ and $B(4, -2)$ lie on the circle whose equation is

$$x^2 + y^2 - 2x + 2y = 8$$

b) Find the equation of the line which passes through B and is perpendicular to AB.

c) Hence find the coordinates of the point C such that AC is a diameter of this circle.

3 A circle has equation $x^2 + y^2 + 8x - 4y - 30 = 0$.

a) Show that the point $P(3, 3)$ lies on this circle.

b) Find the coordinates of the point C which is the centre of the circle.

c) Find the equation of the radius through P, and hence show that the point $X(0, \frac{18}{7})$ lies on this radius.

d) Find the equation of the chord AB of the circle, which passes through X such that $AX = BX$.

4 a) Show that the points $P(2, -1)$ and $Q(6, 7)$ lie on the circle whose equation is

$$x^2 + y^2 - 12x - 4y + 15 = 0$$

b) Find the coordinates of the point M which is the mid-point of the chord PQ.

c) Find the equation of the radius of the circle that passes through M.

d) Find the coordinates of the point, R, where this radius intersects the circle.

3.8 Tangents and normals to a circle

The tangent to a circle at any point P touches the circle at just one point, namely P.

The normal to a circle at any point P is perpendicular to the tangent at P and passes through the centre.

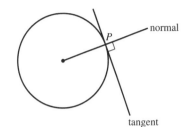

Example 21

Find the equation of the tangent to the circle
$x^2 + y^2 + 2x - 4y - 20 = 0$ at the point $P(2, 6)$.

If you substitute the coordinates of P in the equation of the circle you get:

$$(2)^2 + (6)^2 + 2(2) - 4(6) - 20 = 0$$

which shows that $P(2, 6)$ lies on the circle.

Now:

$$x^2 + 2x + y^2 - 4y - 20 = 0$$
$$\therefore \quad (x + 1)^2 - 1 + (y - 2)^2 - 4 - 20 = 0$$
$$\therefore \quad (x + 1)^2 + (y - 2)^2 = 25$$

Complete the square.

The circle has centre $(-1, 2)$ and radius $r = 5$.

The gradient, m, of the radius through $P(2, 6)$ is given by

$$m = \frac{6 - 2}{2 - (-1)} = \frac{4}{3}$$

This radius is the normal at P and so is perpendicular to the tangent at P.

Therefore, the gradient of the tangent to the circle at $P(2, 6)$ is $-\frac{3}{4}$.

The equation of the tangent through P is of the form $y = -\frac{3}{4}x + c$.
At $P(2, 6)$,

$$6 = -\frac{3}{4}(2) + c \quad \therefore \quad c = \frac{15}{2}$$

The equation of the tangent at the point P is $y = -\frac{3}{4}x + \frac{15}{2}$
or $3x + 4y = 30$.

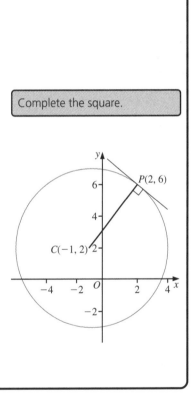

You can draw two tangents to a circle from any point outside the circle. These tangents are equal in length.

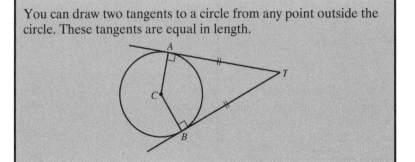

Example 22

Find the length of the tangents from the point $(8, 4)$ to the circle with centre $(3, 0)$ and radius 2.

In the diagram, x is the length to be found. The distance d is given by

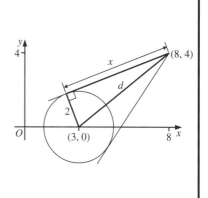

$$d = \sqrt{(8 - 3)^2 + (4 - 0)^2}$$
$$\therefore \quad d = \sqrt{41}$$

By Pythagoras' theorem:

$$d^2 = x^2 + 2^2$$
$$\therefore \quad 41 = x^2 + 4$$
$$\therefore \quad x = \sqrt{37}$$

The length of the tangent is $\sqrt{37}$.

C1

Example 23

Find the equation of the normal to the circle $x^2 + y^2 - 2x - 4y - 20 = 0$ at the point $P(5, 5)$.

The normal is perpendicular to the tangent at P and passes through both P and the centre of the circle.

$$x^2 - 2x + y^2 - 4y - 20 = 0$$
$$(x - 1)^2 - 1 + (y - 2)^2 - 4 - 20 = 0$$
$$\therefore \qquad\qquad (x - 1)^2 + (y - 2)^2 = 25$$

This gives the centre as $C(1, 2)$.

The normal passes through $C(1, 2)$ and $P(5, 5)$. To find the equation, first find the gradient of CP.

$$m_{CP} = \frac{5 - 2}{5 - 1} = \frac{3}{4}$$

Therefore the equation is:

$$y = \tfrac{3}{4}x + c$$

As the normal passes through $P(5, 5)$,

$$5 = \tfrac{3}{4}(5) + c$$
$$\therefore \quad c = \frac{5}{4}$$

The equation of the normal is:

$$y = \tfrac{3}{4}x + \tfrac{5}{4}$$
$$\therefore \qquad\qquad 4y = 3x + 5$$
$$\text{or} \quad 3x - 4y + 5 = 0$$

> To find the centre of the circle, express its equation in the form $(x - a)^2 + (y - b)^2 = r^2$.

> Sketching a diagram helps:
>
>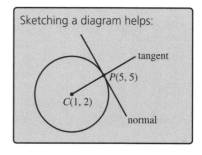

Exercise 3H

1 Find the equations of the tangents to these circles at the points given.
a) $x^2 + y^2 - 2x - 6y + 8 = 0$ at $(2, 2)$
b) $x^2 + y^2 + 6x - 4y + 8 = 0$ at $(-1, 1)$
c) $x^2 + y^2 + 10x + 8y + 39 = 0$ at $(-4, -3)$
d) $x^2 + y^2 + 10y + 20 = 0$ at $(2, -4)$
e) $x^2 + y^2 - 14x + 8y + 57 = 0$ at $(9, -2)$
f) $x^2 + y^2 - 12x - 16y = 0$ at $(0, 0)$

2 Find the equations of the normals to these circles at the points given.
a) $x^2 + y^2 + 4x + 6y - 21 = 0$ at $(1, 2)$
b) $x^2 + y^2 - 8x + 2y + 15 = 0$ at $(3, -2)$
c) $x^2 + y^2 + 8x - 8y - 17 = 0$ at $(3, 4)$
d) $x^2 + y^2 + 4x - 14 = 0$ at $(-5, 3)$
e) $x^2 + y^2 + 10x - 6y - 14 = 0$ at $(2, 6)$
f) $x^2 - 4x + y^2 + 6y - 7 = 0$ at $(4, -1)$

3 a) Find the coordinates of the points where the circle $x^2 + y^2 - 10x - 8y + 21 = 0$ cuts the x-axis.
b) Find the equations of the tangents to the circle at those points.

4 a) Find the coordinates of the points where the circle $x^2 + y^2 - 6x - 8y + 15 = 0$ cuts the y-axis.
b) Find the equations of the tangents to the circle at those points.

5 a) Find the equation of the tangent to the circle $x^2 + y^2 - 4x + 6y - 7 = 0$ at the point $(4, 1)$.
b) Given that this tangent meets the x-axis at the point A, and the y-axis at the point B, find the coordinates of A and B.
c) Find the area of the triangle AOB, where O is the origin.

6 A circle has equation $x^2 + y^2 + 2x - 6y - 19 = 0$.
a) Show that the point $T(4, 1)$ lies on the circle.
b) Find the coordinates of the centre of the circle.
c) Find the equation of the tangent to the circle at T.

7 a) Show that the line $y = 2x + 3$ is a tangent to the circle $x^2 + y^2 - 12x - 15y + 81 = 0$.
b) Find the coordinates of the point where the tangent touches the circle.

8 Find the length of the tangent from the point $(2, 5)$ to the circle $x^2 + y^2 - 14x - 2y + 34 = 0$.

9 a) Find the length of the tangents from the point $(3, -1)$ to the circle $x^2 + y^2 - 10x - 4y + 12 = 0$.
b) Deduce that the shape formed by these two tangents and the two radii through the points of contact of the circle and the tangents, is a square.

3.9 Intersection of a line and a circle

In Chapter 1 you saw that a straight line and a quadratic curve can
intersect at two distinct points, one point or not at all.

◆ Two distinct roots   ◆ One repeated root   ◆ No real roots

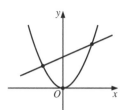   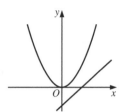

The straight line intersects the   The straight line touches the   The straight line does not
quadratic curve at two distinct points. quadratic curve at one point.   intersect the quadratic curve.

C1

The same three possibilities apply to the intersection of a straight line
and a circle.

To decide how many points of intersection there are you must solve
simultaneously the equations of the straight line and the circle.

The number of roots of the resulting quadratic equation determines
which case applies:

◆ Two distinct roots   ◆ One repeated root   ◆ No real roots

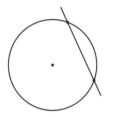   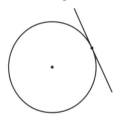   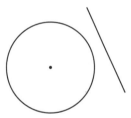

The straight line intersects the   The straight line touches the   The straight line does not
circle at two distinct points.   circle at one point – it is a   intersect the circle.
                                        tangent to the circle.

Example 24

Show that the line $y = x - 2$ is a tangent to the circle
$x^2 + y^2 - 6x + 2y + 8 = 0$.

....

Substitute $y = x - 2$ into the equation of the circle:

$$x^2 + (x - 2)^2 - 6x + 2(x - 2) + 8 = 0$$
$$x^2 + x^2 - 4x + 4 - 6x + 2x - 4 + 8 = 0$$
$$2x^2 - 8x + 8 = 0$$
$$x^2 - 4x + 4 = 0$$
$$(x - 2)(x - 2) = 0$$
$$\therefore \quad x = 2, \text{ a repeated root.}$$

The one repeated root implies that the line $y = x - 2$ touches the
circle at just one point. Therefore, it is a tangent to the circle.

Example 25

Show that the line $x + y = 3$ intersects the circle $x^2 + y^2 + x - 5y + 4 = 0$ at two distinct points. Find the coordinates of these intersection points.

Rearrange $x + y = 3$ to give $y = 3 - x$

Substitute this value of y in the equation of the circle:

$$x^2 + (3 - x)^2 + x - 5(3 - x) + 4 = 0$$
$$x^2 + 9 - 6x + x^2 + x - 15 + 5x + 4 = 0$$
$$2x^2 - 2 = 0$$
$$x^2 - 1 = 0$$

This quadratic equation has two distinct roots and hence the straight line intersects the circle at two distinct points.

Solving the quadratic gives:

$$x^2 = 1$$
$$x = \pm 1$$

When $x = 1$, $y = 3 - 1 = 2$
When $x = -1$, $y = 3 - (-1) = 4$
The points of intersection are $(1, 2)$ and $(-1, 4)$.

C1

Note that you could check this result using the discriminant at this point.
$D = b^2 - 4ac = 0^2 - 4(1)(-1) = 4$, which is positive. This means there are two distinct roots.

Example 26

Determine whether the line $y = x + 1$ intersects the circle $x^2 + y^2 - 6x - 2y + 6 = 0$ at two points, one point or not at all.

Substitute $y = x + 1$ in the equation of the circle:

$$x^2 + (x + 1)^2 - 6x - 2(x + 1) + 6 = 0$$
$$\therefore \quad x^2 + x^2 + 2x + 1 - 6x - 2x - 2 + 6 = 0$$
$$\therefore \quad 2x^2 - 6x + 5 = 0$$

Using the discriminant with $a = 2$, $b = -6$, $c = 5$ gives:

$$D = b^2 - 4ac$$
$$= (-6)^2 - 4(2)(5)$$
$$= 36 - 40$$
$$= -4 \, (< 0)$$

Since the discriminant is negative the quadratic equation $2x^2 - 6x + 5 = 0$ has no real roots. Geometrically this tells you that the line $y = x + 1$ does not intersect the circle $x^2 + y^2 - 6x - 2y + 6 = 0$.

Exercise 3I

1 Find the coordinates of the points of intersection of each of these circles with the corresponding straight lines.
   a) $x^2 + y^2 - 6x - 4y + 9 = 0$ and $y = 7 - x$
   b) $x^2 + y^2 + 8x + 2y - 8 = 0$ and $y = 7x + 2$
   c) $x^2 + y^2 - 8y - 9 = 0$ and $y = 11 - x$
   d) $x^2 + y^2 + 10x - 6y - 31 = 0$ and $y = 5x + 15$

2 Show that the line $y = x - 3$ is a tangent to the circle $x^2 + y^2 - 5x - 9y + 14 = 0$.

3 Show that the line $y = 2x + 3$ is a tangent to the circle $x^2 + y^2 + 6x + y + 8 = 0$.

C1

4 For each of the following determine whether the given straight line intersects the corresponding circle at two points, one point or not at all.
   a) $y = x - 4$ and $x^2 + y^2 - 5x + 3y + 8 = 0$
   b) $y = 3x - 11$ and $x^2 + y^2 - 4x - 30y + 209 = 0$
   c) $y = 2x - 5$ and $x^2 + y^2 - 12x - 4y - 10 = 0$
   d) $y = x + 2$ and $x^2 + y^2 + 3x - y = 0$
   e) $y = x + 2$ and $x^2 + y^2 - 7x - 3y + 11 = 0$
   f) $y = 2x - 1$ and $x^2 + y^2 - 8x + y + 25 = 0$

5 Find the equation of the tangents to the circle $x^2 + y^2 + 4x - 2y - 24 = 0$ at the points where the circle cuts the line $y = x$.

6 Show that the circles $x^2 + y^2 - 10x - 8y + 18 = 0$ and $x^2 + y^2 - 8x - 4y + 14 = 0$ do not intersect.

Summary

You should know how to ...	Check out
1 Find the coordinates of the mid-point of a line.	1 Sketch the positions of A and B in the xy plane and find the coordinates of the mid-point of the line AB. a) $A(1, 4)$, $B(5, 2)$ b) $A(-1, -2)$, $B(4, 3)$ c) $A(-4, 3)$ $B(2, -3)$

2 Find the distance between two points.	**2** For the pairs of points in question 1, calculate the distance AB.
3 Find the gradient of a straight line.	**3** For the pairs of points in question 1, calculate the gradient of the line AB.
4 Find the equation of a straight line in the forms	**4** For the pairs of points in question 1, find the equation of the line AB in the form i) $y = mx + c$ ii) $ax + by + c = 0$
5 Use gradient to find the equation of a line parallel or perpendicular to a given line.	**5** a) Find the equation of the line that is parallel to the line with equation $y = 3x - 7$ and passes through $(2, -1)$. b) Find the equation of the line that is parallel to the line with equation $2x + y + 3 = 0$ and passes through $(-2, 3)$. c) Find the equation of the line that is perpendicular to the line with equation $y = 2x + 3 = 0$ and passes through $(1, 3)$. d) Find the equation of the line that is perpendicular to the line with equation $3x + 2y + 1 = 0$ and passes through $(-1, 2)$.
6 Find the equation of the tangent or normal to a point on a circle.	**6** A circle has equation $(x - 2)^2 + (y + 1)^2 = 13$. a) Show that the point $P(4, 2)$ lies on the circle. b) Find the equation of the tangent at P. c) Find the equation of the normal at P.
7 Interpret the algebraic results of a straight line intersecting a circle or quadratic graph geometrically.	**7** a) The line $x + y = 3$ intersects the curve $y = x^2 - 2x - 3$ at P and Q. b) A circle has equation $(x - 3)^2 + y^2 = 16$. Find, using algebra, whether the line $y = 2x + 4$ intersects this circle.

C1

Revision exercise 3

1 The line $2x - y + 6 = 0$ intersects the coordinate axes at two points, $A(a, 0)$ and $B(0, b)$.

  a) Find the values of a and b.

  b) Find the coordinates of M, the mid-point of AB.

  c) Find the equation of the line through M perpendicular to AB, giving your answer in the form $y = mx + c$.   *(AQA, 2003)*

2 The point A has coordinates $(3, -5)$ and the point B has coordinates $(1, 1)$.

  a) i) Find the gradient of AB.
      ii) Show that the equation of the line AB can be written in the form $rx + y = s$ where r and s are positive integers.

  b) The mid-point of AB is M and the line MC is perpendicular to AB.
      i)   Find the coordinates of M.
      ii) Find the gradient of the line MC.
      iii) Given that C has coordinates $(5, p)$, find the value of the constant p.   *(AQA, 2003)*

3 The points A and B have coordinates $(13, 5)$ and $(9, 2)$ respectively.

  a) i) Find the gradient of AB.
      ii) Find an equation for the line AB.

  b) The point C has coordinates $(2, 3)$ and the point X lies on AB so that XC is perpendicular to AB.
      i) Show that the equation of the line XC can be written in the form $4x + 3y = 17$.
      ii) Calculate the coordinates of X.   *(AQA, 2002)*

4 A circle has the equation $x^2 + y^2 + 4x - 14y + 4 = 0$.

  a) Find the radius of the circle and the coordinates of its centre.

  b) Sketch the circle.

  c) Find the length of a tangent from the point $P(6, 8)$ to the circle.   *(AQA, 2003)*

5 a) Solve the simultaneous equations
$$y = x + 1$$
$$x^2 - 8x + y^2 - 2y + 9 = 0$$

  b) Hence describe the geometrical relationship between the straight line with equation $y = x + 1$, and the circle with equation $x^2 - 8x + y^2 - 2y + 9 = 0$, giving a reason for your answer.   *(AQA, 2001)*

6 The points A and B have coordinates $(1, 7)$ and $(15, 5)$ respectively. The point O is the origin.

  a) Find an equation for the straight line AB in the form $ax + by = c$, where a, b and c are integers.

b) Show that the lines OA and AB are perpendicular.

c) A circle passes through the points O, A and B.
   i) Explain briefly why OB is a diameter.
   ii) Write down the coordinates of the centre of the circle.
   iii) Find the radius of the circle in the form $p\sqrt{10}$, where p is a rational number. *(AQA, 2002)*

7 A circle has the equation $(x - 3)^2 + (y - 4)^2 = 16$.
   The point A has coordinates $\left(\frac{3}{5}, \frac{4}{5}\right)$.

   a) Show that A lies on the circle.

   b) Sketch the circle.

   c) Show that the normal to the circle at A passes through the origin.

   d) Find the equation of the tangent to the circle at A, giving your answer in the form $ax + by = c$, where a, b and c are integers. *(AQA, 2003)*

8 Find the equation of the straight line that is parallel to $y + 20x = 90$ and passes through the point $(4, -10)$. *(AQA/NEAB, 1994)*

9 The point A has coordinates $(2, 3)$ and O is the origin.

   a) Write down the gradient of OA and hence find the equation of the line OA.

   b) Show that the line which has equation $4x + 6y = 13$
   i) is perpendicular to OA.
   ii) passes through the mid-point of OA. *(AQA, 2003)*

10 The equation of the line AB is $5x - 3y = 26$.

   a) Find the gradient of AB.

   b) The point A has coordinates $(4, -2)$ and point C has coordinates $(-6, 4)$.
   i) Prove that AC is perpendicular to AB.
   ii) Find an equation for the line AC, expressing your answer in the form $px + qy = r$ where p, q and r are integers.

   c) The line with equation $x + 2y = 13$ also passes through the point B. Find the coordinates of B. *(AQA, 2002)*

11 The line AB has equation $5x - 2y = 7$, the point A has coordinates $(1, -1)$ and the point B has coordinates $(3, k)$.

   a) i) Find the value of k.
   ii) Find the gradient of AB.

   b) Find an equation for the line through A which is perpendicular to AB.

   c) The point C has coordinates $(-6, -2)$. Show that AC has length $p\sqrt{2}$, stating the value of p. *(AQA, 2003)*

C1

12 The line joining the points $A(0, 5)$ and $B(4, 1)$ is a tangent to a circle whose centre C is at point $(5, 4)$.

   a) Find the equation of line AB.

   b) Find the equation of the line through C which is perpendicular to AB.

   c) Find the coordinates of the point of contact of the line AB with the circle.

   d) Find the equation of the circle.   (*AQA, 2002*)

13 A circle has equation $x^2 + y^2 + 2x - 6y = 0$.

   a) Find the radius of the circle and the coordinates of its centre.

   b) Find the equation of the tangent to the circle at the point $(2, 4)$.   (*AQA, 2002*)

14 A circle has equation $x^2 + y^2 - 4x + 8y + 10 = 0$.

   a) Determine the coordinates of the centre and the radius of the circle.

   b) Explain why the circle lies entirely below the x-axis.

   c) The straight line with the equation $x + 2y + 1 = 0$ cuts the circle at the points P and Q. Find the coordinates of P and Q.

   d) Show that the tangents at P and Q are perpendicular.   (*AQA, 2001*)

4 Differentiation

This chapter will show you how to

- Find the gradient of a curve
- Differentiate simple functions
- Find equations of tangents and normals to curves
- Find stationary points
- Use differentiation in real-life contexts

Before you start

You should know how to ...	Check in
1 Find the gradient of a straight line with equation $y = mx + c$.	**1** Find the gradient and intercept of these straight lines and sketch the graphs. a) $2y + 4 = x$ b) $2x + 3y = 6$ c) $4x - 3y + 12 = 0$ d) $x - \dfrac{y}{2} = 1$
2 Find the gradient of a straight line when two points are known.	**2** Find the gradient of the line AB where: a) $A(6, 4)$, $B(3, 1)$ b) $A(2, 5)$, $B(4, -1)$ c) $A(-3, 1)$, $B(5, 5)$ d) $A(4, -3)$, $B(-4, -2)$
3 Find the equation of a straight line, given the gradient and one point.	**3** Find the equation of the straight line through the point P, with gradient m, if: a) P is $(2, 1)$, $m = 3$ b) P is $(-1, 1)$, $m = -2$ c) P is $(1, 4)$, $m = -\frac{1}{2}$ d) P is $(2, -5)$, $m = \frac{1}{3}$
4 Evaluate a polynomial.	**4** Evaluate these polynomials for the given value of x. a) $p(x) = 2x^2 - 3x + 1$, $x = 2$ b) $p(x) = x^3 + 2x^2 - 5$, $x = -2$ c) $p(x) = 3x^2 - 2x^3$, $x = 1$ d) $p(x) = 5 - x + 2x^3$, $x = -1$ *(continued)*

5 Solve linear and quadratic equations.	**5** Solve these equations. a) $2x - 3 = 9$ b) $5 - 7x = -2$ c) $x^2 - 2x - 3 = 0$ d) $x^2 + 2x - 2 = 0$
6 Factorise polynomial expressions.	**6** Factorise these polynomial expressions. a) $2x^2 - 11x + 15$ b) $3 - 8x - 3x^2$ c) $3x^2 - 2x^3$ d) $2x^3 + 7x^2 - 4x$
7 Sketch quadratic and cubic graphs.	**7** Sketch the graphs of these polynomials, indicating where each graph crosses the coordinate axes. a) $y = (x + 1)(x + 2)$ b) $y = (2x - 1)(x + 5)$ c) $y = (x - 1)(x + 2)(x - 3)$ d) $y = (2x - 1)(1 - 3x)(1 + x)$

C1

4.1 Gradient of a curve

The gradient of a straight line which passes through the points $A(x_1, y_1)$ and $B(x_2, y_2)$ is:

$$m_{AB} = \frac{y_2 - y_1}{x_2 - x_1}$$

The gradient of a straight line is the same at all points on the line. For example, the line with equation $y = 3x - 1$ has gradient of 3 which is a constant.

Consider the piece of curve shown in the diagram.

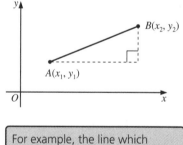

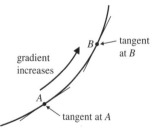

As you move along the curve from point A to point B, the gradient of the curve changes – it becomes steeper.

In the diagram you can see that the gradient of the tangent at B is steeper than that at A. Its gradient is larger. So the gradient of the curve at B is greater than the gradient at A.

For example, the line which passes through the points $A(1, 2)$ and $B(3, 8)$ has gradient

$$m_{AB} = \frac{8 - 2}{3 - 1} = \frac{6}{2} = 3$$

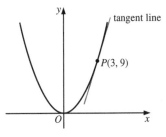

The gradient of a curve at a point P is the gradient of the tangent line to the curve at point P.

To find the gradient of the curve $y = x^2$ at the point $P(3, 9)$, you need to find the gradient of the tangent line to the curve at point P.

Exercise 4A

1 a) Copy and complete the following table.

x	-3	-2	-1	-0.5	0	0.5	1	2	3
x^2									

b) Using a scale of 2 cm to 1 unit, plot the graph of $y = x^2$ for $-3 \leqslant x \leqslant 3$.

c) By drawing a tangent to your curve at the point where $x = 2$, estimate the gradient of the curve at the point $(2, 4)$.

d) By drawing a tangent to your curve at the point where $x = -1$, estimate the gradient of the curve at the point $(-1, 1)$.

2 a) Copy and complete the following table.

x	0	0.5	1	1.5	2	2.5	3
$\frac{1}{4}x^3$							

b) Using a scale of 4 cm to 1 unit, plot the graph of $y = \frac{1}{4}x^3$ for $0 \leqslant x \leqslant 3$.

c) By drawing a tangent to your curve at the point where $x = 1$, estimate the gradient of the curve at the point $(1, \frac{1}{4})$.

d) By drawing a tangent to your curve at the point where $x = 2$, estimate the gradient of the curve at the point $(2, 2)$.

Gradient of a tangent as a limit

Drawing a tangent line by eye is not a very accurate way to find the gradient of a curve. Mathematicians had to develop methods for finding the gradient of any curve at any point on the curve.

To find the gradient of $y = x^2$ at the point $P(2, 4)$, consider the chord PQ of the curve, as shown.

The gradient of the chord PQ is given by

$$m_{PQ} = \frac{9 - 4}{3 - 2} = 5$$

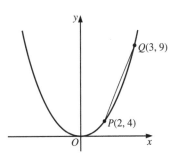

Now imagine that point Q is moving closer and closer to P.

When Q is (2.5, 6.25) the gradient is:

$$m_{PQ} = \frac{6.25 - 4}{0.5} = \frac{2.25}{0.5} = 4.5$$

When Q is (2.1, 4.41) the gradient is:

$$m_{PQ} = \frac{4.41 - 4}{0.1} = \frac{0.41}{0.1} = 4.1$$

When Q is (2.01, 4.0401) the gradient is:

$$m_{PQ} = \frac{4.0401 - 4}{0.01} = \frac{0.0401}{0.01} = 4.01$$

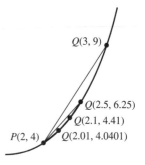

As Q moves closer to P along the curve, the chord approximates to the tangent to the curve at P. The gradient of the chord appears to be tending to the value 4.

The gradient at point P is 4, which you can call the **limit** of the gradient of the chord.

C1

Example 1

Find the gradient of the curve $y = x^2$ at $P(2.5, 6.25)$ by considering the chord PQ, where Q is a suitable point on the curve.

· ·

Let point Q be the point (3, 9), which is suitably 'near' P.
The gradient of the chord PQ is given by:

$$m_{PQ} = \frac{9 - 6.25}{3 - 2.5} = 5.5$$

Now consider the gradient of PQ as point Q moves closer to P.
When Q is (2.6, 6.76) the gradient is:

$$m_{PQ} = \frac{6.76 - 6.25}{0.1} = \frac{0.51}{0.1} = 5.1$$

When Q is (2.51, 6.3001) the gradient is:

$$m_{PQ} = \frac{6.3001 - 6.25}{0.01} = \frac{0.0501}{0.01} = 5.01$$

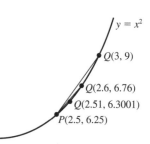

As Q moves closer to P along the curve, the chord approximates to the tangent to the curve at P. The gradient of the chord appears to be tending to the value 5.

The gradient at point P is 5, which is the limit of the gradient of the chord.

If you do more numerical examples, you will discover that this result is always true:

✦ The gradient of $y = x^2$ at the point (x, y) is $2x$.

> At the point (2.5, 6.25) the gradient is $2(2.5) = 5$, which again agrees with the result found in example 1.

Example 2

Find the gradient of the curve $y = x^3$ at $P(2, 8)$ by considering the chord PQ as Q is allowed to move towards P.

Let point Q be the point $(3, 27)$, which is suitably 'near' P.
The gradient of the chord PQ is given by:

$$m_{PQ} = \frac{27 - 8}{3 - 2} = 19$$

Now consider the gradient of PQ as point Q moves closer to P.
When Q is taken to be the point $(2.1, 9.261)$ the gradient is given by:

$$m_{PQ} = \frac{9.261 - 8}{2.1 - 2} = \frac{1.261}{0.1} = 12.61$$

When Q is taken to be the point $(2.01, 8.120\,601)$ the gradient is given by:

$$m_{PQ} = \frac{8.120\,601 - 8}{0.01} = \frac{0.120\,601}{0.01} = 12.0601$$

As Q moves closer to P along the curve, the chord becomes the tangent to the curve at P. The gradient of the chord appears to be tending to the value 12.
The gradient at point P is 12, which is the limit of the gradient of the chord.

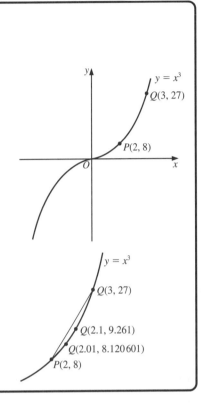

C1

If you do more numerical examples, you will find that this important result is true:

◆ The gradient of $y = x^3$ at the point (x, y) is $3x^2$.

The diagram shows the tangent line to a curve at a point P.

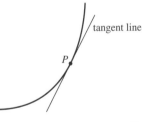

tangent line

P

You can calculate the gradient of the tangent line by finding the difference in y, the difference in x, and dividing:

$$\text{gradient at } P = \frac{\text{difference in } y}{\text{difference in } x} = \frac{dy}{dx}$$

At the point $(2, 8)$ the gradient is $3(2)^2 = 12$, which agrees with the result found in example 2.

See section 3.3.

The expression $\dfrac{dy}{dx}$ is called the **gradient function** or the **derived expression** or the **first derivative** of y with respect to x.

$\dfrac{dy}{dx}$ represents the gradient of a curve at a general point $P(x, y)$.

For example, $\dfrac{dy}{dx} = 2x$ gives the gradient of the curve $y = x^2$.

This tells you that the gradient of any point on the curve $y = x^2$ is twice the x-coordinate of the point. For example, the gradient of the curve $y = x^2$ at the point $P(3, 9)$ is $2 \times 3 = 6$.

You can write this as:

$$\left.\dfrac{dy}{dx}\right|_{x=3} = 2(3) = 6$$

meaning $\dfrac{dy}{dx}$ evaluated when $x = 3$

When $y = x^3$, you can write $\dfrac{dy}{dx} = 3x^2$ for the gradient of the curve.

> Finding $\dfrac{dy}{dx}$ for a function $y = f(x)$ is called **differentiating** or finding the derivative of the function.
>
> **Differentiation** forms part of a branch of mathematics called **calculus**.

C1

Alternative notation

If the equation of a curve is denoted by $y = f(x)$, it is sometimes more convenient to denote $\dfrac{dy}{dx}$ by $f'(x)$.

For example, if $f(x) = x^3$ then you would write $f'(x) = 3x^2$ for the derived function.

The gradient at $x = 2$ is then $f'(2) = 3 \times 2^2 = 12$.

General expression for the derivative of x^n

You can extend the results for $y = x^2$ and $y = x^3$ to find this general result:

> If $y = x^n$ then $\dfrac{dy}{dx} = nx^{n-1}$, where n is any real number.

Example 3

Find $\dfrac{dy}{dx}$ for each of the following.

a) $y = x^4$ b) $y = x^6$

a) When $y = x^4$,

$$\dfrac{dy}{dx} = 4x^{4-1}$$

$$\therefore \dfrac{dy}{dx} = 4x^3$$

b) When $y = x^6$,

$$\dfrac{dy}{dx} = 6x^{6-1}$$

$$\therefore \dfrac{dy}{dx} = 6x^5$$

Another useful result is that:

> If $y = ax^n$ then $\dfrac{dy}{dx} = anx^{n-1}$, where n is any real number.

Example 4

Find $\dfrac{dy}{dx}$ for each of these.

a) $y = 3x^2$ b) $y = 5x^3$

a) When $y = 3x^2$,

$$\frac{dy}{dx} = 3 \times 2x^{2-1}$$

$$\therefore \frac{dy}{dx} = 6x$$

b) When $y = 5x^3$,

$$\frac{dy}{dx} = 5 \times 3x^{3-1}$$

$$\therefore \frac{dy}{dx} = 15x^2$$

Two special cases

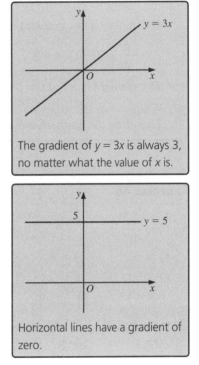

The gradient of $y = 3x$ is always 3, no matter what the value of x is.

Horizontal lines have a gradient of zero.

C1

◆ When the function is a straight line, you know from previous work that the gradient is a constant. For example, the gradient of $y = 3x$ is 3.

You can write $y = 3x$ as $y = 3x^1$. So:

$$\frac{dy}{dx} = 3 \times 1x^{2-1}$$
$$= 3x^0$$
$$= 3 \times 1$$
$$\therefore \frac{dy}{dx} = 3, \text{ a constant as expected.}$$

◆ When the function is a constant, its graph is a horizontal straight line with gradient zero, for example $y = 5$.

You can write $y = 5$ as $y = 5x^0$. So:

$$\frac{dy}{dx} = 5 \times 0x^{0-1}$$

$$\therefore \frac{dy}{dx} = 0, \text{ as expected.}$$

Example 5

Find the gradient of each of these functions at the point indicated.

a) $y = x^2$ at $(3, 9)$ b) $y = -4x^3$ at $(1, -4)$
c) $y = 2x^4$ at $(-1, 2)$ d) $y = 6x$ at $(2, 12)$

a) When $y = x^2$,

$$\frac{dy}{dx} = 2x$$

When $x = 3$ the gradient is given by:

$$\frac{dy}{dx} = 2(3) = 6$$

The gradient is 6 at the point $(3, 9)$.

b) When $y = -4x^3$,

$$\frac{dy}{dx} = -12x^2$$

When $x = 1$ the gradient is given by:

$$\frac{dy}{dx} = -12(1)^2 = -12$$

The gradient is -12 at the point $(1, -4)$.

c) When $y = 2x^4$,

$$\frac{dy}{dx} = 8x^3$$

When $x = -1$ the gradient is given by:

$$\frac{dy}{dx} = 8(-1)^3 = -8$$

The gradient is -8 at the point $(-1, 2)$.

d) When $y = 6x$ the gradient is 6 at all points on the line.
Therefore the gradient is 6 at the point $(2, 12)$.

C1

Exercise 4B

1 Find $\dfrac{dy}{dx}$ for each of these functions.

a) $y = x^5$ b) $y = x^9$ c) $y = x^7$ d) $y = x^{12}$

e) $y = x^{20}$ f) $y = x^8$ g) $y = x^{14}$ h) $y = x^{11}$

i) $y = x^3$ j) $y = x^{17}$ k) $y = x^{100}$ l) $y = x$

2 Differentiate each of these expressions with respect to x.

a) $7x^2$ b) $2x^9$ c) $3x^5$ d) $4x^3$

e) $8x^7$ f) $7x^4$ g) $-5x^3$ h) $12x^2$

i) $9x^4$ j) $-4x^7$ k) $6x$ l) $15x^3$

3 Find the gradient of these functions at the point indicated.

a) $y = x^2$ at $(3, 9)$ b) $y = x^3$ at $(-1, -1)$

c) $y = x^5$ at $(2, 32)$ d) $y = 4x^2$ at $(5, 100)$

e) $y = -x^5$ at $(1, -1)$ f) $y = 3x^3$ at $(-4, -192)$

g) $y = 10x^2$ at $(6, 360)$ h) $y = -7x^4$ at $(-2, -112)$

i) $y = 12x$ at $(13, 156)$ j) $y = 3x^2$ at $(-7, 147)$

k) $y = -10x^7$ at $(1, -10)$ l) $y = 5x^5$ at $(2, 160)$

<u>4</u> Find the coordinates of the points on the curve $y = x^3$ where the gradient is 12.

4.2 Differentiating polynomials

To find the derivative of a function which has more than one term, you need to differentiate each term in turn. For example, the quadratic function $y = x^2 + 4x - 5$ has three terms. Its derivative is:

$$\frac{dy}{dx} = 2x + 4$$

> Notice that the derivative of a constant is always zero.

Example 6

Find $\dfrac{dy}{dx}$ for each of these functions.

a) $y = x^2 - 5x + 8$
b) $y = 3x^3 + \frac{1}{2}x^2 - 2x - 1$
c) $y = 1 - 5x^2 + \frac{1}{2}x^4$

....

a) If $y = x^2 - 5x + 8$ then:

$$\frac{dy}{dx} = 2x - 5$$

b) If $y = 3x^3 + \frac{1}{2}x^2 - 2x - 1$ then:

$$\frac{dy}{dx} = 9x^2 + x - 2$$

c) If $y = 1 - 5x^2 + \frac{1}{2}x^4$ then:

$$\frac{dy}{dx} = -10x + 2x^3$$

C1

You can use differentiation to find the gradient of the graph of a polynomial at any point.

Example 7

Find the gradient of the curve $y = x^3 - 2x^2 + x - 3$ at the point $(2, -1)$.

....

If $y = x^3 - 2x^2 + x - 3$ then:

$$\frac{dy}{dx} = 3x^2 - 4x + 1$$

When $x = 2$,

$$\frac{dy}{dx}\bigg|_{x=2} = 3(2)^2 - 4(2) + 1$$
$$= 12 - 8 + 1$$
$$= 5$$

The gradient of the curve is 5 at the point $(2, -1)$.

You can use the derivative to find the points on a curve where the gradient is zero.

Example 8

Given the function $y = x^3 + x^2 - 8x + 1$, find
a) the gradient of the curve of the function when $x = 1$
b) the x-coordinates of the points on the curve where the gradient is zero.

· ·

a) If $y = x^3 + x^2 - 8x + 1$ then:

$$\frac{dy}{dx} = 3x^2 + 2x - 8$$

When $x = 1$,

$$\left.\frac{dy}{dx}\right|_{x=1} = 3(1)^2 + 2(1) - 8$$

$$= -3$$

The gradient of the curve is -3 at the point where $x = 1$.

b) When the gradient is zero:

$$3x^2 + 2x - 8 = 0$$
$$(3x - 4)(x + 2) = 0$$
$$3x - 4 = 0 \text{ or } x = -2$$
$$\therefore \qquad x = \tfrac{4}{3} \text{ or } x = -2$$

The x-coordinates of the points on the curve where the gradient is zero are $x = \tfrac{4}{3}$ and $x = -2$.

> Factorise the quadratic.

Exercise 4C

· ·

1 Find $\dfrac{dy}{dx}$ for each of these functions.

a) $y = x^2 + 5x + 2$ b) $y = 3x^2 - 7x + 6$

c) $y = 4 - 5x - x^2$ d) $y = 2 + 7x - 5x^2$

e) $y = x^3 - 3x^2 + 4$ f) $y = 5 - x + 2x^2 - x^3$

g) $y = 2x^3 - 5x + 8$ h) $y = 4x^3 - 3x^2 + 7x - 10$

i) $y = 1 - 6x^2 - 4x^3$ j) $y = x^4 - 2x^2 + 6x$

2 Differentiate each of these functions with respect to x, to find $f'(x)$.

a) $f(x) = x^2 - 6x + 8$ b) $f(x) = 5x^2 - 2x + 9$

c) $f(x) = 6 - 7x - x^2$ d) $f(x) = 1 + x - 5x^2$

e) $f(x) = x^3 + 4x + 6$ f) $f(x) = x^3 + 7x^2 - 3x - 3$

g) $f(x) = 2 - 3x - x^3$ h) $f(x) = 6 + 5x - x^2 - x^3$

i) $f(x) = 2x^3 + 4x^2 - 3x$ j) $f(x) = 4x^4 - 3x^2 + 7x + 5$

3 Find the gradient of each of these functions at the point indicated.

a) $y = x^2 - 3x + 2$ at $(2, 0)$ b) $y = x^2 + 2x - 8$ at $(3, 7)$

c) $y = 2 + 3x - 5x^3$ at $(-1, 4)$ d) $y = x^3 - 5x^2 + 6$ at $(2, -6)$

e) $f(x) = 2 - 3x^3$ at $(-1, 5)$ f) $f(x) = 3x^3 - 5x + 2$ at $(0, 2)$

g) $f(x) = 4 - 5x^2 - x^3$ at $(-2, -8)$ h) $f(x) = 3 + 7x - 4x^3$ at $(3, -84)$

4 a) Find the coordinates of the points on the curve $y = x^3 + 2x - 1$ where the gradient is 29.

b) Find the coordinates of the points on the curve $f(x) = x^4 + 2x^3$ where the gradient is zero.

5 Given $y = (2x^2 - 3)^2$, show that $\dfrac{dy}{dx} = 8x(2x^2 - 3)$.

C1

⊛4.3 Gradient as a rate of change

The gradient of a curve is given by

$$\frac{dy}{dx} = \frac{\text{change in } y}{\text{change in } x}$$

The derivative $\dfrac{dy}{dx}$ therefore represents the **rate of change of y with respect to x.**

A common rate of change connects velocity, displacement and time.

Suppose s denotes the displacement of a body at time t, with the graph relating s and t as shown in the diagram.

Suppose P and Q are any two points on the graph. The length QR represents the distance travelled between the two points P and Q. The length PR represents the time taken to travel this distance.

The gradient of the line PQ represents the average velocity of the body during this time interval.

You can use the same technique as in section 4.1 to show that as Q moves closer to P the gradient of the line PQ gets closer to the gradient of the curve at P.

Therefore the gradient of the tangent at P is equal to the velocity at that instant (point). So:

> The velocity v at time t is given by $v = \dfrac{ds}{dt}$.

Similarly, the rate of change of velocity with respect to time is called the acceleration.

> The acceleration a at time t is given by $a = \dfrac{dv}{dt}$.

> This definition of gradient was given for a straight line on page 88.

> For example, if $\dfrac{dy}{dx} = 3$, then y is increasing 3 times as fast as x.

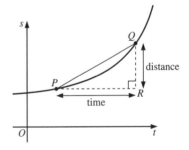

> Acceleration, velocity and displacement will **not** be assessed in the C1 module.

Example 9

The displacement, s metres of a body at a time t seconds is given by $s = t^2 + 3t$. Find

a) the velocity of the body at time t
b) the initial velocity of the body.

a) The velocity v is given by:

$$v = \frac{ds}{dt} = 2t + 3$$

b) The initial velocity v is the velocity when $t = 0$. Substituting $t = 0$ gives:

$$\left.\frac{ds}{dt}\right|_{t=0} = 2(0) + 3 = 3$$

The initial velocity of the body is 3 m s^{-1}.

> When distance is in metres (m) and time in seconds (s), the unit of velocity is metres per second (m s^{-1}).

C1

Example 10

The displacement, s metres, of a body at time t seconds is given by $s = 2t^3 - t^2 + 2$. Find

a) the velocity after 1 second
b) the acceleration after 1 second
c) the time at which the acceleration is zero.

a) If $s = 2t^3 - t^2 + 2$ then the velocity is given by:

$$v = \frac{ds}{dt} = 6t^2 - 2t$$

When $t = 1$,

$$\left.\frac{ds}{dt}\right|_{t=1} = 6(1)^2 - 2(1) = 4$$

The velocity is 4 m s^{-1} after 1 second.

b) The acceleration is given by:

$$a = \frac{dv}{dt} = 12t - 2$$

When $t = 1$,

$$\left.\frac{dv}{dt}\right|_{t=1} = 12(1) - 2 = 10$$

The acceleration is 10 m s^{-2} after 1 second.

> The unit of acceleration is metres per second per second (m s^{-2}).

c) When the acceleration is zero:

$$12t - 2 = 0$$

$$\therefore \quad t = \frac{2}{12} = \frac{1}{6}$$

The acceleration is zero when $t = \frac{1}{6}$ second.

Exercise 4D

1 The displacement, s metres, of a body at a time t seconds is given by the formula $s = t^2 + 3t$.

   a) Find an expression for the velocity of the body at time t.

   b) Calculate the velocity of the body when $t = 2$.

2 A body moves such that its displacement, s metres, at time t seconds, is given by the formula $s = 2t^3 + 5t$.

   a) Find an expression for the velocity of the body at time t.

   b) Calculate the velocity of the body when $t = 3$.

3 Given $s = 3t^2 - 5t^3$, where s is displacement at time t, find

   a) an expression for the velocity, v

   b) an expression for the acceleration, a.

4 Given $s = 1 + t + t^3$, where s is displacement at time t, find

   a) an expression for the velocity, v

   b) an expression for the acceleration, a.

5 The velocity v m s^{-1} of a body at a time t seconds is given by the formula $v = 3t^2 - 2t$.

   a) Find an expression for the acceleration of the body at time t.

   b) Calculate the acceleration of the body when $t = 6$.

6 A body moves in such a way that its velocity v m s^{-1}, at time t seconds, is given by the formula $v = t^3 - 3t^2 + 6t$.

   a) Find an expression for the acceleration of the body at time t.

   b) Calculate the initial acceleration of the body.

7 The displacement, s metres, of a body at a time t seconds is given by the formula $s = t^2 - 8t$.

   a) Find an expression for the velocity of the body at time t.

   b) Calculate the value of t when the body is at rest.

8 A body moves such that its displacement, s metres, at time t seconds, is given by the formula $s = t^3 - 6t^2 + 9t + 5$.

   a) Calculate the times at which the body is at rest.

   b) Find the values of s at these times.

9 A body moves such that its displacement, s metres, at time t seconds, is given by the formula $s = 14 + 9t^2 - t^3$. Find the maximum velocity of the body.

C1

4.4 Tangents and normals to a curve

Equation of a tangent

You can use differentiation to find the equation of the tangent line to a curve at a particular point.

Example 11

Find the equation of the tangent to the curve $y = x^2$ at the point $P(3, 9)$.

$y = x^2$, so:

$$\frac{dy}{dx} = 2x$$

> The gradient of the tangent to the curve at point P is given by $\frac{dy}{dx}$ evaluated when $x = 3$.

At the point $P(3, 9)$:

$$\left.\frac{dy}{dx}\right|_{x=3} = 2(3) = 6$$

The tangent is a straight line, so its equation is given by $y = mx + c$. The gradient of the tangent at point P is 6, so the equation of the line is:

$$y = 6x + c$$

The tangent passes through $P(3, 9)$. Therefore:

$$9 = 6(3) + c$$
$$\therefore \quad c = -9$$

The equation of the tangent is therefore $y = 6x - 9$.

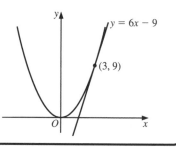

Equation of a normal

The **normal** to a curve at a point P is the straight line through P which is perpendicular to the tangent at P.

Since the tangent and normal are perpendicular to each other, if the gradient of the tangent is m, then the gradient of the normal is $-\dfrac{1}{m}$ (see page 66).

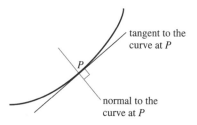

Example 12

Find the equation of the normal to the curve $y = 3x^2 + 7x - 2$ at the point P where $x = -1$.

When $x = -1$,

$$y = 3(-1)^2 + 7(-1) - 2 = -6$$

Therefore, P has coordinates $(-1, -6)$.

$$y = 3x^2 + 7x - 2 \quad \therefore \quad \frac{dy}{dx} = 6x + 7.$$

At the point $P(-1, -6)$,

$$\left.\frac{dy}{dx}\right|_{x=-1} = 6(-1) + 7 = 1$$

The gradient of the tangent line at P is 1. Therefore, the gradient of the normal at P is $-\dfrac{1}{(1)} = -1$.

The equation of the normal at P is

$$y = -x + c$$

The normal passes through $P(-1, -6)$. Therefore:

$$-6 = -(-1) + c$$
$$\therefore \quad c = -7$$

Therefore, the equation of the normal to the curve at the point $P(-1, -6)$ is $y = -x - 7$ or $x + y + 7 = 0$.

C1

Example 13

Find the equations of the normals to the curve $y = x^3 - 3x^2 + 4$ which are perpendicular to the line $y - 24x = 1$.

....

$y - 24x = 1$ can be written as $y = 24x + 1$.

$\quad\therefore$ The gradient of the line is 24.

The required normals are perpendicular to the line $y = 24x + 1$, so they must have a gradient of $-\frac{1}{24}$. Therefore, the gradient of the corresponding tangents to the curve is 24.

$$y = x^3 - 3x^2 + 4 \quad \therefore \quad \frac{dy}{dx} = 3x^2 - 6x$$

> Differentiate to find an expression for the gradient of the tangents.

Now $\dfrac{dy}{dx} = 24$. Therefore,

$$3x^2 - 6x = 24$$
$$3x^2 - 6x - 24 = 0$$
$$x^2 - 2x - 8 = 0$$
$$\therefore \quad (x + 2)(x - 4) = 0$$

> Solve the quadratic to find the points where the normals intersect the curve.

Solving gives $x = -2$ or $x = 4$.

When $x = -2$: $\qquad y = (-2)^3 - 3(-2)^2 + 4 = -16$

When $x = 4$: $\qquad y = (4)^3 - 3(4)^2 + 4 = 20$

So you want the normals to the curve at the points $P(-2, -16)$ and $Q(4, 20)$.

Both the required normals have equations of the form $y = -\frac{1}{24}x + c$. Since one of the normals passes through $P(-2, -16)$, it follows that

$$-16 = -\frac{1}{24}(-2) + c$$

$$\therefore \quad c = -\frac{193}{12}$$

The equation of the normal through $P(-2, -16)$ is

$$y = -\tfrac{1}{24}x - \tfrac{193}{12} \text{ or } 24y + x + 386 = 0$$

The second normal passes through $Q(4, 20)$. Therefore

$$20 = -\frac{1}{24}(4) + c$$

$$\therefore c = \frac{121}{6}$$

Therefore, the equation of the normal through $Q(4, 20)$ is

$$y = -\tfrac{1}{24}x + \tfrac{121}{6} \text{ or } 24y + x - 484 = 0$$

Exercise 4E

C1

1 Find the equation of the tangent to each of these curves at the point given.
   a) $y = x^2$ at $(4, 16)$ b) $y = 2x^3 - 4$ at $(2, 12)$
   c) $y = 3 - 4x^2$ at $(1, -1)$ d) $y = x^3 - 7x$ at $(-2, 6)$
   e) $y = x + x^3$ at $(1, 2)$ f) $y = 2 - x - 3x^2$ at $(0, 2)$

2 Find the equation of the normal to each of these curves at the point given.
   a) $y = x^3$ at $(1, 1)$ b) $y = 2 + 3x^2$ at $(-1, 5)$
   c) $y = 5x^2 - 6x$ at $(2, 8)$ d) $y = x^3 + 5x$ at $(-1, -6)$
   e) $y = 1 + x - x^2$ at $(3, -5)$ f) $y = x^4 - 2x$ at $(0, 0)$

3 Find the equation of the tangent to the curve $y = x^2 + 4x - 3$ at the point where $x = 2$.

4 Find the equation of the tangent to the curve $y = 7 - 3x^2$ at the point where $x = 3$.

5 Find the equation of the normal to the curve $y = 2x - x^2$ at the point where $x = 4$.

6 The curve $y = x^2 - 3x + 1$ cuts the y-axis at the point P.
   a) Find the coordinates of P.
   b) Find the equation of the tangent to the curve at the point P.

7 The curve $y = x^3 - 8$ cuts the x-axis at the point C.
   a) Find the coordinates of C.
   b) Find the equation of the normal to the curve at the point C.

8 The curve $y = x^2 - 5x + 4$ cuts the x-axis at the points P and Q.
   a) Find the coordinates of P and Q.
   b) Find the equation of the tangent to the curve at the points P and Q.
   c) Given that these two tangents intersect at the point X, find the coordinates of X.

9 The line $y = 9$ meets the curve $y = x^2$ at the points C and D.

a) Find the coordinates of C and D.

b) Find the equation of the tangent to the curve at the points C and D.

c) Find the coordinates of the point of intersection of these two tangents.

10 The curve $y = x^2 - x - 6$ cuts the x-axis at the points A and B.

a) Find the coordinates of A and B.

b) Find the equations of the normals to the curve at the points A and B.

c) Given that these two normals intersect at the point X, find the coordinates of X.

11 The normal to the curve $y = x^2 + 5x - 2$ at the point where $x = -3$, and the tangent to the same curve at the point where $x = 1$, meet at the point Q. Find the coordinates of Q.

12 a) Find the values of x for which the gradient of the curve $y = x^3 - 3x^2 - 9x + 10$ is 15.

b) Hence find the equations of the tangents to the curve which have gradient 15.

C1

4.5 Stationary points

Maximum, minimum and point of inflection

A point on a curve at which the gradient is zero, where $\dfrac{dy}{dx} = 0$, is called a **stationary point**.

At a stationary point, the tangent to the curve is horizontal and the curve is 'flat'.

There are three types of stationary point.

Minimum point

In this case, the gradient of the curve is negative to the left of point P. To the right of point P, the gradient of the curve is positive.

To the left of P	At point P	To the right of P
$\dfrac{dy}{dx} < 0$	$\dfrac{dy}{dx} = 0$	$\dfrac{dy}{dx} > 0$

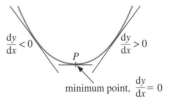

Maximum point

In this case, the gradient of the curve is positive to the left of point P. To the right of point P, the gradient of the curve is negative.

To the left of P	At point P	To the right of P
$\dfrac{dy}{dx} > 0$	$\dfrac{dy}{dx} = 0$	$\dfrac{dy}{dx} < 0$

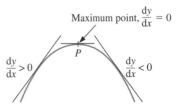

Point of inflection

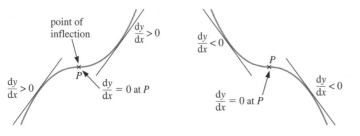

In this case, the gradient has the *same sign* each side of the stationary point. A point of inflection which has zero gradient (such as this one) is called a **horizontal point of inflection** or **saddle point**.

Maximum and minimum points are also called **turning points** as this is where the graph 'turns' and the gradient changes from positive to negative or negative to positive.

> Points of inflection will not be assessed in the C1 module and are included here for completeness.

Example 14

Find the coordinates of the stationary point on the curve $y = 8x - 2x^2$ and determine its nature.

....

$y = 8x - 2x^2$ ∴ $\dfrac{dy}{dx} = 8 - 4x.$

At a stationary point $\dfrac{dy}{dx} = 0$. Therefore:

$$8 - 4x = 0$$
$$\therefore \quad x = 2$$

When $x = 2$, $y = 8(2) - 2(2)^2 = 8$.

The coordinates of the stationary point are $(2, 8)$.

To determine the nature of the stationary point, you must examine the gradient each side of the point.

x	1	2	3
$\dfrac{dy}{dx}$	4	0	−4

        positive   negative

The stationary point $(2, 8)$ is a maximum.

In this case the coefficient of the x^2 term is negative so you know that the quadratic graph is ∩ shaped and hence the turning point is a maximum.

> A simple sketch can help with changing gradient.
> Positive, zero, negative gradient would look like:

Example 15

Find the coordinates of the stationary point on the curve
$y = x^3 + 3x^2 + 1$ and determine their nature. Sketch the curve.

$y = x^3 + 3x^2 + 1$ $\therefore$ $\dfrac{dy}{dx} = 3x^2 + 6x$

Differentiate the function.

At a stationary point $\dfrac{dy}{dx} = 0$. Therefore:

$$3x^2 + 6x = 0$$
$$\therefore \quad 3x(x + 2) = 0$$

Solve the quadratic for x.

Solving gives $x = 0$ or $x = -2$.

When $x = 0$: $y = (0)^3 + 3(0)^2 + 1 = 1$

When $x = -2$: $y = (-2)^3 + 3(-2)^2 + 1 = 5$

Find the corresponding y-coordinates.

The coordinates of the stationary points are $(0, 1)$ and $(-2, 5)$.

To determine the nature of the stationary point, you must examine
the value of the gradient function each side of the point.

For the point $(0, 1)$:

x	-1	0	1
$\dfrac{dy}{dx}$	-3	0	9

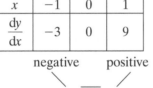

negative   positive
$\searrow$ $-$ $\nearrow$

Note that when you choose
x values on each side of $x = 0$,
the chosen interval must not
include any other stationary
points.

The stationary point $(0, 1)$ is a minimum.

For the point $(-2, 5)$:

x	-3	-2	-1
$\dfrac{dy}{dx}$	9	0	3

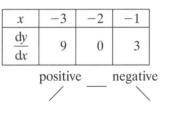

positive   negative
$\nearrow$ $-$ $\searrow$

The stationary point $(-2, 5)$ is a maximum.

There are two stationary points on the curve: $(0, 1)$ a minimum
and $(-2, 5)$ a maximum.

To sketch the curve, plot the stationary points and notice that the
curve $y = x^3 + 3x^2 + 1$ cuts the y-axis at the point $(0, 1)$.

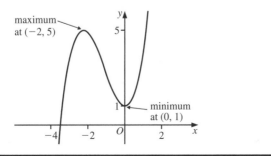

The second derivative

You can differentiate $\dfrac{dy}{dx}$, to get $\dfrac{d}{dx}\left(\dfrac{dy}{dx}\right)$. This is written as $\dfrac{d^2y}{dx^2}$ and is called the **second derivative of y with respect to x**.

In the alternative notation, the first derivative of $f(x)$ is $f'(x)$, and $f''(x)$ is the **second derivative of $f(x)$ with respect to x**.

Example 16

Given that $y = x^3 - 3x^2 + 1$, find $\dfrac{dy}{dx}$ and $\dfrac{d^2y}{dx^2}$.

....

$y = x^3 - 3x^2 + 1$ $\quad \therefore \quad \dfrac{dy}{dx} = 3x^2 - 6x$

$\qquad\qquad$ and $\quad \dfrac{d^2y}{dx^2} = 6x - 6$

> Differentiate again to find $\dfrac{d^2y}{dx^2}$.

C1

Stationary points and the second derivative

The second derivative of a function can be thought of as the gradient of the gradient graph. It can be used to determine the nature of a stationary point on a curve – whether it is a maximum or a minimum.

Consider the graph of a function $y = f(x)$ which has maximum and minimum turning points. The graph of its derived function is also shown.

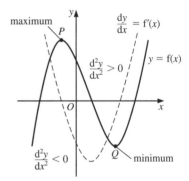

◆ At the maximum point P, the gradient of the derived function is negative. That is:

$$\dfrac{d^2y}{dx^2} < 0 \text{ at a maximum}$$

◆ At the minimum point Q, the gradient of the derived function is positive. That is:

$$\dfrac{d^2y}{dx^2} > 0 \text{ at a minimum}$$

Example 17

Find the coordinates of the stationary point on the curve $y = 3x^2 + 6x + 4$ and determine its nature.

....

$y = 3x^2 + 6x + 4$ $\quad \therefore \quad \dfrac{dy}{dx} = 6x + 6$

At a stationary point $\dfrac{dy}{dx} = 0$. Therefore:

$\qquad 6x + 6 = 0$

$\qquad \therefore \quad x = -1$

When $x = -1$: $\quad y = 3(-1)^2 + 6(-1) + 4 = 1$

The coordinates of the stationary point are $(-1, 1)$.

$$\dfrac{d^2y}{dx^2} = 6$$

Since $\dfrac{d^2y}{dx^2} > 0$ the stationary point is a minimum.

> You can tell from the fact that the coefficient of the x^2 term is positive that the quadratic graph is U shaped and hence the turning point is a minimum.

The next example uses function notation.

Example 18

Find the coordinates of the stationary points on the curve $f(x) = x^3 - 6x^2 - 15x + 1$, and use the second derivative to determine their nature.

$$f(x) = x^3 - 6x^2 - 15x + 1$$
$$\therefore \qquad f'(x) = 3x^2 - 12x - 15$$

At stationary points, $f'(x) = 0$. So:

$$3x^2 - 12x - 15 = 0$$
$$3(x^2 - 4x - 5) = 0$$
$$\therefore \quad 3(x - 5)(x + 1) = 0$$

Solving gives $x = 5$ or $x = -1$.

When $x = 5$: $\qquad f(5) = (5)^3 - 6(5)^2 - 15(5) + 1 = -99$

When $x = -1$: $\qquad f(-1) = (-1)^3 - 6(-1)^2 - 15(-1) + 1 = 9$

The stationary points are $(5, -99)$ and $(-1, 9)$.

The second derivative is $f''(x) = 6x - 12$.

At the point $(5, -99)$:

$$f''(5) = 6(5) - 12 = 18 > 0$$

Therefore, the stationary point $(5, -99)$ is a minimum.

At the point $(-1, 9)$:

$$f''(-1) = 6(-1) - 12 = -18 < 0$$

Therefore, the stationary point $(-1, 9)$ is a maximum.

C1

Exercise 4F

1 Find the coordinates of the points on each of these curves at which the gradient is zero.

a) $y = x^2 - 4x + 3$

b) $y = x^2 + 6x + 5$

c) $y = 6 - x^2$

d) $y = 3 - 5x + x^2$

e) $y = 2x^2 - 3x + 1$

f) $y = x^3 - 3x + 2$

g) $y = x^3 - 6x^2 - 36x$

h) $y = 6 + 9x - 3x^2 - x^3$

i) $y = 5 + 3x^2 - x^3$

j) $y = 2x^3 - 54x + 7$

k) $y = 5 - 12x + 9x^2 - 2x^3$

l) $y = 3x^3 - 18x^2 + 18x - 14$

2 Find $\dfrac{d^2y}{dx^2}$ for each of these functions.

a) $y = 3x - 4x^2$

b) $y = 3x^2 - 7$

c) $y = x^3 + 5x$

d) $y = x^3 + 2x^2$

e) $y = 5x^3 - 3x^2 + 1$

f) $y = 3 - 7x - 4x^3$

g) $y = x^4 + 3x^2 - 1$

h) $y = x^3 - 5x^4$

i) $y = 2x^5 + 7x^3 - 6$

j) $y = x + x^3 - x^5 - x^7$

k) $y = 1 - 9x^3 - 2x^6$

l) $y = x^8 + 2x^6 - x^4 + 1$

3 Find the coordinates of the stationary points on each of these
curves, and determine their nature.
a) $y = x^2 - 2x + 5$ b) $y = x^2 + 4x + 2$
c) $y = 3 + x - x^2$ d) $y = x^2 - 6x + 8$
e) $f(x) = 6x^2 + 15x - 9$ f) $f(x) = x^2 - 10x + 25$
g) $f(x) = x^3 + 6x^2 - 36x$ h) $f(x) = x^3 - 5x^2 + 3x + 1$

4 Find the coordinates of the stationary points on each of these
curves. In each case determine their nature and sketch the curve.
a) $y = x^2 - 6x + 12$ b) $y = x^2 - 10x + 21$
c) $y = x^3 - 3x + 3$ d) $y = 1 + 24x + 3x^2 - x^3$
e) $y = 2x^3 - 9x^2 + 12x - 4$ f) $y = -x^3 + 6x^2 - 9x$

5 Sketch the curve $y = x^3 - 9x^2 + 27x - 19$, paying particular
attention to what happens at $x = 3$.

6 By sketching the curve $y = x^4 - 4x^3 - 2x^2 + 12x + 12$, show that
the equation $x^4 - 4x^3 - 2x^2 + 12x + 12 = 0$ has no real solutions.

C1

4.6 Practical applications of maxima and minima

Differentiation can be used to solve practical problems. For example, it
can be used to find the maximum possible value of an area or volume.

Example 19

In the right-angled triangle ABC shown, the lengths AB and BC vary
such that their sum is always 6 cm.
a) If the length of AB is x cm, write down, in terms of x, the length BC.
b) Find the maximum area of triangle ABC.

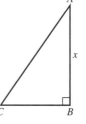

a) $AB + BC = 6$
        $x + BC = 6$
     $\therefore$ $BC = 6 - x$

b) The area, A, of triangle ABC is given by
$$A = \tfrac{1}{2} \times BC \times AB$$
$$= \tfrac{1}{2}(6 - x)x$$
$$\therefore \quad A = 3x - \frac{x^2}{2} \qquad [1]$$

You can see that A reaches a maximum value because the
coefficient of the x^2 term is negative. (That is, the graph of x
against A is $\cap$ shaped.)

The maximum value of A occurs when $\dfrac{dA}{dx} = 0$.

$$\frac{dA}{dx} = 3 - x$$

When $\dfrac{dA}{dx} = 0$: $3 - x = 0$
                    $\therefore$ $x = 3$

> **Remember:**
> Area of a triangle
> $= \tfrac{1}{2} \times$ base $\times$ height

> You can prove that $x = 3$ gives
> a maximum by finding $\dfrac{d^2A}{dx^2}$.
> $$\frac{dA}{dx} = 3 - x$$
> $$\frac{d^2A}{dx^2} = -1 (< 0)$$
> $\therefore$ maximum value.

The area of the triangle is a maximum when $x = 3$. Therefore, the maximum area of triangle ABC is found by substituting $x = 3$ into [1], which gives:

$$A_{\text{max}} = 3(3) - \frac{(3)^2}{2} = \frac{9}{2} = 4.5$$

The maximum area of triangle ABC is 4.5 cm².

Example 20

A right circular cylinder of base radius r metres and height h metres is to be made so that the sum of its radius and its height is 12 m.

a) Show that the volume, V, of the cylinder is given by
$$V = 12\pi r^2 - \pi r^3$$

b) Find the maximum volume of the cylinder.

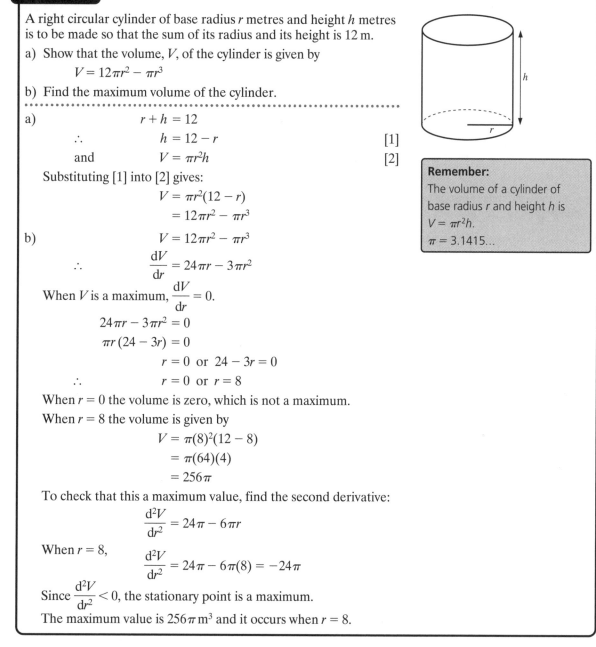

a)
$$r + h = 12$$
$$\therefore \qquad h = 12 - r \qquad [1]$$
$$\text{and} \qquad V = \pi r^2 h \qquad [2]$$

Substituting [1] into [2] gives:
$$V = \pi r^2 (12 - r)$$
$$= 12\pi r^2 - \pi r^3$$

b)
$$V = 12\pi r^2 - \pi r^3$$
$$\therefore \qquad \frac{dV}{dr} = 24\pi r - 3\pi r^2$$

When V is a maximum, $\dfrac{dV}{dr} = 0$.
$$24\pi r - 3\pi r^2 = 0$$
$$\pi r (24 - 3r) = 0$$
$$r = 0 \ \text{ or } \ 24 - 3r = 0$$
$$\therefore \qquad r = 0 \ \text{ or } \ r = 8$$

When $r = 0$ the volume is zero, which is not a maximum.
When $r = 8$ the volume is given by
$$V = \pi(8)^2(12 - 8)$$
$$= \pi(64)(4)$$
$$= 256\pi$$

To check that this a maximum value, find the second derivative:
$$\frac{d^2V}{dr^2} = 24\pi - 6\pi r$$

When $r = 8$,
$$\frac{d^2V}{dr^2} = 24\pi - 6\pi(8) = -24\pi$$

Since $\dfrac{d^2V}{dr^2} < 0$, the stationary point is a maximum.
The maximum value is $256\pi \, \text{m}^3$ and it occurs when $r = 8$.

Remember:
The volume of a cylinder of base radius r and height h is $V = \pi r^2 h$.
$\pi = 3.1415...$

C1

Exercise 4G

1 The profit, £y, generated from the sale of x items of a certain luxury product is given by the formula $y = 600x + 15x^2 - x^3$. Calculate the value of x which gives a maximum profit, and determine that maximum profit.

2 The profit, y hundred pounds, generated from the sale of x thousand items of a certain product is given by the formula $y = 72x + 3x^2 - 2x^3$. Calculate how many items should be sold in order to maximise the profit, and determine that maximum profit.

3 At a speed of x mph a certain car will travel y miles on each gallon of petrol, where

$$y = 15 + x - \frac{x^2}{110}$$

Calculate the speed at which the car should aim to travel in order to maximise the distance it can cover on a single tank of petrol.

4 At a speed of x mph, a transporter can cover y miles on 1 gallon of diesel fuel, where

$$y = 5 + \frac{x}{2} + \frac{x^2}{60} - \frac{x^3}{1800}$$

Calculate the maximum distance which the transporter can travel on 30 gallons of diesel fuel.

5 A ball is thrown vertically upwards. At time t seconds after the instant of projection, its height, y metres above the point of projection, is given by the formula $y = 15t - 5t^2$. Calculate the time at which the ball is at its maximum height, and find the value of y at that time.

6 A rectangular pen is formed from 40 m of fencing with a long wall forming one side of the pen, as shown in the diagram.

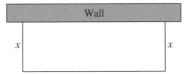

Given that the two opposite sides of the pen which touch the wall each have length x metres,

a) find, in terms of x, the length of each of the other two sides.

Given also that the area enclosed is a maximum,

b) find the value of x, and hence calculate the area enclosed.

7 An open cuboidal tank of height h metres is to be made with a square base of length x metres and breadth x metres. The external surface area of the tank is to be 48 m².

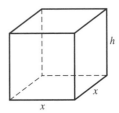

a) Show that $h = \dfrac{48 - x^2}{4x}$

b) Deduce that the volume, V m³, of the tank is given by
$$V = 12x - \frac{x^3}{4}.$$

c) Find an expression for $\dfrac{\mathrm{d}V}{\mathrm{d}x}$.

d) Given that the volume of the tank has to be a maximum, calculate the value of x, and find this maximum volume.

8 A cuboidal plastic bar of length l cm is to be made with a rectangular cross-section of width $2x$ cm and height x cm. The external surface area of the bar is to be 75 m².

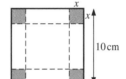

a) Show that $l = \dfrac{75 - 4x^2}{6x}$.

b) Deduce that the volume, V m³, of the bar is given by
$V = 25x - \dfrac{4x^3}{3}$.

c) Find an expression for $\dfrac{dV}{dx}$.

d) Given that the volume of the bar has to be a maximum, calculate the value of x, and find this maximum volume.

9 An *open* cardboard box is to be made by cutting small squares of side x cm from each of the four corners of a larger square of card of side 10 cm, and folding along the dashed lines, as shown in the diagram. Find the value of x such that the box has a maximum volume.

4.7 Increasing and decreasing functions

The function $f(x) = x$ increases as the values of x increase, and this is true for all real values of x. The graph of the function shows this.

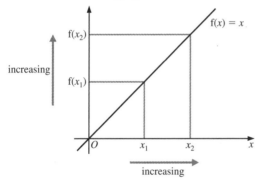

> This is an example of a function that increases for all values of x.

The function $g(x) = x^2$ behaves differently.

$g(x)$ increases as the values of x increase for $x > 0$.

$g(x)$ decreases as the values of x increase for $x < 0$.

x > 0   **x < 0**

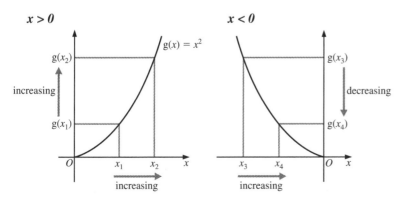

> This function increases for $x > 0$ but decreases for $x < 0$.

Generally a function f(x) is increasing when $x = a$ if $f'(a) > 0$. It is decreasing if $f'(a) < 0$.

It is useful to be able to identify the turning points on the graph of a function when finding where the function increases or decreases.

Example 21

Determine the range of values of x for which these functions are increasing or decreasing.

a) $f(x) = x^2 - 6x$ b) $f(x) = x^4 - 8x^2 - 3$

a) $f(x) = x^2 - 6x$ $\therefore$ $f'(x) = 2x - 6$

At a stationary point $f'(x) = 0$.

$$2x - 6 = 0$$
$$\therefore \quad x = 3$$

Now, $f''(x) = 2$.

Therefore, at $x = 3$, the curve has a minimum value.

From the graph it is clear that f(x) is increasing for $x > 3$, and decreasing for $x < 3$.

Note that 0 and 6 are the **zeros** of the function $f(x) = x^2 - 6x$.

b) $f(x) = x^4 - 8x^2 - 3$ $\therefore$ $f'(x) = 4x^3 - 16x$

At a stationary point $f'(x) = 0$. So:

$$4x^3 - 16x = 0$$
$$\therefore \quad 4x(x - 2)(x + 2) = 0$$
$$\therefore \quad\quad\quad x = -2, x = 0 \text{ or } x = 2.$$

Now, $f''(x) = 12x^2 - 16$.

When $x = -2$, $f''(-2) = 12(-2)^2 - 16 = 32 > 0$. Therefore, at $x = -2$, the curve has a minimum value.

When $x = 0$, $f''(0) = 12(0)^2 - 16 = -16 < 0$. Therefore, at $x = 0$, the curve has a maximum value.

When $x = 2$, $f''(2) = 12(2)^2 - 16 = 32 > 0$. Therefore, at $x = 2$, the curve has a minimum value.

From the graph it is clear that f(x) is increasing for $-2 < x < 0$ and $x > 2$, and that f(x) is decreasing for $x < -2$ and $0 < x < 2$.

Exercise 4G

1 Determine the range of values of x for which these functions increase or decrease.

a) $f(x) = x^2 - 8x + 3$ b) $f(x) = 7 - 2x - x^2$

c) $f(x) = x^3 - 3x^2 - 9x + 4$ d) $f(x) = 2x^3 - 21x^2 + 36x - 5$

e) $f(x) = 5 + 36x - 3x^2 - 2x^3$ f) $f(x) = x^4 + 4x^3 - 8x^2 - 48x + 20$

2 Use a graph to explain why $f(x) = -x^3$ is a decreasing function for all values of x.

3 Prove that $f(x) = x^3 - 3x^2 + 3x + 8$ is an increasing function for all values of x.

C1

Summary

You should know how to ...	Check out
1 Differentiate a polynomial expression.	**1** Differentiate $y = x^3 - 3x^2 + 4x - 3$
2 Use the first derivative to find the gradient of a curve at a point.	**2** Find the gradient of the curve $y = 3x^2 - x + 4$ at the point where $x = -1$.
3 Interpret the gradient as a rate of change in different contexts.	**3** A bowl is filling with water, so that the volume of water, V cm^3, at time t seconds is given by $V = 3t^2 + 4$. Find $\dfrac{dV}{dt}$ at $t = 2$, and explain what the result means.
4 Use the gradient at a point to find the equation of the tangent and normal to the curve at that point.	**4** Find the equation of i) the tangent ii) the normal to these curves: a) $y = x(x - 3)$ at $x = 2$ b) $y = 14 + 3x - 2x^2$ at $x = -1$
5 Use the first derivative to find the coordinates of stationary points.	**5** Find the coordinates of the stationary points on these curves. a) $f(x) = x^3 - 5x^2 - 8x + 10$ b) $y = x^4 - 3x^2 + 4$
6 Use the second derivative to determine the nature of stationary points.	**6** Determine the nature of the stationary points on the curves in question 5.

7 Use the first derivative to find where a function is increasing or decreasing.

7 a) For $f(x) = x^3 - 5x^2 - 8x + 10$,
   i) find $f'(x)$ at $x = 2$ and $x = -2$.
   ii) is the function increasing or decreasing at $x = 2$ and $x = -2$?
   iii) sketch the curve.
   b) For the curve of $y = x^4 - 4x^2 + 4$,
   i) find the coordinates of the stationary points
   ii) sketch the curve.

Revision exercise 4

C1

1 The function $f(x)$ is given by $f(x) = 6x^3 - 3x^2 - 60x + 85$.

a) Write down an expression for $f'(x)$.

b) Calculate the values of x for which $f(x)$ has stationary values.

c) Calculate $f(2)$ and hence sketch the graph of $y = f(x)$.
   State the number of roots of $f(x) = 0$.   *(AQA/NEAB, 1994)*

2 Find the equation of the tangent to the curve $y = x^3 + 2x^2 + 3x + 6$
   at the point where $x = -1$.   *(AQA/NEAB, 1996)*

3 Use calculus to find the values of x for which $y = 3x^4 + 8x^3 + 6x^2 - 1$
   has stationary points.   *(AQA/NEAB, 1997)*

4 A curve has equation $y = x^3 - x^2 - px + q$ where p and q are
   positive constants.

a) Find in terms of p and q, the equation of the tangent to the curve
   at the point where the curve intersects the y-axis.

b) Given that the curve intersects the x-axis at three points, sketch
   $y = x^3 - x^2 - px + q$.   *(AQA/NEAB, 1998)*

5 Use calculus to find the exact coordinates of the minimum point of
   the graph of $f(x) = 12x^2 - 16x + 5$.

   Write down the range of $f(x)$.   *(AQA/NEAB, 1999)*

6 A function f is defined by $f(x) = (x - 2)(11 - 5x)$.

a) Write down the zeros of the function $f(x)$.

b) Find an expression for $f'(x)$ and find the coordinates of the
   stationary point of $f(x)$.

c) $f(x)$ can be written in the form $k(x + a)^2 + b$. Find the values
   of k, a and b.   *(AQA, NEAB, 2000)*

7 The height, h centimetres, of water in a river above its normal level at a time, t days, after a thunderstorm is given by

$$h = 3t^2 - t^3 \quad 0 \leqslant t \leqslant 3$$

a) Find $\dfrac{dh}{dt}$.

b) Find the rate of change, in centimetres per day, of the height of the water in the river after 2.5 days.

c) Find the values of t for which the height of water is increasing.   *(AQA, 2002)*

8 The diagram shows a thin metal component.

The component consists of a rectangle of height h cm and a right-angled triangle whose shorter sides are of length $3x$ cm and $4x$ cm. The perimeter of the component is 240 cm.

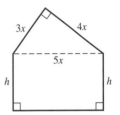

a) i) Show that $h = 120 - 6x$.

   ii) The total surface area of the front face of the component is A cm². By eliminating h show that

$$A = 600x - 24x^2$$

b) i) Find $\dfrac{dA}{dx}$ and hence find the value of x for which A has a stationary value.

   ii) Find $\dfrac{d^2A}{dx^2}$ and hence determine whether this stationary value is a maximum or a minimum.   *(AQA, 2003)*

9 An open topped box has height h cm and a square base of side x cm.

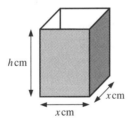

The box has a capacity V cm³. The area of its external surface, consisting of its horizontal base and four vertical faces, is A cm².

a) Find expressions for V and A in terms of x and h.

b) It is given that $A = 3000$.

   i) Show that

$$V = 750x - \tfrac{1}{4}x^3$$

   ii) Find the positive value of x for which $\dfrac{dV}{dx} = 0$, giving your answer in surd form.

   iii) Hence find the maximum possible value of V, giving your answer in the form $p\sqrt{10}$ where p is an integer.   *(AQA, 2001)*

C1

10 a) Express $3(x + 1)^2$ in the form $px^2 + qx + c$.

b) Find the gradient of the curve with equation $y = 3(x + 1)^2$ at the point where $x = 4$.   *(AQA, 2002)*

11 Given that $y = 3x^3 + x^2 + x + 4$, find $\dfrac{dy}{dx}$.

Hence calculate the exact values of x for which the gradient is equal to 1.   *(AQA/NEAB, 1995)*

12 a) It is given that $V = 2400x - 140x^2 + 2x^3$.

Write down an expression for $\dfrac{dV}{dx}$ and hence solve the equation $\dfrac{dV}{dx} = 0$, giving your answers to one decimal place.

The net of a closed box is to be cut from sheet of steel measuring 80 cm by 60 cm, as shown below. The height of the box is x cm.

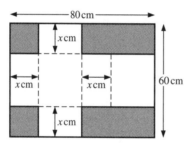

b) Show that the volume, V cm³, of the box is given by

$$V = x(2400 - 140x + 2x^2)$$

c) Find the dimensions of the box for which the volume is a maximum.   *(AQA/NEAB, 2001)*

13 The size of a population, P, of birds on an island is modelled by $P = 59 + 117t + 57t^2 - t^3$ where t is the time in years after 1970.

a) Find $\dfrac{dP}{dt}$.

b) i) Find the positive value of t for which P has stationary value.

ii) Determine whether this stationary value is a maximum or minimum.

c) i) State the year when the model predicts that the population will reach its maximum value.

ii) Determine what the model predicts will happen in the year 2029.   *(AQA, 2002)*

5 Integration

This chapter will show you how to

✦ Integrate simple functions
✦ Evaluate definite integrals
✦ Find the area under curves

Before you start

You should know how to ...	Check in
1 Find the derivatives of a, ax, ax^2, ax^3, where a is a constant.	**1** Find $\dfrac{dy}{dx}$ if: a) $y = 3x^2$ b) $y = x^3$ c) $y = -5x$ d) $y = 7$
2 Differentiate polynomials.	**2** Find $\dfrac{dy}{dx}$ if: a) $y = 4x^3 - 7x$ b) $y = 4 - 2x^2$ c) $y = 3x^2 - 4x^5$ d) $y = 5 + \dfrac{x^2}{2} - \dfrac{x^4}{4}$
3 Evaluate a polynomial function at a given point.	**3** a) Find f(3) if $f(x) = 2x^2 - 3x$ b) Find f(−2) if $f(x) = x^3 - \frac{1}{2}x^2$ c) If $f(x) = 2x + x^2$ find f(3) − f(1). d) If $f(x) = x^3 - 3x$ find f(2) − f(−2).
4 Find where a curve crosses the coordinate axes.	**4** Find the coordinates of the points where these curves cross the coordinate axes. a) $y = x^2 - 4x$ b) $y = 2x^2 + 7x - 15$ c) $y = 2x^3 + x^2$ d) $y = x^3 - 3x^2 + 4$

5.1 Reversing differentiation

You know that if $y = x^2$, then $\dfrac{dy}{dx} = 2x$. Now suppose that you are given $\dfrac{dy}{dx} = 2x$ and asked to find y in terms of x. This process is the reverse of differentiation and is called **integration**.

In this particular case, you know that $y = x^2$ will satisfy $\dfrac{dy}{dx} = 2x$, but so will $y = x^2 + 1$ and $y = x^2 + 2$. In fact, $y = x^2 + c$, where c is a constant, will also satisfy $\dfrac{dy}{dx} = 2x$.

Since you do not know the value of the constant term, you can write $y = x^2 + c$, where c is called the **constant of integration**.

$y = x^2 + c$ is called the **integral** of $2x$ with respect to x. This is written as:

$$\underset{\text{integral}}{\int 2x} \quad \underset{\substack{\text{with respect} \\ \text{to the variable } x}}{dx} \quad = x^2 + c$$

> This is called **indefinite integration**, because c could have any value.

To find $\int x^4 \, dx$, notice that x^5 differentiates to give $5x^4$, which is the required power of x. However, the coefficient 5 is unrequired. To remove it, multiply x^5 by $\frac{1}{5}$. Now you have:

$$\tfrac{1}{5}x^5 \text{ differentiates to give } x^4$$

So:

$$\int x^4 \, dx = \tfrac{1}{5}x^5 + c$$

> Don't forget to add the constant of integration.

In general:

If $\dfrac{dy}{dx} = ax^n$, then

$$y = \frac{ax^{n+1}}{n+1} + c \quad (n \neq -1)$$

> $\neq$ means 'not equal to'.

That is:

$$\int ax^n \, dx = \frac{ax^{n+1}}{n+1} + c \quad (n \neq -1)$$

> One way of remembering this is 'add 1 to the power and divide by the new power'.

Note also that $\int ax^n \, dx = a \times \int x^n \, dx$, where a is a constant.

Example 1

Find these integrals.

a) $\int 3x^2 \, dx$ b) $\int 2x^4 \, dx$ c) $\int \frac{1}{3}x^5 \, dx$ d) $\int 7 \, dx$

a) Using the result given:

$$\int 3x^2 \, dx = \frac{3x^3}{3} + c$$
$$= x^3 + c$$

b) $\int 2x^4 \, dx = \frac{2x^5}{5} + c$

c) $\int \frac{1}{3}x^5 \, dx = \frac{1}{3} \times \frac{x^6}{6} + c$
$$= \frac{x^6}{18} + c$$

d) Writing $7 = 7x^0$ and using the result given:

$$\int 7x^0 \, dx = \frac{7x^1}{1} + c$$
$$= 7x + c$$

To differentiate a polynomial, you should differentiate each term of the polynomial in turn. The same technique applies to the integration of polynomials.

Example 2

Find these integrals.

a) $\int (x^2 + 6x - 3) \, dx$ b) $\int (2x - 1)^2 \, dx$ c) $\int 3x(x + 5)^2 \, dx$

a) Integrating term by term gives:

$$\int (x^2 + 6x - 3) \, dx = \int x^2 \, dx + \int 6x \, dx - \int 3 \, dx$$
$$= \frac{x^3}{3} + \frac{6x^2}{2} - \frac{3x}{1} + c$$
$$= \frac{x^3}{3} + 3x^2 - 3x + c$$

> The constant c represents the sum of the constants from each of the integrations.

b) First expand $(2x - 1)^2$ to obtain a polynomial:

$$\int (2x - 1)^2 \, dx = \int (4x^2 - 4x + 1) \, dx$$
$$= \int 4x^2 dx - \int 4x dx + \int 1 dx$$
$$= \frac{4x^3}{3} - \frac{4x^2}{2} + \frac{1x}{1} + c$$
$$= \frac{4x^3}{3} - 2x^2 + x + c$$

C1

c) First expand $3x(x+5)^2$ to obtain a polynomial:

$$\int 3x(x+5)^2\,dx = \int 3x(x^2 + 10x + 25)\,dx$$
$$= \int (3x^3 + 30x^2 + 75x)\,dx$$
$$= \frac{3x^4}{4} + \frac{30x^3}{3} + \frac{75x^2}{2} + c$$
$$= \frac{3x^4}{4} + 10x^3 + \frac{75x^2}{2} + c$$

If you know the coordinates of a point on the curve, you can find the constant of integration.

C1

Example 3

The gradient of a curve at the point (x, y) on the curve is given by $\frac{dy}{dx} = 3x^2 - 4x$. Given that the point $(1, 2)$ lies on the curve, determine the equation of the curve.

Integrating gives

$$y = \int 3x^2 - 4x\,dx$$
$$\therefore \quad y = \frac{3x^3}{3} - \frac{4x^2}{2} + c$$
$$= x^3 - 2x^2 + c$$

The curve passes through the point $(1, 2)$. Substituting gives:

$$2 = (1)^3 - 2(1)^2 + c$$
$$\therefore \quad c = 3$$

The equation of the curve is $y = x^3 - 2x^2 + 3$.

Exercise 5A

1 Integrate each of these terms with respect to x.
a) x^3 b) x^4 c) $3x^2$ d) $12x^5$ e) $-4x$ f) $15x^4$
g) $2x^3$ h) 3 i) $\frac{1}{2}x^5$ j) $\frac{2}{3}x^3$ k) $-\frac{1}{3}x^2$ l) $\frac{2}{3}$

2 Find each of these integrals.
a) $\int 3x^2 + 7\,dx$
b) $\int 4x^3 - 2x\,dx$
c) $\int 2 - 6x^5\,dx$
d) $\int 4x - 6x^2\,dx$
e) $\int 5 - 8x\,dx$
f) $\int x - x^3\,dx$
g) $\int 1 + x + x^2\,dx$
h) $\int 2 - 5x + 8x^2\,dx$
i) $\int 4x - 3x^3 + 7x^6\,dx$
j) $\int 3x - 2x^3 + 3x^8\,dx$

3 Integrate each of these expressions with respect to x.

a) $x(x-4)$

b) $x(2x-3)$

c) $3x(x+2)$

d) $5x(3x-2)$

e) $x^2(x+1)$

f) $x^3(5x-2)$

g) $2x^2(6-5x)$

h) $(x+1)(x+2)$

4 In each of these, use the information given to find an expression for y in terms of x.

a) $\dfrac{dy}{dx} = 10x + 3, y = 24$ when $x = 2$

b) $\dfrac{dy}{dx} = 3x^2 - 4x, y = 12$ when $x = 3$

c) $\dfrac{dy}{dx} = 6x - 12x^2, y = -35$ when $x = 2$

d) $\dfrac{dy}{dx} = 15x - 4, y = 2$ when $x = -1$

e) $\dfrac{dy}{dx} = 4x^3 + 2x, y = 91$ when $x = 3$

f) $\dfrac{dy}{dx} = 1 - 10x, y = -20$ when $x = -2$

g) $\dfrac{dy}{dx} = 6x^5 - 2x^2, y = 3$ when $x = -1$

h) $\dfrac{dy}{dx} = -2(1 + 2x), y = 12$ when $x = 0$

5 The gradient of a curve at the point (x, y) on a curve is given by $\dfrac{dy}{dx} = 3x^2 + 4$. Given that the point $(1, 7)$ lies on the curve, determine the equation of the curve.

6 A curve passes through the point $(-2, 8)$ and its gradient function is $4x^3 - 6x$. Find the equation of the curve.

7 The gradient of a curve at the point (x, y) is $16x^3 + 2x + 1$. Given that the curve passes through the point $(\tfrac{1}{2}, 3)$ find the equation of the curve.

8 A curve has an equation which satisfies $\dfrac{d^2y}{dx^2} = 6x - 4$. The point $P(2, 11)$ lies on the curve, and the gradient of the curve at the point P is 9. Determine the equation of the curve.

9 Find y as a function of x given that $\dfrac{d^2y}{dx^2} = 12x^2 - 6$, and that when $x = 1, \dfrac{dy}{dx} = -2$ and $y = 1$.

10 The curve with equation $y = ax^2 + bx + c$ passes through the points $P(2, 6)$ and $Q(3, 16)$, and has a gradient of 7 at the point P. Find the values of the constants a, b and c.

5.2 Definite integrals

You can find a numerical value for an integral if you evaluate it between two given limits.

> If $\int f'(x)\,dx = f(x) + c$
>
> then $\int_a^b f'(x)\,dx = \left[f(x)\right]_a^b = f(b) - f(a)$

$\int_a^b f(x)\,dx$ is called a **definite integral**, since it gives a definite answer.

✦   The constant a is called the lower limit of the integral.
✦   The constant b is called the upper limit of the integral.
✦   The dx indicates that the limits a and b are x limits.

For example, to evaluate the definite integral $\int_0^1 2x\,dx$, first integrate to obtain

$$\int_0^1 2x\,dx = \left[x^2 + c\right]_0^1$$

Substituting the values $x = 1$ and $x = 0$ gives

$$\int_0^1 2x\,dx = (1^2 + c) - (0^2 + c) = 1 - 0$$

$$\therefore \quad \int_0^1 2x\,dx = 1$$

Notice that the constants of integration cancel. You can ignore the constants of integration when working with definite integrals.

> Notice that square brackets are used here.

> You subtract the expression containing the lower limit from the expression containing the upper limit.

C1

Example 4

Evaluate these definite integrals.

a) $\displaystyle\int_0^2 4x^3\,dx$ b) $\displaystyle\int_1^3 3x^2 - 1\,dx$ c) $\displaystyle\int_{-1}^2 4x + 1\,dx$

....

a) $\displaystyle\int_0^2 4x^3\,dx = \left[x^4\right]_0^2$
$\qquad\qquad = 2^4 - 0^4 = 16$

b) $\displaystyle\int_1^3 3x^2 - 1\,dx = \left[x^3 - x\right]_1^3$
$\qquad\qquad\quad = (3^3 - 3) - (1^3 - 1)$
$\qquad\qquad\quad = 24 - 0 = 24$

c) $\displaystyle\int_{-1}^2 4x + 1\,dx = \left[2x^2 + x\right]_{-1}^2$
$\qquad\qquad\quad = (2(2)^2 + 2) - (2(-1)^2 + (-1))$
$\qquad\qquad\quad = 10 - 1 = 9$

Exercise 5B

Work out each of these definite integrals.

1 $\int_0^3 x^2 \, dx$

2 $\int_0^2 8x^3 \, dx$

3 $\int_2^5 4x \, dx$

4 $\int_1^3 2x + 1 \, dx$

5 $\int_3^5 3x^2 - 1 \, dx$

6 $\int_{-1}^3 5 - 2x \, dx$

7 $\int_{-3}^3 x^2 + 1 \, dx$

8 $\int_0^2 8x^3 + 4x \, dx$

9 $\int_{-1}^2 2x^7 \, dx$

10 $\int_{-2}^1 2 - 3x^2 \, dx$

11 $\int_3^6 x(x - 1) \, dx$

12 $\int_{-2}^{-1} (x + 2)^2 \, dx$

5.3 Area under a curve

Consider the area under the straight line $y = 2x$ between the limits $x = 0$ and $x = a$.

You can see from the diagram that the area A under $y = 2x$ between $x = 0$ and $x = a$ is given by $A = a^2$. In other words, $A = x^2$ is an area function for this straight line.

If you differentiate this area function $A = x^2$, you get

$$\frac{dA}{dx} = 2x$$

In fact,

$$A = \int_0^a 2x \, dx$$

for the area under $y = 2x$ between $x = 0$ and $x = a$.

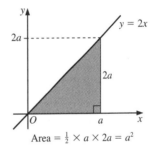

Area $= \frac{1}{2} \times a \times 2a = a^2$

Example 5

Find the area under $y = 2x$ between $x = 1$ and $x = 3$.

$$\begin{aligned} \text{Area} &= \int_1^3 2x \, dx \\ &= \left[x^2 \right]_1^3 \\ &= (3)^2 - (1)^2 \\ &= 8 \end{aligned}$$

> More precisely you would say that the area is 8 square units.

The example shows that you can interpret a definite integral as the area under a line. This is also true for the area under a curve.

In general, the area under the curve $y = f(x)$ between the limits $x = a$ and $x = b$ is given by

$$A = \int_a^b y \, dx \quad \text{or} \quad \int_a^b f(x) \, dx$$

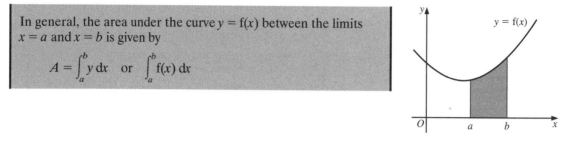

Example 6

Find the area under the curve $y = x^2 - 6x + 5$.
a) between the limits $x = 0$ and $x = 1$
b) between the limits $x = 1$ and $x = 4$.

A sketch graph is always useful. In this case the positive x^2 term indicates a $\cup$ shaped curve. Factorising gives:

$$x^2 - 6x + 5 = (x - 1)(x - 5)$$

Therefore the graph intersects the x-axis at $x = 1$ and $x = 5$ and the sketch graph is shown in the diagram.

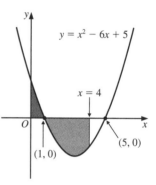

a) Let A be the required area, then:

$$A = \int_0^1 x^2 - 6x + 5 \, dx$$
$$= \left[\frac{x^3}{3} - 3x^2 + 5x \right]_0^1$$
$$= \left(\frac{1}{3} - 3 + 5 \right) - (0)$$
$$= \frac{7}{3}$$

The required area is $\frac{7}{3}$ or $2\frac{1}{3}$.

b) Let A be the required area, then:

$$A = \int_1^4 x^2 - 6x + 5 \, dx$$
$$= \left[\frac{x^3}{3} - 3x^2 + 5x \right]_1^4$$
$$= \left(\frac{4^3}{3} - 3(4)^2 + 5(4) \right) - \left(\frac{1}{3} - 3(1)^2 + 5(1) \right)$$
$$= \left(\frac{64}{3} - 48 + 20 \right) - \left(\frac{7}{3} \right)$$
$$= -\frac{27}{3} = -9$$

Notice that in this case the definite integral gives a negative value. The minus sign tells you that the area is below the x-axis. Therefore the required area is 9.

Example 7

Given the cubic function $y = x^3 - 6x^2 + 5x + 12$,

a) show that the cubic curve intersects the x-axis at $x = 3$ and $x = 4$. Hence find the third point of intersection with the x-axis and sketch the graph of the cubic function.

b) find the area under the cubic curve between $x = -1$ and $x = 1$.

a) When $x = 3$

$$y = (3)^3 - 6(3)^2 + 5(3) + 12 = 0$$

When $x = 4$

$$y = (4)^3 - 6(4)^2 + 5(4) + 12 = 0$$

> To show that the curve intersects the x-axis at the point $x = 3$ and $x = 4$, evaluate y for each of these x values.

Therefore $(x - 3)$ and $(x - 4)$ are factors of y.

$$\therefore \quad y = (x - 3)(x - 4)(?)$$

> Remember the Factor Theorem (page 36).

C1

The missing factor must be linear and since $-3 \times -4 = 12$, the constant must be 1. This gives $(x + 1)$ as the third factor. So:

$$y = (x - 3)(x - 4)(x + 1)$$

Therefore the curve also intersects the x-axis at $x = -1$. The sketch graph is shown.

b) Let A be the required area. Then:

$$A = \int_{-1}^{1} x^3 - 6x^2 + 5x + 12 \, dx$$

$$= \left[\frac{x^4}{4} - 2x^3 + \frac{5x^2}{2} + 12x \right]_{-1}^{1}$$

$$= \left(\frac{1}{4} - 2 + \frac{5}{2} + 12 \right) - \left(\frac{1}{4} + 2 + \frac{5}{2} - 12 \right)$$

$$= \frac{51}{4} + \frac{29}{4} = 20 \quad \text{The required area is 20.}$$

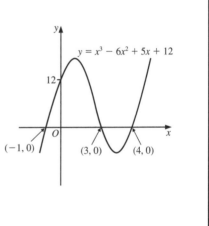

Example 8

Find the area enclosed between the line with equation $y = x$ and the curve with equation $y = x^2$.

First sketch the graph:

Find the intersection points.

$$x^2 = x, \text{ or } x^2 - x = 0$$

$$x(x - 1) = 0$$

$$\therefore \quad x = 0, \quad x = 1$$

When $x = 0, y = 0$ and when $x = 1$, $y = 1$.

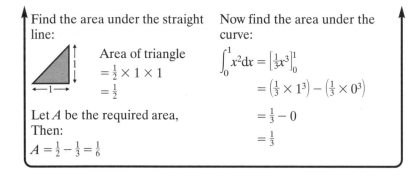

Find the area under the straight line:

Area of triangle
$= \frac{1}{2} \times 1 \times 1$
$= \frac{1}{2}$

Let A be the required area,
Then:

$A = \frac{1}{2} - \frac{1}{3} = \frac{1}{6}$

Now find the area under the curve:

$\int_0^1 x^2 dx = \left[\frac{1}{3}x^3\right]_0^1$

$= \left(\frac{1}{3} \times 1^3\right) - \left(\frac{1}{3} \times 0^3\right)$

$= \frac{1}{3} - 0$

$= \frac{1}{3}$

Exercise 5C

C1

1 Work out the shaded area on each of these diagrams.

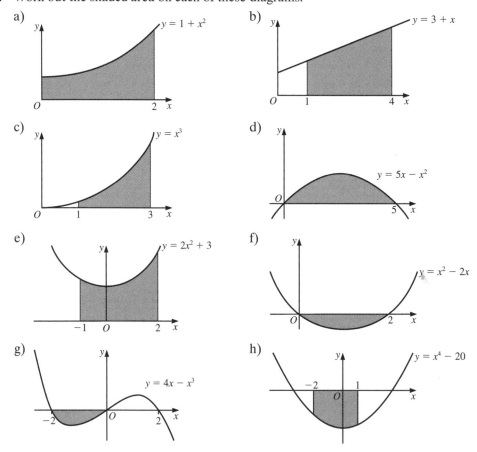

a) $y = 1 + x^2$

b) $y = 3 + x$

c) $y = x^3$

d) $y = 5x - x^2$

e) $y = 2x^2 + 3$

f) $y = x^2 - 2x$

g) $y = 4x - x^3$

h) $y = x^4 - 20$

2 Find the areas enclosed by the x-axis and these curves and straight lines.

a) $y = x^2 + 3x$, $x = 2, x = 5$

b) $y = \frac{1}{8}x^3 + 2x$, $x = 2, x = 4$

c) $y = 2 - x^3$, $x = -3, x = -2$

d) $y = x(3x - 2)$, $x = 1, x = 2$

e) $y = x(x + 1)^2$, $x = 0, x = 2$

f) $y = (3x - 4)^2$, $x = 1, x = 3$

3 Sketch the graph of the region bounded by the curve $y = x^3 - 5$, the lines $x = 2$ and $x = 4$, and the x-axis. Find the area of the region.

4 Find the area enclosed above the x-axis and below the curve $y = 16 - x^2$.

5 Sketch the curve $y = (x - 2)(x - 3)$, showing where it crosses the x-axis. Hence find the area enclosed below the x-axis and above the curve.

6 Sketch the curve with equation $y = (x - 2)^2$. Calculate the area of the region bounded by the curve and the x- and y-axes.

7 Find the area of the region above the x-axis bounded by the line $y = 4x$ and the curve $y = x^3$.

8 a) Sketch the curve $y = x(x + 1)(x - 3)$, showing where it cuts the x-axis.

b) Calculate the area of the region, above the x-axis, bounded by the x-axis and the curve.

c) Calculate the area of the region, below the x-axis, bounded by the x-axis and the curve.

9 a) Sketch the curve $y = x^2(x - 1)(x + 2)$.

b) Calculate the area of the region bounded by the positive x-axis and the curve.

c) Calculate the area of the region bounded by the negative x-axis and the curve.

C1

Summary

You should know how to ...	Check out
1 Integrate polynomial expressions.	**1** Find a) $\int 2x^2 - 3x - 5 \, dx$ b) $\int 4x^3 - 6x + 3 \, dx$
2 Use integration to find an area between a curve and the x-axis.	**2 a)** Use your result from question 1(a) to find the area shown in the diagram. 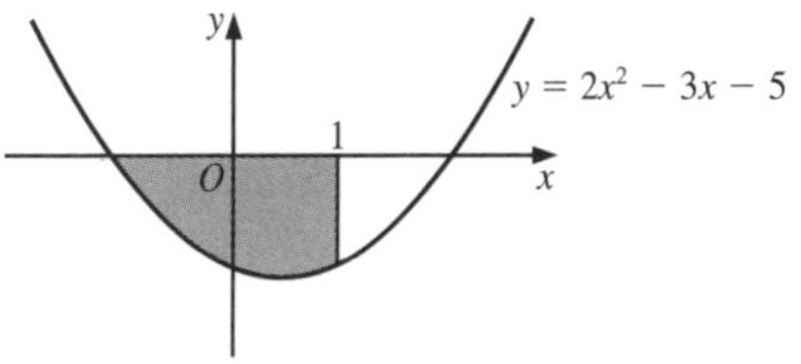 **b)** Use your result from question 1(b) to find the area under the curve $y = 4x^3 - 6x + 3$ between the points $x = 1$ and $x = 3$.

Revision exercise 5

1

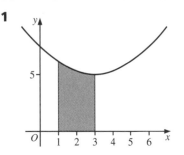

The graph of $y = (x + a)^2 + b$ is sketched above.

a) Write down the values of a and b.

b) Use algebraic integration to find the area of the shaded region
   shown above.   (*AQA/NEAB, 1997*)

2 a) Find $\int x(x^2 - 4)\,dx$.

 b) Evaluate $\int_{-1}^{1} x(x^2 - 4)\,dx$.

 c) Explain the significance of your answer to part b) in terms of the
    graph of $y = x(x^2 - 4)$.   (*AQA/NEAB, 1998*)

3 A road hump is 40 cm wide and 10 cm high at its peak.
   The cross-section, as shown above, is modelled by a
   function of the form $kx(w - x)$, where k and w
   are constants.

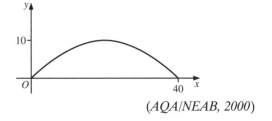

 a) Find the value of w and k.

 b) Use algebraic integration to estimate the volume
    of the hump, given that the road is 6 m wide.   (*AQA/NEAB, 2000*)

4 The diagram shows the straight line $y = 3x$ and the curve $y = x^3 - 3x^2 + 3x$.

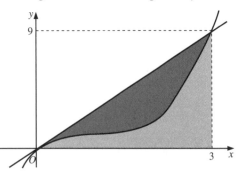

 a) i) Differentiate $x^3 - 3x^2 + 3x$
    ii) Find the coordinates of the stationary point on the curve $y = x^3 - 3x^2 + 3x$.

 b) i) Find $\int (x^3 - 3x^2 + 3x)\,dx$
    ii) Show that the areas of the two shaded regions are equal.   (*AQA, 2004*)

C1

5 The diagram shows the graph of $y = 12 - 3x^2$ and the tangent to the curve at the point $P(2, 0)$. The region enclosed by the tangent, the curve and the y-axis is shaded.

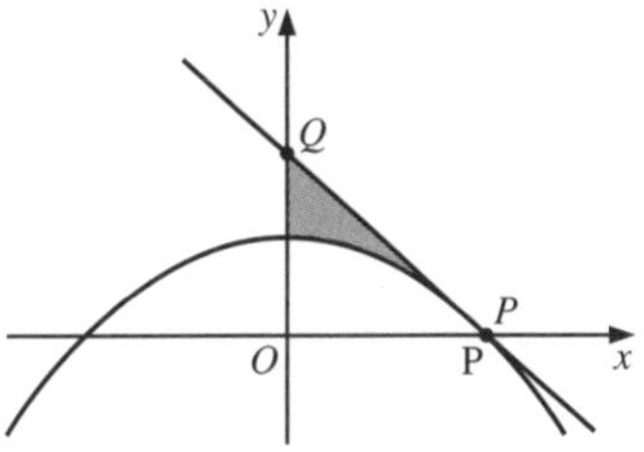

a) Find $\int_0^2 12 - 3x^2 \, dx$.

b) i) Find the gradient of the curve $y = 12 - 3x^2$ at the point P.
    ii) Find the coordinates of the point Q where the tangent at P crosses the y-axis.

c) Find the area of the shaded region.

(AQA, 2002)

6 The function f is defined for all values of x by $f(x) = x^3 - 7x^2 + 14x - 8$. It is given that $f(1) = 0$ and $f(2) = 0$.

a) Find the values of $f(3)$ and $f(4)$.

b) Write $f(x)$ as the product of three linear factors.

c) The diagram shows the graph of $y = x^3 - 7x^2 + 14x - 8$.

C1

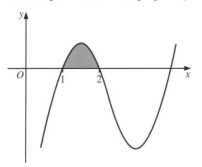

i) Find $\dfrac{dy}{dx}$

ii) State, giving a reason, whether the function f is increasing or decreasing at the point where $x = 3$.

iii) Find $\int (x^3 - 7x^2 + 14x - 8) \, dx$.

iv) Hence find the area of the shaded region enclosed by the graph of $y = f(x)$ for $1 \leqslant x \leqslant 2$, and the x-axis.

(AQA, 2003)

7 The diagram shows the graph of $y = x^3 - x, x \geqslant 0$. The points on the graph for which $x = 1$ and $x = 2$ are labelled A and B respectively.

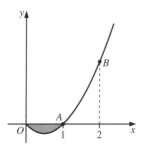

a) Find the y-coordinate of B and hence find the equation of the straight line AB, giving your answer in the form $ax + by + c = 0$.

b) Find by integration the area of the shaded region.

(AQA, 2002)

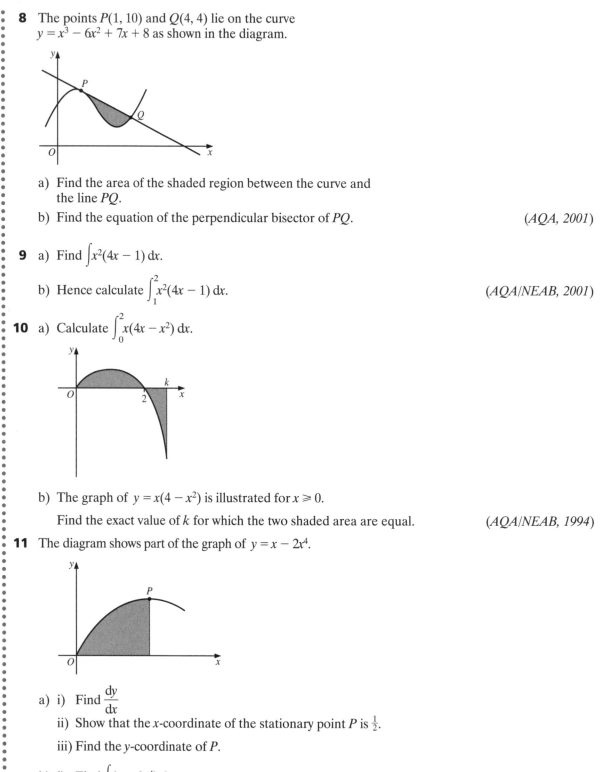

8 The points $P(1, 10)$ and $Q(4, 4)$ lie on the curve
$y = x^3 - 6x^2 + 7x + 8$ as shown in the diagram.

a) Find the area of the shaded region between the curve and
the line PQ.

b) Find the equation of the perpendicular bisector of PQ.   (*AQA, 2001*)

9 a) Find $\int x^2(4x - 1)\,dx$.

b) Hence calculate $\int_1^2 x^2(4x - 1)\,dx$.   (*AQA/NEAB, 2001*)

10 a) Calculate $\int_0^2 x(4x - x^2)\,dx$.

b) The graph of $y = x(4 - x^2)$ is illustrated for $x \geqslant 0$.

Find the exact value of k for which the two shaded area are equal.   (*AQA/NEAB, 1994*)

11 The diagram shows part of the graph of $y = x - 2x^4$.

a) i)   Find $\dfrac{dy}{dx}$

ii) Show that the x-coordinate of the stationary point P is $\frac{1}{2}$.

iii) Find the y-coordinate of P.

b) i)   Find $\int (x - 2x^4)\,dx$.

ii) Hence find the area of the shaded region.   (*AQA, 2003*)

12 The curve with equation $y = x^3 - 6x^2 + 9x + 16$ is sketched.

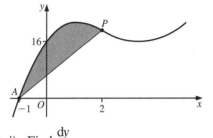

a) i) Find $\dfrac{dy}{dx}$.

ii) Hence find the coordinates of the stationary points of the curve.

b) i) Find $\displaystyle\int_{-1}^{2} (x^3 - 6x^2 + 9x + 16)\,dx$.

ii) Hence find the area of the shaded region.   *(AQA, 2003)*

C1 Practice Paper

✦ *The time allowed is 1 hour and 30 minutes.*
✦ *All necessary working should be shown; otherwise marks for method may be lost.*
✦ *Calculators(scientific and graphical) are **not** permitted in this paper.*
✦ *The maximum mark for this paper is 75.*

1 a) Show that $\sqrt{208} = 4\sqrt{13}$ (*2 marks*)

   b) Write $\dfrac{9}{\sqrt{13} - 2}$ in the form $a + b\sqrt{13}$ (*4 marks*)

   c) Find the exact roots of the equation $2x^2 + 8x - 5 = 0$ giving your answers in their simplest form. (*3 marks*)

2 The straight line $y - x = 2$ intersects the circle $x^2 + 5x + y^2 = 9$ at the points A and B. Find the coordinates of A and B. (*6 marks*)

3 The function f is given as $f(x) = x^3 + 4x^2 + 9x + 10$.

   a) Use the Factor Theorem to show that $(x + 2)$ is a factor of f. (*1 mark*)

   b) Divide $f(x)$ by $(x + 2)$ to find a quadratic factor of f. (*2 marks*)

   c) By considering the quadratic factor show that $f(x)$ has only one linear factor. (*2 marks*)

   d) Sketch the graph of $f(x)$, indicating the coordinates of the points where the graph crosses the x and y axes. (*3 marks*)

4 a) Write $x^2 - 6x + 7$ in the form $(x + a)^2 + b$. (*2 marks*)

   b) Hence sketch the graph of $y = x^2 - 6x + 7$ indicating the coordinates of the vertex. (*3 marks*)

   c) State the equation of the line of symmetry of the curve. (*1 mark*)

   d) Describe the geometrical transformation by which this graph can be obtained from the graph of $y = x^2$. (*2 marks*)

5 The points A and B have coordinates $(1, 4)$ and $(-1, 1)$ respectively.

   a) Find the gradient of the line AB. (*2 marks*)

   b) Find the equation of the line AB. Give your answer in the form $ax + by + c = 0$. (*3 marks*)

   c) Find the equation of the line that is parallel to AB and passes through the point C which has coordinates $(4, 0)$. (*3 marks*)

   d) Find the distance between the points A and C. (*2 marks*)

C1

6 The points P and Q have coordinates $(-2, 4)$ and $(-6, 2)$ respectively. P and Q lie at either end of a chord of a circle.

a) Find the coordinates of the mid-point M of the line AB. *(1 mark)*

b) Find the equation of the line that passes through M and the centre of the circle. *(5 marks)*

c) Given that the centre of the circle is at $(-3, 1)$ find the equation of the circle. *(5 marks)*

7 The diagram shows part of the curve $y = 2x^3 - 3x^2$. The curve intersects the x-axis at Q and there is a stationary point at P.

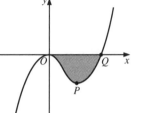

a) i) Find $\dfrac{dy}{dx}$. *(2 marks)*

   ii) Find the coordinates of P. *(3 marks)*

b) i) Find the value of $\dfrac{d^2y}{dx^2}$ at P. *(1 mark)*

   ii) Hence show that the curve has a minimum value at P. *(2 marks)*

c) i) Find $\int 2x^3 - 3x^2 \, dx$ *(2 marks)*

   ii) Find the area of the shaded region in the diagram. *(4 marks)*

8 A company works out the profit it makes on selling widgets using the function

$$f(x) = 7x - x^2, x \geqslant 0$$

where x is the number sold in thousands and $f(x)$ is the profit in thousands of pounds.

a) i) Find $f'(x)$. *(2 marks)*

   ii) For what range of values of x are profits increasing? *(2 marks)*

   iii) What is the maximum profit the company can make through selling widgets? *(2 marks)*

b) Given that the company wants to make a profit of at least £6000, show that

$$x^2 - 7x + 6 \leqslant 0$$

and hence find the range of values for the number of widgets the company must sell. *(3 marks)*

C1

6 Transformations of functions

This chapter will show you how to

◆ Transform the graphs of functions by translation, reflection and stretching

Before you start

You should know how to ...	Check in

1 Translate a shape; reflect a shape in a given axis; stretch a shape in a given direction by a scale factor.	**1** On graph paper, draw axes Ox and Oy using 1 cm to 1 unit for $-6 \leqslant x \leqslant 12$, $-10 \leqslant y \leqslant 16$. Plot the points $O(0, 0), A(0, 5), B(2, 2)$. Draw the images of triangle OAB under these transformations.
	
	 a) Translations
	
	    i) $\binom{5}{6}$ ii) $\binom{4}{-7}$ iii) $\binom{-6}{0}$ iv) $\binom{-4}{-4}$
	
	 b) Reflection in i) Ox ii) Oy.
	
	 c) i) Stretch, scale factor 5, parallel to Ox
	    ii) Stretch, scale factor $\frac{1}{2}$, parallel to Ox
	    iii) Stretch, scale factor 3, parallel to Oy.

2 Use function notation.	**2** If $f(x) = x^2$, find the value of a) $f(3)$ b) $f(3) + 2$ c) $-f(3)$ d) $f(-3)$ e) $3f(3)$ Write an expression for $f(2x)$. If $g(x) = 4x - 1$, find the value of f) $g(-2)$ g) $g(-2)-2$ h) $-g(-2)$ i) $g(2)$ j) $-2g(-2)$ Write an expression for $g(-2x)$.
3 Draw sketch graphs of the basic functions.	**3** Draw sketch graphs of a) $y = x$ b) $y = x^2$ c) $y = x^3$ d) $y = \dfrac{1}{x}$ e) $y = 2^x$ Confirm your results using a graphics calculator if possible.

You can often write the equation of a curve as

$y = $ some expression in x

or, using functional notation, as

$y = f(x)$

For example, you could write $y = x^2$ as $f(x) = x^2$. To evaluate the function when $x = 3$ you would write

$f(3) = 3^2$

$\therefore\ \ f(3) = 9$

You can say that 9 is the **image** of 3 under the function f, and also that 'f of 3 equals 9'.

Some functions are defined for all values of x. For example,

$f(x) = 2x - 3, \ \ f(x) = x^2, \ \ f(x) = x^3 + x - 1.$

For any value of x, there is a corresponding value of $f(x)$.

However, there are functions that are only defined for certain values of x. For example,

$f(x) = \dfrac{1}{x}, \ \ f(x) = \sqrt{x}.$

When $x = 0$, $f(x) = \dfrac{1}{x}$ has no finite value and $f(x) = \sqrt{x}$ is not defined for negative x.

C2

6.1 Translations

Here are five functions whose graphs you need to know:

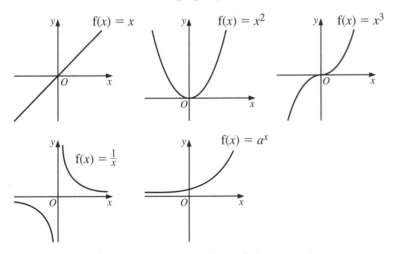

You have already met translations of $y = x^2$, for example, transformations of the form $y = (x - 1)^2$ and $y = x^2 + 2$.

Translations parallel to the y-axis

Consider the function f(x) defined by $f(x) = x^2, x \in \mathbb{R}$.

Now consider the functions

(i) $f(x) + 1 = x^2 + 1$ and   (ii) $f(x) - 1 = x^2 - 1$

Plotting graphs of both (i) and (ii) on the same set of axes as $f(x) = x^2$ gives the curves shown.

In case (i), the graph of f(x) has been translated $+1$ unit parallel to the y-axis (it moves up).

In case (ii), the graph of f(x) has been translated -1 unit parallel to the y-axis (it moves down).

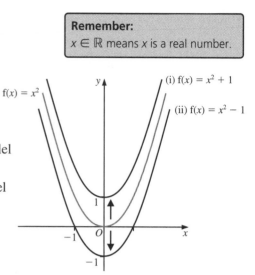

C2

In general:
- The algebraic transformation **f(x) + a**, where a is a constant, causes a geometric transformation of the graph of f(x), namely a **translation of a units parallel to the y-axis.**
- The algebraic transformation **f(x) − a**, where a is a constant, causes a geometric transformation of the graph of f(x), namely a **translation of $-a$ units parallel to the y-axis.**

Example 1

The function f(x) is defined by $f(x) = x^3, x \in \mathbb{R}$. Sketch the graph of f(x). Hence sketch the graph of $g(x) = x^3 - 4$.

The graph of f(x) is shown in diagram a).

Since $g(x) = f(x) - 4$, you obtain the graph of g by translating the graph of f(x) by -4 units parallel to the y-axis.
This is shown in diagram b).

Translations parallel to the *x*-axis

Look again at the function $f(x) = x^2$.

If you simplify expressions for i) $f(x + 2)$ and ii) $f(x - 2)$, you get

(i) $f(x + 2) = (x + 2)^2$ and (ii) $f(x - 2) = (x - 2)^2$

Plotting graphs of both (i) and (ii) on the same set of axes gives the curves shown.

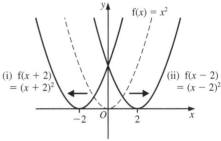

In case (i), the graph of f has been translated -2 units parallel to the *x*-axis (it moves left).

In case (ii), the graph of f has been translated $+2$ units parallel to the *x*-axis (it moves right).

In general:
- The algebraic transformation **f(x + a)**, where *a* is a constant, causes a geometric transformation of the graph of f(*x*), namely a **translation of −a units parallel to the *x*-axis**.
- The algebraic transformation **f(x − a)**, where *a* is a constant, causes a geometric transformation of the graph of f(*x*), namely a **translation of a units parallel to the *x*-axis**.

C2

Example 2

The function $f(x)$ is defined by $f(x) = x^2 + 1$, for all real values of x.
a) Sketch the graph of $f(x)$.
b) State the transformation by which the graph of $f(x + 3)$ can be obtained from the graph of $f(x)$.
c) Hence sketch the graph of $f(x + 3)$.
d) Express $f(x + 3)$ in the form $ax^2 + bx + c$.

a) Sketching the graph of $f(x) = x^2 + 1$ gives the curve shown.

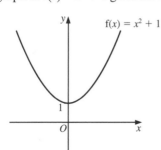

b) The graph of $f(x + 3)$ can be obtained from the graph of $f(x)$ by a translation of -3 units parallel to the *x*-axis.

c) The graph of f(x + 3) is shown.

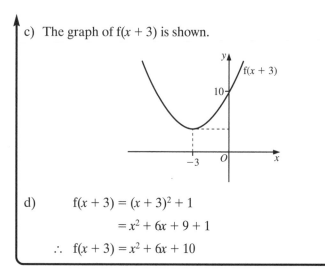

Use a graphics calculator to confirm the shape of this graph.

d) $f(x + 3) = (x + 3)^2 + 1$
              $= x^2 + 6x + 9 + 1$
     $\therefore$ $f(x + 3) = x^2 + 6x + 10$

C2

Example 3

The function f is defined for all real values of x by $f(x) = 3^{x-2}$.
Sketch the graph of $y = f(x)$.

The graph of 3^x is shown.

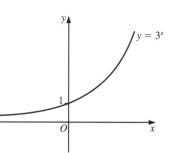

You can sketch the graph of $y = 3^x$ by considering a few values.

x	-1	0	1	2
y	$\frac{1}{3}$	1	3	9

$y = 3^x$ is an example of an **exponential function**, in which the variable x is contained within the power.

The graph of $f(x) = 3^{x-2}$ is obtained by translating the graph of $y = 3^x$ by $+2$ units parallel to the x-axis.

Therefore the graph of $f(x)$ is as shown.

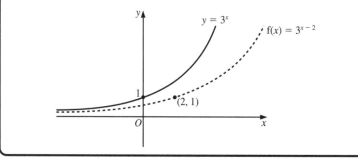

6.2 Reflection transformations

Again consider the function $f(x) = x^2$ defined for all real values of x.

Now consider the functions

    (i) $-f(x) = -x^2$ and (ii) $f(-x) = (-x)^2 = x^2$.

In case (i), the graph of $f(x)$ has been reflected in the x-axis.

In case (ii), the graph of $f(x)$ has been reflected in the y-axis.

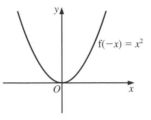

> ✦ The algebraic transformation $-\mathbf{f(x)}$ causes a geometric transformation of the graph of $f(x)$, namely a **reflection in the x-axis**.
> ✦ The algebraic transformation $\mathbf{f(-x)}$ causes a geometric transformation of the graph of $f(x)$, namely a **reflection in the y-axis**.

C2

Example 4

The function $f(x)$ is defined for all real values of x and given by $f(x) = x + 1$.

a) Sketch the graph of $f(x)$.

b) Sketch the graph of the function $g(x)$ obtained by reflecting the graph of $f(x)$ in the x-axis.

c) Write down and simplify an expression for the function $g(x)$.

. . . .

a) The graph of $f(x) = x + 1$ is shown below.

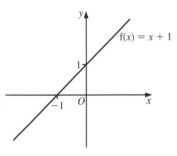

b) The reflection of the graph of $f(x)$ in the x-axis is shown below.

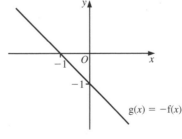

c) The function $g(x)$ is given by:

$$g(x) = -f(x)$$
$$= -(x + 1) \quad \therefore \ g(x) = -x - 1$$

The next example is a reflection of an exponential function.

Example 5

The function f(x) is defined for all real values of x and given by
f(x) = 2^{-x}. Sketch the graph of y = f(x).

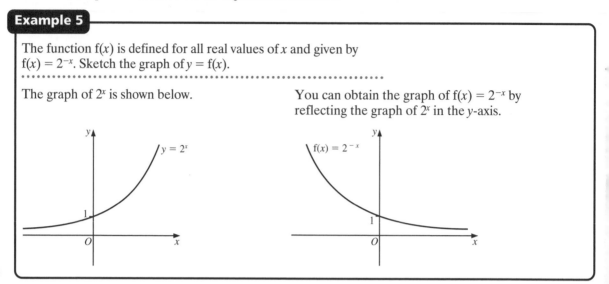

The graph of 2^x is shown below.

You can obtain the graph of f(x) = 2^{-x} by reflecting the graph of 2^x in the y-axis.

6.3 Stretch transformations

Once again consider the function f(x) = x^2 defined for all real values of x.

Now consider the functions (i) f($2x$) and (ii) 2f(x).

    (i) f($2x$) = $(2x)^2$ = $4x^2$ and   (ii) 2f(x) = $2x^2$

> **Remember:**
> A scale factor of 2 means that lengths in the direction of stretch are doubled.

In case (i), the graph of f(x) has been stretched parallel to the x-axis by a scale factor of $\frac{1}{2}$.

In case (ii), the graph of f(x) has been stretched parallel to the y-axis by a scale factor of 2.

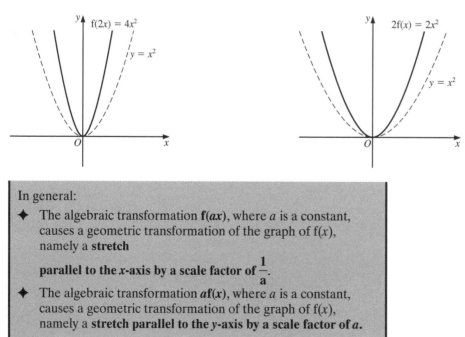

In general:

◆ The algebraic transformation **f(ax)**, where a is a constant, causes a geometric transformation of the graph of f(x), namely a **stretch**

    parallel to the x-axis by a scale factor of $\dfrac{1}{a}$.

◆ The algebraic transformation a**f(x)**, where a is a constant, causes a geometric transformation of the graph of f(x), namely a **stretch parallel to the y-axis by a scale factor of a.**

C2

Example 6

The function f(x) is defined by $f(x) = 2x + 5, x \in \mathbb{R}$.
a) Sketch the graph of f(x).
b) Describe a geometric transformation which, when applied to the graph of f(x), will give the graph of $g(x) = 6x + 5$.

$x \in \mathbb{R}$ means that the function is defined for real values of x.

a) Sketching the graph of $f(x) = 2x + 5$ gives the line shown.

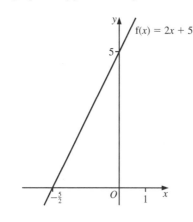

b) $g(x) = 6x + 5$
          $= 2(3x) + 5$
$\therefore \ g(x) = f(3x)$

Therefore, you can obtain the graph of g(x) by stretching the graph of f(x) parallel to the x-axis by a scale factor of $\frac{1}{3}$. This means that the intercept of g(x) with the x-axis will be $\frac{1}{3}$ the intercept of f(x).

So g(x) cuts the x-axis at

$$-\tfrac{5}{2} \times \tfrac{1}{3} = -\tfrac{5}{6}$$

and $g(0) = f(0) = 5$

Therefore the y-intercept is still at (0, 5).

This gives the graph of g(x) as shown.

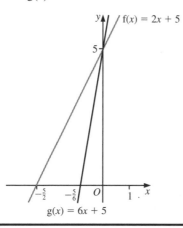

C2

Example 7

The function $f(x) = \dfrac{1}{x}$ is defined for all real x except $x = 0$.

Here is its graph.

Describe the transformation by which the graph of each function $g(x)$ can be obtained from the graph of $f(x)$, and sketch the graph of $g(x)$.

a) $g(x) = \dfrac{1}{x - 1}$ $(x \neq 1)$

b) $g(x) = \dfrac{1}{3x}$ $(x \neq 0)$

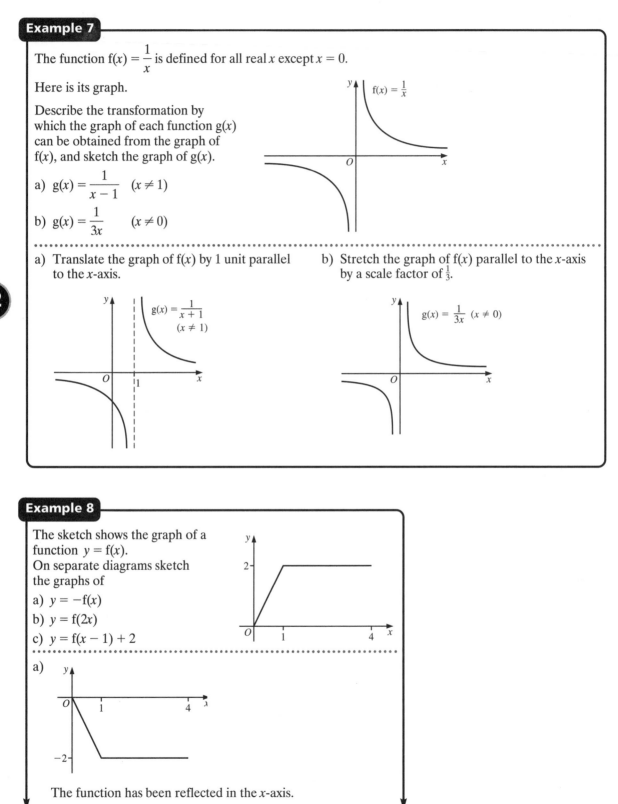

a) Translate the graph of $f(x)$ by 1 unit parallel to the x-axis.

b) Stretch the graph of $f(x)$ parallel to the x-axis by a scale factor of $\frac{1}{3}$.

Example 8

The sketch shows the graph of a function $y = f(x)$.
On separate diagrams sketch the graphs of

a) $y = -f(x)$

b) $y = f(2x)$

c) $y = f(x - 1) + 2$

a)

The function has been reflected in the x-axis.

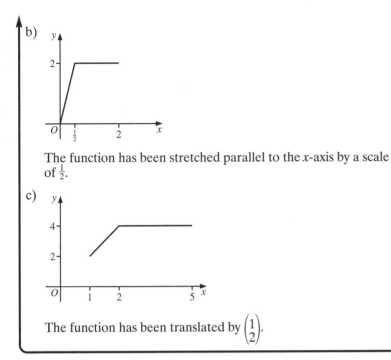

b)

The function has been stretched parallel to the x-axis by a scale of $\frac{1}{2}$.

c)

The function has been translated by $\begin{pmatrix} 1 \\ 2 \end{pmatrix}$.

C2

Exercise 6A

In each part of questions 1 to 4, sketch the graphs of the original function and the given function on one set of axes. In each case state the geometrical transformation which transforms the original function to the related graph.

1 Original function $y = x^2$

a) $y = x^2 + 3$ b) $y = (x - 4)^2$

c) $y = 2x^2$ d) $y = -x^2$

e) $y = (x + 2)^2$ f) $y = \frac{1}{3}x^2$

2 Original function $y = x^3$

a) $y = -x^3$ b) $y = x^3 + 1$

c) $y = 2x^3$ d) $y = (x - 4)^3$

e) $y = x^3 - 6$ f) $y = (x + 2)^3$

<u>3</u> Original function $y = \dfrac{1}{x}$

a) $y = \dfrac{4}{x}$ b) $y = \dfrac{1}{x - 2}$ c) $y = \dfrac{1}{x} + 3$

d) $y = -\dfrac{1}{x}$ e) $y = \dfrac{1}{x + 1}$ f) $y = \dfrac{1}{2x}$

4 Original function $y = 2^x$

a) $y = 2^{x + 3}$ b) $y = 2^{-x}$ c) $y = -2^x$

d) $y = 2^{3x}$ e) $y = 2^{\frac{x}{2}}$ f) $y = 2^x - 5$

5 Given $f(x) = x^2$, sketch the graph of each of these functions on the same set of axes.

    a) $y = f(x)$ b) $y = -f(x)$ c) $y = f(x - 2)$ d) $y = f(x) + 3$

6 Given $f(x) = \dfrac{1}{x}$, sketch the graph of $y = f(x + 3)$.

7 Given $f(x) = 3^x$, sketch the graph of $y = f(-x)$.

8 Given $f(x) = 5^x$, sketch the graph of $y = f(x) + 2$.

In each of questions 9 to 14, a diagram is given for the graph of a function $f(x)$, where $f(x) = 0$ for $x < 0$ or $x > 4$. On separate axes, sketch the graphs of the functions listed below each diagram.

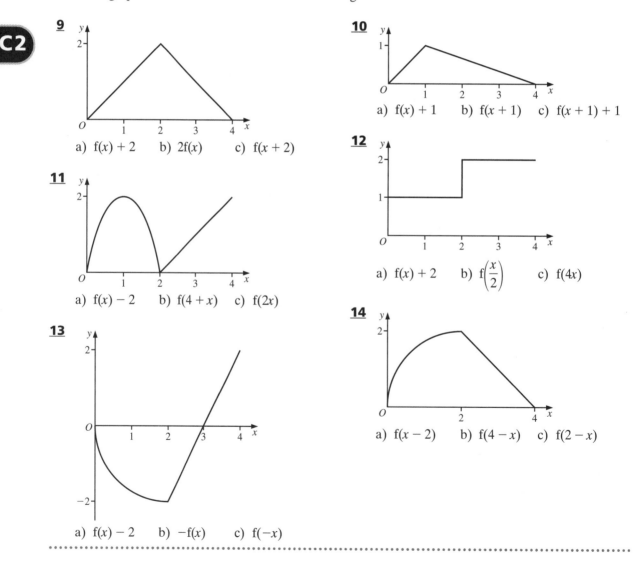

9

    a) $f(x) + 2$ b) $2f(x)$ c) $f(x + 2)$

10

    a) $f(x) + 1$ b) $f(x + 1)$ c) $f(x + 1) + 1$

11

    a) $f(x) - 2$ b) $f(4 + x)$ c) $f(2x)$

12

    a) $f(x) + 2$ b) $f\!\left(\dfrac{x}{2}\right)$ c) $f(4x)$

13

    a) $f(x) - 2$ b) $-f(x)$ c) $f(-x)$

14

    a) $f(x - 2)$ b) $f(4 - x)$ c) $f(2 - x)$

Summary

You should know how to ...	Check out

1 Recognise the transformation of a graph as a translation, reflection in the coordinate axes or a stretch parallel to the coordinate axes. Fully describe such transformations.	**1** a) The graph $y = x^2$ is transformed to $y = x^2 + 2$.
	  i) Describe this transformation.
	  ii) Sketch the graph.
	  b) The graph $y = x^2$ is transformed to $y = 3x^2$.
	  i) Describe this transformation.
	  ii) Sketch the graph.
	  c) By what transformation does $y = x^2$ become $y = \dfrac{x^2}{4}$?

2 Use a given transformation applied to basic linear, quadratic, cubic, reciprocal and exponential graphs to find the equation of the transformed graphs.	**2** a) The graph of $y = x^2 + 2$ is reflected in the x-axis.
	  i) Sketch the graph.
	  ii) What is the equation of the tranformed graph?
	  b) For the graph $y = x^3$, give the equation of the transformed graph and sketch the transformed graph for:
	  i) a translation $\begin{pmatrix} 3 \\ 0 \end{pmatrix}$
	  ii) a stretch parallel to the x-axis, scale factor $\frac{1}{3}$
	  iii) a stretch parallel to the y-axis, scale factor 3
	  iv) a reflection in the y-axis.
	  c)
	  For the function $f(x) = 2^x$, describe the transformation and sketch the graph of these tranformed functions:
	  i) $f(x - 5)$ ii) $5f(x)$
	  iii) $f(5x)$ iv) $-2f(x)$

C2

Revision exercise 6

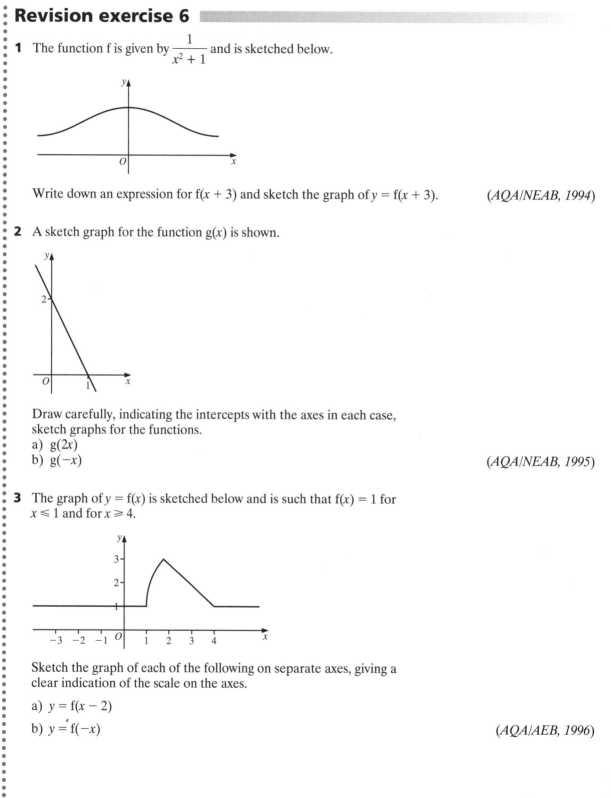

1 The function f is given by $\dfrac{1}{x^2 + 1}$ and is sketched below.

Write down an expression for f(x + 3) and sketch the graph of y = f(x + 3). *(AQA/NEAB, 1994)*

2 A sketch graph for the function g(x) is shown.

Draw carefully, indicating the intercepts with the axes in each case, sketch graphs for the functions.
a) g($2x$)
b) g($-x$) *(AQA/NEAB, 1995)*

3 The graph of y = f(x) is sketched below and is such that f(x) = 1 for $x \leqslant 1$ and for $x \geqslant 4$.

Sketch the graph of each of the following on separate axes, giving a clear indication of the scale on the axes.

a) y = f(x − 2)

b) y = f($-x$) *(AQA/AEB, 1996)*

C2

4

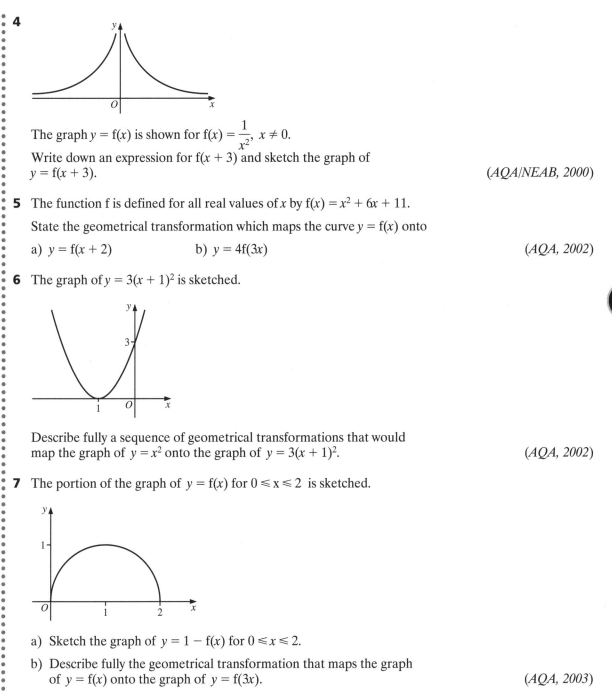

The graph $y = f(x)$ is shown for $f(x) = \dfrac{1}{x^2}$, $x \neq 0$.

Write down an expression for $f(x + 3)$ and sketch the graph of
$y = f(x + 3)$.   (*AQA/NEAB, 2000*)

5 The function f is defined for all real values of x by $f(x) = x^2 + 6x + 11$.

State the geometrical transformation which maps the curve $y = f(x)$ onto

a) $y = f(x + 2)$ b) $y = 4f(3x)$ (*AQA, 2002*)

6 The graph of $y = 3(x + 1)^2$ is sketched.

Describe fully a sequence of geometrical transformations that would
map the graph of $y = x^2$ onto the graph of $y = 3(x + 1)^2$.   (*AQA, 2002*)

C2

7 The portion of the graph of $y = f(x)$ for $0 \leqslant x \leqslant 2$ is sketched.

a) Sketch the graph of $y = 1 - f(x)$ for $0 \leqslant x \leqslant 2$.

b) Describe fully the geometrical transformation that maps the graph
of $y = f(x)$ onto the graph of $y = f(3x)$.   (*AQA, 2003*)

7 Sequences and series

This chapter will show you how to

- Use a recurrence relationship
- Find the nth term of arithmetic and geometrical progressions
- Find the sum of arithmetic and geometric series
- Find the sum to infinity of a geometric series
- Expand binomial expressions

Before you start

You should know how to ...	Check in
1 Describe a rule for continuing a sequence of numbers.	**1** Describe these number sequences and explain how to continue them, giving the next two terms. a) 2, 4, 7, 11, 16, ... b) 3, 8, 15, 24, 35, ... c) 7, 4, 1, -2, -5, ...

2 Use a formula to find the nth term of a sequence.	**2** a) The nth term of the sequence of numbers known as the triangular numbers, 1, 3, 6, 10, 15, ..., is $\frac{1}{2}n(n+1)$.
	     i) Use the formula to confirm that the 6th triangular number is 21.
	     ii) What is the 21st triangular number?
	
	 b) The nth term of the sequence of numbers 3, 8, 13, 18, 23, ... is given by $5n - 2$.
	     i) What is the 6th term?
	     ii) Find the 26th term.
	     iii) Explain why 333 must be a member of this sequence. What number term in the sequence is 333?

7.1 Sequences

A **sequence** is a set of numbers in a particular order where each number is derived from a particular rule. For example, 3, 6, 9, 12, ... is a sequence.

The first term is 3, the second term is 6, the nth term is given by $3n$.

You write the nth term as u_n. In this example,

$$u_n = 3n \quad \text{for } n \geqslant 1$$

> When $n = 1$, $u_1 = 3 \times 1 = 3$
> When $n = 2$, $u_2 = 3 \times 2 = 6$
> and so on.

Example 1

Write down the first three terms of the sequence whose nth term is given by

$$u_n = n^2 + 6n \quad \text{for } n \geqslant 1$$

Let $n = 1$, then: $\quad u_1 = (1)^2 + 6(1) = 7$

Let $n = 2$, then: $\quad u_2 = (2)^2 + 6(2) = 16$

Let $n = 3$, then: $\quad u_3 = (3)^2 + 6(3) = 27$

The first three terms of the sequence are 7, 16 and 27.

> u_n can be called the **general term** of the sequence.

Example 2

Write down an expression, in terms of n, for the nth term of the sequence 5, 9, 13, 17, ...

The difference between each of the consecutive terms is 4.
Consider the sequence defined by $u_n = 4n$:

$$4, 8, 12, 16, \dots$$

Each of these numbers is one less than the numbers in the given sequence. So the sequence 5, 9, 13, 17, ... is defined by $u_n = 4n + 1$.

C2

You can also define a sequence by giving an expression that relates one general term of the sequence to another. This relationship between the terms occurs throughout the sequence and is therefore called a **recurrence relation**.

> You also need to know the first one or two terms of the sequence.

Converging sequences

Consider the recurrence relation $u_{n+1} = f(u_n)$ given by

$$u_{n+1} = \tfrac{1}{2}u_n + 2$$

where the first term is $u_1 = 1$.

Substituting successive values of u generates the sequence

$$1, 2, 5, 3.25, 3.625, 3.8125, 3.906\,25, 3.953\,125, \dots$$

which appears to be getting closer to the value 4.

> $u_1 = 1$
> $u_2 = \tfrac{1}{2}u_1 + 2 = 2.5$
> $u_3 = \tfrac{1}{2}u_2 + 2 = 3.25$
> and so on.

You can show this graphically by sketching the graphs of $y = \tfrac{1}{2}x + 2$ and $y = x$ on the same set of axes.

The first term is 1.

If you draw a perpendicular from 1 on the x-axis to the line $y = \tfrac{1}{2}x + 2$, it meets it at $y = 2.5$, which is the second term.

If you then draw a horizontal line from $y = 2.5$ to the line $y = x$, and a perpendicular up to $y = \tfrac{1}{2}x + 2$, you get $y = 3.25$, which is the third term.

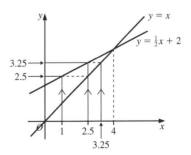

This process represents substituting into the recurrence relation to find the second term 2.5, third term 3.25, and so on.

Repeating this produces the sketch graph shown.

The sequence appears to be converging to the value 4.

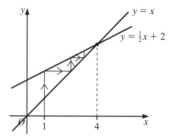

To find this value algebraically, notice that it is the point at which the graph of $y = \frac{1}{2}x + 2$ intersects the graph of $y = x$.

A sequence whose nth term gets closer to a finite number L as n approaches infinity is called a **convergent** or **converging** sequence – it converges on the number L, which is called the **limit** of the sequence.

> Generally, the limit, L, of a sequence defined by $u_{n+1} = f(u_n)$, is given by $L = f(L)$.

C2

In this case, let L be the limit. Then $L = f(L)$ gives:

$$L = \tfrac{1}{2}L + 2$$
$$\therefore \ \tfrac{1}{2}L = 2$$
$$\therefore \ \ L = 4 \text{ as expected.}$$

Example 3

A sequence is defined by the recurrence relation

$$u_{n+1} = \frac{2u_n + 1}{3}$$

Given that $u_1 = 2$, find

a) the first four terms of the sequence

b) the limit of the sequence.

. . . .

a) If $u_1 = 2$,

$$u_2 = \frac{2(2) + 1}{3} = \frac{5}{3}$$

$$u_3 = \frac{2\left(\frac{5}{3}\right) + 1}{3} = \frac{13}{9}$$

$$u_4 = \frac{2\left(\frac{13}{9}\right) + 1}{3} = \frac{35}{27}$$

b) Let L be the limit of the sequence. Then $L = f(L)$ gives:

$$L = \frac{2L + 1}{3}$$

$$\therefore \ 3L = 2L + 1$$
$$\therefore \ \ L = 1$$

> If the terms of a sequence move through a regular cycle, the sequence is **periodic**.
> For example, the sequence 5, 8, 3, 5, 8, 3, 5, 8, 3 is said to be periodic of period 3.

If the terms of a sequence do not tend to a limit as n increases, the sequence is **divergent**.

Exercise 7A

1 Write down the first six terms of the following sequences, and decide which of the sequences appear to be convergent and which appear to be divergent. For those which appear convergent, determine the limiting value to which they are tending.

a) $u_n = 2n + 1$

b) $u_n = 3n - 2$

c) $u_n = 5 - 2n$

d) $u_n = n^2 + 3$

e) $u_n = \dfrac{1}{n}$

f) $u_n = \dfrac{n}{n + 1}$

g) $u_n = \dfrac{1}{n^2 + 1}$

h) $u_n = 3 + \dfrac{1}{n(n + 1)}$

i) $u_n = n(n + 1)(n + 2)$

j) $u_n = 2^n$

k) $u_n = (-1)^n n$

l) $u_n = \dfrac{(-1)^{n + 1}}{n^2}$

2 Find a formula, in terms of n, for the nth term of each of these sequences.

a) 4, 8, 12, 16, 20 ...

b) 5, 7, 9, 11, 13, ...

c) 4, 9, 14, 19, 24, ...

d) 8, 11, 14, 17, 20 ...

e) $\frac{1}{2}, \frac{1}{3}, \frac{1}{4}, \frac{1}{5}, \frac{1}{6}, \ldots$

f) $\frac{1}{3}, \frac{1}{6}, \frac{1}{9}, \frac{1}{12}, \frac{1}{15}, \ldots$

g) $\frac{2}{5}, \frac{2}{8}, \frac{2}{11}, \frac{2}{14}, \frac{2}{17}, \ldots$

h) $\frac{1}{2}, \frac{2}{3}, \frac{3}{4}, \frac{4}{5}, \frac{5}{6}, \ldots$

i) $\frac{2}{1}, \frac{3}{4}, \frac{4}{7}, \frac{5}{10}, \frac{6}{13}, \ldots$

j) $\frac{3}{5}, \frac{5}{11}, \frac{7}{17}, \frac{9}{23}, \frac{11}{29}, \ldots$

k) $\frac{12}{7}, \frac{11}{12}, \frac{10}{17}, \frac{9}{22}, \frac{8}{27}, \ldots$

l) $\frac{4}{5}, \frac{1}{12}, -\frac{2}{19}, -\frac{5}{26}, -\frac{8}{33}, \ldots$

3 Write down an expression, in terms of n, for the nth term of each of these sequences.

a) 2, 4, 8, 16, 32, ...

b) 10, 20, 40, 80, 160, ...

c) 5, 10, 20, 40, 80, ...

d) 4, 12, 36, 108, 324, ...

e) 2, −6, 18, −54, 162, ...

f) $1, -\frac{1}{2}, \frac{1}{4}, -\frac{1}{8}, \frac{1}{16}, \ldots$

g) 1, 4, 9, 16, 25, ...

h) $\frac{1}{4}, \frac{2}{9}, \frac{3}{16}, \frac{4}{25}, \frac{5}{36}, \ldots$

i) −2, 6, −12, 20, −30, ...

j) $\frac{2}{3}, \frac{3}{8}, \frac{4}{15}, \frac{5}{24}, \frac{6}{35}, \ldots$

k) $0, \frac{1}{4}, -\frac{2}{9}, \frac{3}{14}, -\frac{4}{19}, \ldots$

l) 1, 4, 27, 256, 3125, ...

4 Write down the first six terms of each of the following sequences, and decide which of the sequences appear to be (i) convergent, (ii) divergent, (iii) periodic. For those which appear convergent, determine the limiting value to which they are tending.

a) $u_{n+1} = 2 + u_n$, $u_1 = 5$ b) $u_{n+1} = 6 + u_n$, $u_1 = 3$

c) $u_{n+1} = 3 + u_n$, $u_1 = 2$ d) $u_{n+1} = 1 + 2u_n$, $u_1 = 3$

e) $u_{n+1} = 8 - 3u_n$, $u_1 = 3$ f) $u_{n+1} = 10 - u_n$, $u_1 = 5$

g) $u_{n+1} = \dfrac{1}{u_n}$, $u_1 = 7$ h) $u_{n+1} = \dfrac{2}{u_n^2}$, $u_1 = 1$

i) $u_{n+1} = u_n^2 - 3$, $u_1 = 2$

5 A sequence is given by $u_{n+1} = \frac{1}{2}u_n + 4$, where $u_1 = -2$.

a) Write down the first five terms in the sequence.

b) Calculate the limit to which the sequence is converging.

6 A sequence is given by $u_{n+1} = 5 - \frac{1}{3}u_n$, where $u_1 = 6$.

a) Write down the first five terms in the sequence.

b) Calculate the limit to which the sequence is converging.

7 a) Write down the first five terms in the sequence

$$u_{n+1} = \frac{u_n + 2}{4}, \text{ where } u_1 = 22$$

b) Calculate the limit to which the sequence is converging.

8 A sequence is given by the formula

$$u_{n+1} = 1 + \frac{6}{u_n}, \text{ where } u_1 = 4$$

a) Write down the first five terms in the sequence.

b) Calculate the limit to which the sequence is converging.

7.2 Series and sigma notation

A **series** is the sum of the terms of a sequence. You can write the sum of the first n terms of a sequence as S_n, where

$$S_n = u_1 + u_2 + u_3 + \dots + u_n$$

This is an example of a **finite** series since there is a finite number of terms. It can be expressed more concisely using sigma (Σ) notation, as:

$$u_1 + u_2 + u_3 + \dots + u_n = \sum_{r=1}^{n} u_r$$

Σ is the Greek capital 'S' and in mathematics means 'the sum of'.

For example, the finite series $7 + 11 + 15 + 19$ can be written as

$$\sum_{r=1}^{4} (4r + 3)$$

Some series continue forever, and are described as **infinite**.

The infinite series $1 + 4 + 9 + 16 + \ldots$ can be written as $\sum\limits_{r=1}^{\infty} r^2$

which means 'the sum from r equals 1 to r equals infinity of r^2'.

> ∞ is the symbol for infinity.

Example 4

Find the sum of the first four terms of the sequence defined by
$$u_r = (-1)^r 3^{r+1} \quad for \ r \geqslant 1$$

S_4, the sum of the first four terms, is given by:

$$S_4 = \sum_{r=1}^{4} (-1)^r 3^{r+1}$$
$$= (-1)3^2 + (-1)^2 3^3 + (-1)^3 3^4 + (-1)^4 3^5$$
$$= -3^2 + 3^3 - 3^4 + 3^5$$
$$\therefore \ S_4 = 180$$

The sum of the first four terms is 180.

 C2

If you are given the first few terms in a series you can often find a formula for the sum of the series.

Example 5

Write each of the following series in Σ notation.
a) $-1 + 2 + 7 + 14 + 23$ b) $6 - 7 + 8 - 9 + \ldots$

a) The series whose terms are defined by $u_r = r^2$ is:

$$1 + 4 + 9 + 16 + 25$$

So you want the series whose rth term is given by $u_r = r^2 - 2$. Therefore, the given series can be written as

$$\sum_{r=1}^{5} (r^2 - 2)$$

> The nth term and the rth term are just different ways of expressing the general term of a series.

b) Notice that this is an infinite series.
If you ignore the alternating plus and minus signs, you see that the terms increase by 1. The rth term of the series $6 + 7 + 8 + 9 + \ldots$ is given by $u_r = r + 5$.

So the rth term of the given series is defined by:

$$u_r = (-1)^{r+1}(r+5)$$

and can be written as

$$\sum_{r=1}^{\infty} (-1)^{r+1}(r+5)$$

> The first term is $u_1 = 1 + 5 = 6$.

The term $(-1)^{r+1}$ simply gives you the alternating sign.
When $(r+1)$ is even, you get a positive term.
When $(r+1)$ is odd, you get a negative term.
Notice that this series could also be written as

$$\sum_{r=5}^{\infty} (-1)^{r+1}(r+1)$$

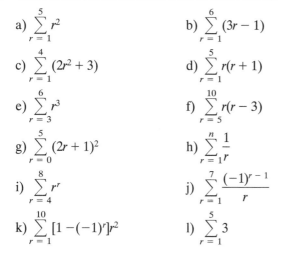

Example 6

Find $\displaystyle\sum_{r=3}^{6} 2r + 1$.

Substitute values from $r = 3$ to $r = 6$:

$$\sum_{r=3}^{6} 2r + 1 = [2(3) + 1] + [2(4) + 1] + [2(5) + 1] + [2(6) + 1]$$
$$= 7 + 9 + 11 + 13$$
$$= 40$$

Exercise 7B

1 Write down all the terms in each of these series.

a) $\displaystyle\sum_{r=1}^{5} r^2$

b) $\displaystyle\sum_{r=1}^{6} (3r - 1)$

c) $\displaystyle\sum_{r=1}^{4} (2r^2 + 3)$

d) $\displaystyle\sum_{r=1}^{5} r(r + 1)$

e) $\displaystyle\sum_{r=3}^{6} r^3$

f) $\displaystyle\sum_{r=5}^{10} r(r - 3)$

g) $\displaystyle\sum_{r=0}^{5} (2r + 1)^2$

h) $\displaystyle\sum_{r=1}^{n} \frac{1}{r}$

i) $\displaystyle\sum_{r=4}^{8} r^r$

j) $\displaystyle\sum_{r=1}^{7} \frac{(-1)^{r-1}}{r}$

k) $\displaystyle\sum_{r=1}^{10} [1 - (-1)^r]r^2$

l) $\displaystyle\sum_{r=1}^{5} 3$

2 Write each of these series in Σ notation.

a) $1 + 2 + 3 + 4 + 5$

b) $1^3 + 2^3 + 3^3 + 4^3 + 5^3 + 6^3 + 7^3$

c) $7 + 10 + 13 + 16 + 19 + 22 + 25$

d) $\frac{1}{3} + \frac{1}{4} + \frac{1}{5} + \dots + \frac{1}{20}$

e) $5 \times 6 + 6 \times 7 + 7 \times 8 + \dots + 18 \times 19$

f) $3^4 + 4^4 + 5^4 + \dots + n^4$

g) $1 - 2 + 3 - 4 + 5 - 6 + 7$

h) $4 - 8 + 16 - 32 + 64 - 128 + 256 - 512 + 1024$

i) $\dfrac{5}{5^2 - 1} + \dfrac{6}{6^2 - 1} + \dfrac{7}{7^2 - 1} + \dots + \dfrac{n}{n^2 - 1}$

j) $\dfrac{1}{2 \times 3} + \dfrac{2}{3 \times 4} + \dfrac{3}{4 \times 5} + \dots + \dfrac{n}{(n + 1)(n + 2)}$

k) $1 \times 4 - 3 \times 7 + 5 \times 10 - \dots + 29 \times 46$

l) $\frac{2}{3} + \frac{5}{9} + \frac{8}{27} + \frac{11}{81} + \frac{14}{243} + \frac{17}{729}$

3 a) Sketch the graph of $y = \dfrac{1}{x^2}$, for $x > 0$.

b) By comparing the area under your graph, for values of x between $x = r - 1$ and $x = r$, with the area of an appropriate rectangle over the same interval, show that

$$\frac{1}{r^2} < \int_{r-1}^{r} \frac{1}{x^2}\, dx \quad \text{where} \quad r \geq 2$$

c) Deduce that

$$\sum_{r=2}^{N} \frac{1}{r^2} < \int_{1}^{N} \frac{1}{x^2}\, dx$$

d) Hence show that

$$\sum_{r=1}^{N} \frac{1}{r^2} < 2 \text{ for all } N.$$

> This question is beyond the scope of C2 and is included here to provide a challenge.

7.3 Arithmetic progressions

Consider the sequence of numbers 1, 3, 5, 7, … . You can obtain each term from the previous term by adding 2. This sequence is an example of an **arithmetic progression** (AP).

> An **arithmetic progression** is a sequence of numbers in which any term can be obtained from the previous term by adding a certain number called the **common difference**.

✦ The first term of an AP is denoted by a.
✦ Its common difference is denoted by d.

In the example above, $a = 1$ and $d = 2$. You can write down an expression for the nth term in terms of a and d.

Write 1, 3, 5, 7, … as

$$1, 1 + 2, 1 + (2 \times 2), 1 + (3 \times 2), \dots$$

or

$$a, a + d, a + 2d, a + 3d, \dots$$

$$u_1 = a, u_2 = a + d, u_3 = a + 2d, \dots$$

$$\therefore u_n = a + (n - 1)d$$

> The general expression for the nth term of an arithmetical progression is $a + (n - 1)d$.

Example 7

Write down the nth term for each of these APs.
a) $2, 5, 8, 11, \ldots$ b) $10, 6, 2, -2, \ldots$

a) The first term is $a = 2$ and the common difference is
   $d = 5 - 2 = 3$. The nth term is given by

$$\begin{aligned} a + (n-1)d &= 2 + 3(n-1) \\ &= 2 + 3n - 3 \\ &= 3n - 1 \end{aligned}$$

b) The first term is $a = 10$ and the common difference is
   $d = 6 - 10 = -4$. The nth term is given by

$$\begin{aligned} a + (n-1)d &= 10 + (n-1)(-4) \\ &= 10 - 4n + 4 \\ &= 14 - 4n \end{aligned}$$

C2

If you know the first term, the last term and the common difference,
you can find the number of terms in an arithmetic progression.

Example 8

Find the number of terms in the arithmetic progression
$$4, 4\tfrac{1}{2}, 5, 5\tfrac{1}{2}, \ldots, 10$$

The first term is $a = 4$ and the common difference is $d = \tfrac{1}{2}$.

Let the number of terms be n, then the nth term is 10. So:

$$\begin{aligned} 10 &= a + (n-1)d \\ 10 &= 4 + (n-1) \times \tfrac{1}{2} \\ 12 &= n - 1 \\ \therefore \ n &= 13 \end{aligned}$$

Exercise 7C

1 Decide which of these sequences are arithmetic progressions. For
those which are, write down the value of the common difference.

a) $8, 11, 14, 17, 20, 23$

b) $83, 72, 61, 50, 39, 28$

c) $1, 2, 4, 8, 16, 32$

d) $1, 1.1, 1.11, 1.111, 1.1111, 1.11111$

e) $1, 1.1, 1.2, 1.3, 1.4, 1.5$

f) $\tfrac{1}{2}, \tfrac{4}{5}, \tfrac{11}{10}, \tfrac{7}{5}, \tfrac{17}{10}, 2$

g) $1, \tfrac{1}{2}, \tfrac{1}{3}, \tfrac{1}{4}, \tfrac{1}{5}$

h) $1, -2, 3, -4, 5, -6$

2 Write down the term indicated in square brackets in each of the
following arithmetic progressions.

a) 1, 5, 9, ... [10th term]

b) 7, 9, 11, ... [30th term]

c) 20, 17, 14, ... [16th term]

d) −6, −11, −16, ... [12th term]

e) 1.2, 1.4, 1.6, ... [14th term]

f) 81, 77, 73, ... [nth term]

g) 0.1, −0.2, −0.5, ... [25th term]

h) $1\frac{1}{2}$, 2, $2\frac{1}{2}$, ... [100th term]

3 Find the number of terms in each of these arithmetic progressions.

a) 5, 6, 7, ..., 15

b) 10, 20, 30, ..., 210

c) 5, 8, 11, ..., 302

d) −8, −6, −4, − ..., 78

e) 97, 85, 73, ..., 13

f) 46, 42, 38, ..., −26

g) 9, −11, −31, ..., −571

h) 2.1, 3.2, 4.3, ..., 31.8

C2

Arithmetic series

The sum of an arithmetic progression is called an **arithmetic series**.

Consider the sum of the first 10 natural numbers:

$$\sum_{r=1}^{10} r = 1 + 2 + 3 + \ldots + 10$$

Simply adding these up gives 55. However, a useful technique for
calculating such a sum is to pair off terms. Notice that the first and
last terms added together give $1 + 10 = 11$. The second and next to
last terms added together give $2 + 9 = 11$. In fact, by pairing off in this
way you get:

$$1 + 10 = 11$$
$$2 + 9 = 11$$
$$3 + 8 = 11$$
$$4 + 7 = 11$$
$$5 + 6 = 11$$

This gives 5 pairings of 11. The sum is $5 \times 11 = 55$. In other words
you can calculate the sum by using

$$\frac{10}{2} \times (1 + 10) = 55$$

If you write S_n for the sum, then:

$$S_n = \frac{n}{2}(a + l)$$

where l is the last term.

As the last term is the nth term $a + (n − 1)d$, you can write

$$S_n = \frac{n}{2}[a + a + (n − 1)d]$$

$$= \frac{n}{2}[2a + (n − 1)d]$$

General formula for the sum of an AP

Consider the sum of the first n terms of an AP

$$S_n = \qquad a \qquad + \qquad [a + d] \qquad\qquad + \dots + \; [a + (n-1)d] \qquad [1]$$

Write the terms on the right in reverse order:

$$S_n = [a + (n-1)d] \qquad + \quad [a + (n-2)d] \qquad\quad + \dots + \qquad a \qquad [2]$$

Adding [1] and [2] gives

$$2S_n = \{a + [a + (n-1)d]\} + \{(a+d) + [a + (n-2)d]\} + \dots + \{[a + (n-1)d] + a\}$$
$$= [2a + (n-1)d] \qquad + \qquad [2a + (n-1)d] \qquad + \dots + [2a + (n-1)d]$$
$$= n[2a + (n-1)d]$$

$$\therefore \; S_n = \frac{n}{2}[2a + (n-1)d]$$

The sum of the first n terms of an arithmetic series is given by

$$S_n = \frac{n}{2}[2a + (n-1)d] \quad \text{or} \quad S_n = \frac{n}{2}(a + l)$$

C2

Example 9

Find the sum of the first 20 terms of the arithmetic progression

$$\frac{1}{2}, \frac{5}{2}, \frac{9}{2}, \dots$$

The first term is $a = \frac{1}{2}$ and the common difference is given by
$d = \frac{5}{2} - \frac{1}{2} = 2$. Therefore the sum of the first 20 terms is given by

$$S_{20} = \frac{20}{2}\left[2\left(\frac{1}{2}\right) + (20 - 1) \times 2\right]$$
$$= 10(1 + 38)$$
$$= 390$$

A useful result is the sum of the first n natural numbers.

The sum of the first n natural numbers is $S_n = \dfrac{n}{2}(n + 1)$.

Example 10

a) Show that the sum of the first n natural numbers can be written as:

$$\frac{n}{2}(n + 1).$$

b) Hence find

$$\sum_{r=1}^{n}(2r - 1)$$

Remember:
The natural numbers are the positive integers 1, 2, 3, ...

a) The first n natural numbers form an arithmetic series with first term $a = 1$ and common difference 1. So:

$$S_n = \frac{n}{2}(a + l)$$

$$= \frac{n}{2}(n + 1)$$

The last term is n.

Using sigma notation, this can be written as:

$$\sum_{r=1}^{n} r = \frac{n}{2}(n + 1)$$

b) $$\sum_{r=1}^{n}(2r - 1) = \sum_{r=1}^{n} 2r - \sum_{r=1}^{n} 1$$

$$\sum_{r=1}^{n} 1 = 1 \times n = n$$

$$= 2\sum_{r=1}^{n} r - \sum_{r=1}^{n} 1$$

$$= 2 \times \frac{n}{2}(n + 1) - n$$

$$= n(n + 1) - n$$

$$= n^2$$

C2

Exercise 7D

1 Find the sum, as far as the term indicated in square brackets, of each of these arithmetic series.

a) $1 + 2 + 3 + \ldots$ [10th term]   b) $5 + 7 + 9 + \ldots$ [25th term]

c) $4 + 9 + 14 + \ldots$ [18th term]   d) $60 + 55 + 50 + \ldots$ [12th term]

e) $9 + 5 + 1 + \ldots$ [20th term]   f) $7 + 10 + 13 + \ldots$ [nth term]

g) $9 - 1 - 11 - \ldots$ [25th term]   h) $-2 - \frac{1}{2} + 1 + \ldots$ [30th term]

2 Find the sum of each of these arithmetic series.

a) $1 + 2 + 3 + \ldots + 100$ b) $6 + 8 + 10 + \ldots + 30$

c) $9 + 13 + 17 + \ldots + 41$ d) $62 + 60 + 58 + \ldots + 38$

e) $8 + 3 - 2 - \ldots - 42$ f) $1.3 + 1.6 + 1.9 + \ldots + 4.6$

g) $3\frac{1}{3} + 4 + 4\frac{2}{3} + \ldots + 12\frac{2}{3}$ h) $9\frac{1}{5} + 8\frac{4}{5} + 8\frac{2}{5} + \ldots + 3\frac{3}{5}$

3 a) Prove that $\displaystyle\sum_{r=1}^{n} r = \frac{n}{2}(n + 1)$

b) Use your answer to part a) to deduce the following.

i) $\displaystyle\sum_{r=1}^{n}(3r - 1) = \frac{n}{2}(3n + 1)$ ii) $\displaystyle\sum_{r=1}^{n}(5r - 3) = \frac{n}{2}(5n - 1)$

iii) $\displaystyle\sum_{r=0}^{n}(r + 5) = \frac{1}{2}(n + 1)(n + 10)$ iv) $\displaystyle\sum_{r=3}^{n}(2r + 3) = (n + 6)(n - 2)$

v) $\displaystyle\sum_{r=6}^{n}(4 + 3r) = \frac{1}{2}(n - 5)(3n + 26)$ vi) $\displaystyle\sum_{r=n+1}^{2n} r = \frac{n}{2}(3n + 1)$

4 In an AP, the 1st term is 13 and the 15th term is 111. Find the common difference and the sum of the first 20 terms.

5 In an arithmetic series, the 3rd term is 4 and the 8th term is 49. Find the 1st term, the common difference and the sum of the first ten terms.

6 The 2nd term of an AP is 7 and the 7th term is -8. Find the 1st term, the common difference and the sum of the first 14 terms.

7 The 5th term of an arithmetic series is 7 and the common difference is 4. Find the 1st term and the sum of the first ten positive terms.

8 The sum of the first ten terms of an AP is 95, and the sum of the first 20 terms of the same AP is 290. Calculate the 1st term and the common difference.

9 The sum of the first n terms of a series is $n(n + 2)$. Find the first three terms of the series.

10 The sum of the first n terms of a series is $\dfrac{n}{2}(n + 8)$. Find the 1st, 2nd and 10th terms.

11 An AP has a common difference of 3. Given the the nth term is 32, and the sum of the first n terms is 185, calculate the value of n.

12 The 1st, 2nd and 3rd terms of an AP are $8 - x$, $3x$ and $4x + 1$, respectively. Calculate the value of x, and find the sum of the first eight terms of the progression.

13 Given that a^2, b^2 and c^2 are in arithmetic progression show that $\dfrac{1}{b + c}$, $\dfrac{1}{c + a}$ and $\dfrac{1}{a + b}$ are also in arithmetic progression.

14 Given that
$$\sum_{r=n+3}^{2n} r = 312$$
find the value of n.

7.4 Geometric progressions

Consider the sequence of numbers 2, 6, 18, 54, … . You can find each term of this sequence by multiplying the previous term by 3. This is an example of a **geometric progression** (GP).

> A **geometric progression** is a sequence of numbers in which any term can be obtained from the previous term by multiplying by a certain number called the **common ratio**.

✦ The first term of a GP is denoted by a.
✦ Its common ratio is denoted by r.

In this example, $a = 2$ and $r = 3$. You can write down an expression for the nth term in terms of a and r.

Write 2, 6, 18, 54, ... as

$$2, 2 \times 3, 2 \times 3^2, 2 \times 3^3, ...$$

or

$$a, ar, ar^2, ar^3, ...$$
$$u_1 = a, u_2 = ar^1, u_3 = ar^2, ...$$
$$\therefore u_n = ar^{n-1}$$

> The general expression for the nth term of a geometrical progression is ar^{n-1}.

C2

Example 11

Write down the nth term for each of these geometric progressions.

a) 3, 12, 48, ...   b) 10, 5, 2.5, ...

a) The first term is 3 and the common ratio is $r = \frac{12}{3} = 4$.
Therefore the nth term is

$$ar^{n-1} = 3(4)^{n-1}$$

b) The first term is 10 and the common ratio is $r = \frac{5}{10} = \frac{1}{2}$.
Therefore the nth term is

$$ar^{n-1} = 10\left(\tfrac{1}{2}\right)^{n-1}$$

Exercise 7E

1 Decide which of the following sequences are geometric progressions. For those which are, write down the value of the common ratio.

a) 3, 9, 27, 81, 243, 729
b) 3, −6, 12, −24, 48, −96
c) 3, 9, 15, 21, 27, 33
d) 1, 1.1, 1.11, 1.111, 1.1111, 1.111 11
e) 1, 1.2, 1.44, 1.728, 2.0736, 2.488 32
f) 1, 2, −4, −8, 16, 32
g) $1, \frac{1}{3}, \frac{1}{6}, \frac{1}{9}, \frac{1}{12}, \frac{1}{15}$
h) $1, \frac{1}{2}, \frac{1}{4}, \frac{1}{8}, \frac{1}{16}, \frac{1}{32}$

2 Write down the term indicated in square brackets in each of the following GPs.

a) 2, 4, 8, ... [10th term]
b) 1, −3, 9, ... [7th term]
c) 5, 10, 20, ... [8th term]
d) 2, 3, $4\frac{1}{2}$, ... [9th term]
e) 81, −54, 36, ... [8th term]
f) $2, \frac{2}{5}, \frac{2}{25}, ...$ [5th term]
g) $1, \frac{1}{2}, \frac{1}{4}, ...$ [12th term]
h) $1, -\frac{1}{3}, \frac{1}{9}, - ...$ [6th term]

3 Find the number of terms in each of these geometric progressions.

a) 2, 10, 50, ... , 1250
b) 3, 6, 12, ... , 768
c) 2, 6, 18, ... , 1458
d) 1, −2, 4, ... , 1024
e) 4, −12, 36, ... , −972
f) 5, 20, 80, ... , 5120
g) $54, 18, 6, ... , \frac{2}{27}$
h) $64, 32, 16, ... , \frac{1}{8}$

4 A GP has 3rd term 75 and 4th term 375. Find the common ratio and the first term.

5 In a GP the 2nd term is -12 and the 5th term is 768. Find the common ratio and the first term.

6 The 4th term of a geometric progression is 48, and the 6th term is 12. Find the possible values of the common ratio and the corresponding values of the 1st term.

7 A GP has 3rd term 7 and 5th term 847. Find the possible values of the common ratio, and the corresponding values of the 4th term.

Geometric series

The sum of all the terms of a geometric progression is called a **geometric series**. Consider the sum of the first 8 terms of the geometric progression with $a = 1, r = 3$:

$$S_8 = 1 + 3 + 9 + 27 \qquad + \ldots + 2187 \qquad [1]$$

$$\therefore 3S_8 = \qquad 3 + 9 + 27 + 81 + \ldots + 2187 + 6561 \qquad [2]$$

> Multiply by the common ratio of 3.

Subtract [1] from [2]:

$$3S_8 - S_8 = 6561 - 1$$
$$\therefore \ 2S_8 = 6560$$
$$\therefore \quad S_8 = 3280$$

So the sum of this GP is 3280.

This technique can be used to find the sum of any geometric progression.

General formula for the sum of a GP

The sum of the first n terms is

$$S_n = a + \ ar + \ ar^2 + \ldots + ar^{n-1} \qquad [1]$$

Multiply throughout by r:

$$rS_n = ar + ar^2 + ar^3 + \ldots + ar^n \qquad [2]$$

Subtract [2] from [1]:

$$S_n - rS_n = (a + ar + \ldots + ar^{n-1}) - (ar + ar^2 + \ldots + ar^n)$$

$$S_n(1 - r) = a - ar^n$$

$$\therefore \ S_n = \frac{a(1 - r^n)}{1 - r} = a\left(\frac{1 - r^n}{1 - r}\right) \qquad [3]$$

Multiplying both the numerator and the denominator of [3] by -1 gives

$$S_n = a\left(\frac{r^n - 1}{r - 1}\right)$$

which is an alternative form.

The sum of the first n terms of a GP is given by

$$S_n = a\left(\frac{1 - r^n}{1 - r}\right) = a\left(\frac{r^n - 1}{r - 1}\right)$$

Example 12

Given the GP 2, 6, 18, 54, … find

a) the common ratio r

b) the 10th term

c) the sum of the first 10 terms.

a) The first term is $a = 2$ and the common ratio is given by $r = \frac{6}{2} = 3$.

b) The 10th term is given by

$$ar^9 = 2(3)^9 = 39\,366$$

c) The sum of the first 10 terms is

$$S_{10} = a\left(\frac{r^{10} - 1}{r - 1}\right)$$

$$= 2\left(\frac{3^{10} - 1}{3 - 1}\right)$$

$$= 2\left(\frac{59\,048}{2}\right)$$

$$= 59\,048$$

C2

Example 13

The sum of the 2nd and 3rd terms of a GP is 12. The sum of the 3rd and 4th terms is -36. Find the first term and the common ratio.

The sum of the 2nd and 3rd terms is:

$$ar + ar^2 = 12$$

$$ar(1 + r) = 12$$

$$\therefore \quad 1 + r = \frac{12}{ar} \qquad\qquad [1]$$

The sum of the 3rd and 4th terms is:

$$ar^2 + ar^3 = -36$$

$$\therefore \quad ar^2(1 + r) = -36 \qquad\qquad [2]$$

Substituting [1] into [2] gives:

$$ar^2\left(\frac{12}{ar}\right) = -36$$

$$12r = -36$$

$$\therefore \qquad r = -3$$

From [1]: $a = \dfrac{12}{r(1 + r)}$

Substituting $r = -3$ gives

$$a = \dfrac{12}{(-3)(1 - 3)} = 2$$

The 1st term of the GP is 2 and the common ratio is -3.

C2

Example 14

Show that there are two possible GPs in each of which the 1st term is 8 and the sum of the first three terms is 14. For the GP with positive common ratio find, in term of n, an expression for the sum of the first n terms.

· ·

Since the 1st term is 8 and the sum of the first three terms is 14, you have

$$8 + 8r + 8r^2 = 14$$
$$8r^2 + 8r - 6 = 0$$
$$\therefore \quad 2(2r - 1)(2r + 3) = 0$$

Solving gives $r = \frac{1}{2}$ or $r = -\frac{3}{2}$.

Hence, there are two GPs which have a first term of 8 and have the sum of their first three terms equal to 14.

To find the sum of the first n terms of the GP with positive common ratio, use

$$S_n = a\left(\dfrac{1 - r^n}{1 - r}\right) \text{ with } a = 8 \text{ and } r = \tfrac{1}{2}$$

This gives

$$S_n = 8\left[\dfrac{1 - \left(\tfrac{1}{2}\right)^n}{1 - \left(\tfrac{1}{2}\right)}\right] = 16[1 - (2^{-1})^n]$$

$$\therefore \ S_n = 16(1 - 2^{-n})$$

Example 15

A GP has a 1st term of 1 and a common ratio of $\frac{1}{4}$. Find the sum of the first four terms and show that the nth term is given by $4^{(1-n)}$.

· ·

The sum of the first four terms is given by

$$S_4 = 1\left[\dfrac{1 - \left(\tfrac{1}{4}\right)^4}{1 - \left(\tfrac{1}{4}\right)}\right] = \dfrac{85}{64}$$

The sum of the first four terms is $\frac{85}{64}$.

The nth term is given by

$$u_n = ar^{n-1}$$
$$= 1\left(\tfrac{1}{4}\right)^{n-1} = (4^{-1})^{n-1}$$
$$\therefore \ u_n = 4^{(1-n)}$$

Geometric progressions occur in everyday situations.

Example 16

An employee of a company starts on a salary of £20 000 per year
with an annual increase of 4% of the previous year's salary

a) Show that the amounts of annual salary form a geometric
progression.

b) Find i) how much the employee earns in the tenth year with
the company.
ii) the total amount earned by the employee over the
first ten years with the company.

a) The starting salary is £20 000. In the second year the employee
will earn £20 000 $\times$ 1.04 = £20 800. In the third year the
employee will earn

$$(£20\,000 \times 1.04) \times 1.04 = £20\,000 \times 1.04^2$$
$$= £21\,632$$

In the fourth year the employee will earn

$$(£20\,000 \times 1.04^2) \times 1.04 = £20\,000 \times 1.04^3$$
$$= £22\,497.28$$

The amounts form a GP with first term $a = 20\,000$ and
common ratio $r = 1.04$.

b) i) In the tenth year the salary will be given by the 10th term of
the progression:

$$ar^9 = £20\,000 \times (1.04)^9$$
$$= £28\,466.24$$

ii) The total amount earned over the first 10 years with the
company is given by the sum of the first 10 terms of the GP:

$$S_{10} = a\left(\frac{r^9 - 1}{r - 1}\right)$$

$$= £20\,000\left(\frac{(1.04)^9 - 1}{1.04 - 1}\right)$$

$$= £211\,655.91$$

C2

Exercise 7F

1 Find the sum, as far as the term indicated in square brackets, of
each of these geometric series.

a) $3 + 6 + 12 + \ldots$ [10th term]   b) $3 - 6 + 12 - \ldots$ [10th term]

c) $3 - 6 + 12 - \ldots$ [11th term]   d) $5 + 10 + 20 + \ldots$ [8th term]

e) $-2 + 8 - 32 + \ldots$ [6th term]   f) $1 + 10 + 100 + \ldots$ [7th term]

g) $1 + \frac{1}{3} + \frac{1}{9} + \ldots$ [7th term]   h) $\frac{8}{9} + \frac{4}{3} + 2 + \ldots$ [6th term]

2 Find the sum of each of these geometric series.

  a) $3 + 6 + 12 + \dots + 384$ b) $2 + 6 + 18 + \dots + 1458$

  c) $4 - 12 + 36 - \dots - 972$ d) $7 - 14 + 28 - \dots + 448$

  e) $36 + 12 + 4 + \dots + \frac{4}{27}$ f) $20 + 10 + 5 + \dots + \frac{5}{16}$

  g) $\frac{1}{4} + \frac{1}{16} + \frac{1}{64} + \dots + \frac{1}{4096}$ h) $\frac{1}{3} - \frac{1}{9} + \frac{1}{27} - \dots - \frac{1}{729}$

3 Find the sum of the first ten terms of a GP which has 3rd term 20 and 8th term 640.

4 In a GP the 2nd term is 15 and the 5th term is -405. Find the sum of the first eight terms.

5 A GP has common ratio -3. Given that the sum of the first nine terms of the progression is 703, find the 1st term.

6 Find the 1st term of the geometric series in which the common ratio is 2 and the sum of the first ten terms is 93.

7 The common ratio of a GP is -5 and the sum of the first seven terms of the progression is 449. Find the first three terms.

8 A GP is such that the sum of the 4th and 5th terms is -108, and the sum of the 5th and 6th terms is 324. Calculate the common ratio and the value of the 1st term.

9 Find the first five terms in the geometric series which is such that the sum of the 1st and 3rd terms is 50, and the sum of the 2nd and 4th terms is 150.

7.5 Infinite geometric progressions

The geometric series

$$1 + \tfrac{1}{2} + \tfrac{1}{4} + \tfrac{1}{8} + \dots + \left(\tfrac{1}{2}\right)^{n-1} + \dots$$

can be written as

$$\sum_{n=1}^{\infty} \left(\tfrac{1}{2}\right)^{n-1}$$

This series is the sum of an infinite geometric progression in which $a = 1$ and $r = \tfrac{1}{2}$. Therefore:

$$S_n = \left[\frac{1 - \left(\tfrac{1}{2}\right)^n}{1 - \tfrac{1}{2}}\right] = 2\left[1 - \left(\tfrac{1}{2}\right)^n\right]$$

> As n gets larger, S_n gets closer to 2: the series is convergent (see page 149).

Look at S_n for $n = 2, 10, 20$ and 30:

n	2	10	20	30
S_n	1.5	1.998	1.999 998 093	1.999 999 998

> $n \to \infty$ means 'n tends to infinity', that is, it gets bigger and bigger.

As $n \to \infty$, the term $\left(\tfrac{1}{2}\right)^n \to 0$, therefore $S_n \to 2$. So 2 is the **limit** of the series, written as:

$$\lim_{n \to \infty} S_n = 2$$

This limit is called the **sum to infinity** of the GP.

General formula for the sum to infinity of a GP

The sum of the first n terms of a GP is given by

$$S_n = a\left(\frac{1 - r^n}{1 - r}\right)$$

If $-1 < r < 1$ then as $n \to \infty$, $r^n \to 0$. Therefore, as $n \to \infty$

$$S_n \to a\left(\frac{1 - 0}{1 - r}\right) = \frac{a}{1 - r}$$

> Notice that the proof of this result hangs on the fact that $-1 < r < 1$. If this is not the case, the sum to infinity does not exist.
> Another way of writing $-1 < r < 1$ is to write $|r| < 1$.
> $|r|$ is known as the modulus, or absolute value of r.

The sum to infinity of a GP is given by

$$S_\infty = \sum_{n=1}^{\infty} ar^{n-1} = \frac{a}{1 - r}$$

where $-1 < r < 1$.

C2

Example 17

Calculate the sum to infinity of the series $2 + \frac{1}{2} + \frac{1}{8} + \frac{1}{32} + \dots$

This is a geometric series with $a = 2$ and $r = \frac{1}{4}$. Therefore:

$$S_\infty = \frac{2}{1 - \frac{1}{4}} = \frac{8}{3}$$

A rational number which is a recurring decimal can be written as a geometric series.

Example 18

Write the recurring decimal 0.3232... as the sum of a GP. Hence write this recurring decimal as a rational number.

Now

$$0.323\,232\dots = \frac{32}{100} + \frac{32}{10\,000} + \frac{32}{1\,000\,000} + \dots$$

This is a geometric series with $a = \frac{32}{100}$ and $r = \frac{1}{100}$.
Since $-1 < r < 1$ the sum to infinity exists and is given by

$$S_\infty = \frac{\left(\frac{32}{100}\right)}{\left(1 - \frac{1}{100}\right)} = \frac{32}{99}$$

The recurring decimal $0.\dot{3}\dot{2}$ can be written as $\frac{32}{99}$.

> $0.\dot{3}\dot{2}$ means $0.323\,232\dots$

Example 19

The sum to infinity of a GP is 7 and the sum of the first two terms is $\frac{48}{7}$. Show that the common ratio, r, satisfies the equation

$$1 - 49r^2 = 0$$

Hence find the first term of the GP with positive common ratio.

· ·

Since the sum to infinity is 7, you have

$$\frac{a}{1-r} = 7 \quad \therefore \ a = 7(1-r) \hspace{3cm} [1]$$

The sum of the first two terms is $\frac{48}{7}$, so:

$$a + ar = \tfrac{48}{7} \quad \therefore \ a(1+r) = \tfrac{48}{7} \hspace{2cm} [2]$$

Substituting [1] into [2] gives

$$7(1-r)(1+r) = \tfrac{48}{7}$$
$$\therefore \quad 49(1-r^2) = 48$$
$$\therefore \quad 1 - 49r^2 = 0$$

as required.

Solving gives $r = \frac{1}{7}$ or $r = -\frac{1}{7}$.

The positive common ratio is $r = \frac{1}{7}$. So from [1] the first term of the required GP is given by

$$a = 7(1-r)$$
$$= 7\left(1 - \tfrac{1}{7}\right)$$
$$\therefore \ a = 6$$

The first term of the GP with positive common ratio is 6.

Exercise 7G

· ·

1 Work out each of these sums.

a) $\displaystyle\sum_{r=0}^{\infty} \left(\tfrac{1}{2}\right)^r$

b) $\displaystyle\sum_{r=0}^{\infty} \left(\tfrac{1}{3}\right)^r$

c) $\displaystyle\sum_{r=1}^{\infty} \left(\tfrac{1}{5}\right)^r$

d) $\displaystyle\sum_{r=0}^{\infty} \left(-\tfrac{1}{4}\right)^r$

e) $\displaystyle\sum_{r=2}^{\infty} \left(-\tfrac{1}{8}\right)^r$

f) $\displaystyle\sum_{r=0}^{\infty} \left(\tfrac{1}{9}\right)^{r+1}$

g) $\displaystyle\sum_{r=1}^{\infty} (0.3)^{r+1}$

h) $\displaystyle\sum_{r=0}^{\infty} (-0.7)^{r+2}$

i) $\displaystyle\sum_{r=0}^{\infty} 4 \times \left(\tfrac{1}{3}\right)^r$

j) $\displaystyle\sum_{r=1}^{\infty} 3 \times \left(-\tfrac{1}{5}\right)^r$

k) $\displaystyle\sum_{r=0}^{\infty} a^r, \ |a| < 1$

l) $\displaystyle\sum_{r=1}^{\infty} (3x)^{r+1}, \ |x| < \tfrac{1}{3}$

2 Express each of these recurring decimals as a fraction in its simplest form.

a) $0.\dot{5}$

b) $0.\dot{8}$

c) $0.\dot{7}\dot{2}$

d) $0.\dot{1}0\dot{2}$

e) $2.\dot{4}$

f) $3.2\dot{8}1\dot{4}$

3 Find the 1st term of a GP that has a common ratio of $\frac{2}{5}$ and a sum to infinity of 20.

4 Find the 3rd term of a GP that has a common ratio of $-\frac{1}{3}$ and a sum to infinity of 18.

5 A GP has a 1st term of 6 and a sum to infinity of 60. Find the common ratio.

6 Find the common ratio of a GP that has a 1st term of 6 and a sum to infinity of 4.

7 Find the common ratio of a geometric series which has a 2nd term of 6 and a sum to infinity of 24.

8 A GP has a 2nd term of 6 and a sum to infinity of 27. Write down the possible value of the first three terms.

C2

7.6 Binomial expansions

You need to know how to expand **binomial** expressions.

> A binomial expression has only two terms.

You can use ordinary algebraic multiplication to show that:

$$(1+x) = 1+x$$
$$(1+x)^2 = (1+x)(1+x) = 1 + 2x + x^2$$
$$(1+x)^3 = (1+x)^2(1+x) = 1 + 3x + 3x^2 + x^3$$
$$(1+x)^4 = (1+x)^3(1+x) = 1 + 4x + 6x^2 + 4x^3 + x^4$$

and so on.

The coefficients of the terms in these expansions can be written as a triangle:

```
          1       1
      1       2       1
  1       3       3       1
1       4       6       4       1
...     ...     ...     ...     ...
```

> Blaise Pascal (1623–1662) was a French mathematician who first studied this number pattern.

This triangular array of numbers is known as **Pascal's triangle**.

The next row is obtained like this:

> Work out the next five rows of the triangle.

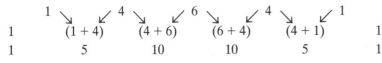

```
      1 ↘   ↙ 4 ↘   ↙ 6 ↘   ↙ 4 ↘   ↙ 1
1       (1 + 4)    (4 + 6)    (6 + 4)    (4 + 1)       1
1          5          10         10         5          1
```

The entry in the 5th row, 3rd position from the left is 10. Therefore, the coefficient of the x^2 term in the expansion of $(1+x)^5$ is 10.

The entry in the 3rd row, 2nd position from the left is 3. Therefore, the coefficient of the x term in the expansion of $(1+x)^3$ is 3.

A general expression for the coefficient of the $(r+1)$th term in the expansion of $(1+x)^n$ is:

$$\binom{n}{r} = \frac{n!}{r!(n-r)!}$$

where

$$n! = n(n-1)(n-2)\ldots 3 \times 2 \times 1 \quad \text{(called } n \text{ factorial)}$$

and where, by definition, $0! = 1$.

For example:
$$4! = 4 \times 3 \times 2 \times 1$$
$$= 24$$

$\binom{n}{r}$ often appears on calculators as ${}^nC_r$ or ${}_nC_r$.

C2

Example 20

Evaluate: a) $\binom{5}{1}$ b) $\binom{6}{4}$

a) $\binom{5}{1} = \dfrac{5!}{1!(5-1)!}$

$= \dfrac{5!}{1! \times 4!}$

$= \dfrac{5 \times 4 \times 3 \times 2 \times 1}{1 \times 4 \times 3 \times 2 \times 1}$

$= 5$

b) $\binom{6}{4} = \dfrac{6!}{4!(6-4)!}$

$= \dfrac{6!}{4! \times 2!}$

$= \dfrac{6 \times 5 \times 4 \times 3 \times 2 \times 1}{4 \times 3 \times 2 \times 1 \times 2 \times 1}$

$= 15$

Using this result, you can write down a general formula for the expansion of $(1+x)^n$:

$$(1+x)^n = 1 + \binom{n}{1}x + \binom{n}{2}x^2 + \binom{n}{3}x^3 + \ldots + x^n$$

This is known as the **binomial expansion** of $(1+x)^n$, for positive integer n. It can also be written using sigma notation:

$$(1+x)^n = \sum_{r=0}^{n} \binom{n}{r} x^r$$

Alternatively, the binomial expansion of $(1+x)^n$ can be written as:

$$(1+x)^n = 1 + nx + \frac{n(n-1)}{2!}x^2 + \frac{n(n-1)(n-2)}{3!}x^3 + \ldots + x^n$$

Notice that this expansion ends at the term x^n when n is a positive integer.

Example 21

Find the coefficients of the x^2 and x^3 terms in the expansion of $(1+x)^7$.

The coefficient of the x^2 term is

$$\binom{7}{2} = \frac{7!}{2!(7-2)!} = 21$$

$n = 7, r = 2$

The coefficient of the x^2 term in the expansion of $(1+x)^7$ is 21.

The coefficient of the x^3 term is

$$\binom{7}{3} = \frac{7!}{3!(7-3)!} = 35$$

$n = 7, r = 3$

The coefficient of the x^3 term in the expansion of $(1+x)^7$ is 35.

Example 22

Write down the expansion of $(1+x)^8$.

Use Pascal's triangle to generate the coefficients:

$$(1+x)^8 = 1 + 8x + 28x^2 + 56x^3 + 70x^4 + 56x^5 + 28x^6 + 8x^7 + x^8.$$

C2

Exercise 7H

1 Evaluate each of these quantities.

a) $\binom{5}{3}$ b) $\binom{6}{2}$ c) $\binom{9}{7}$ d) $\binom{6}{5}$

e) $\binom{5}{5}$ f) $\binom{12}{2}$ g) $\binom{7}{4}$ h) $\binom{100}{99}$

2 Expand:
a) $(1+x)^4$ b) $(1+x)^5$ c) $(1+3x)^4$ d) $(1-x)^3$
e) $(1-2x)^4$ f) $(1-5x)^3$ g) $\left(1+\frac{1}{2}x\right)^4$ h) $\left(1-\frac{1}{5}x\right)^2$

3 Find the coefficient of the term indicated in square brackets in the expansion of each of these expressions.
a) $(1+x)^7$ $[x^4]$ b) $(1+x)^9$ $[x^2]$ c) $(1+2x)^5$ $[x^3]$
d) $(1+5x)^8$ $[x^2]$ e) $(1-3x)^6$ $[x^3]$ f) $(1-6x)^7$ $[x]$
g) $(1-4x)^4$ $[x^2]$ h) $(1+2x)^5$ $[x^4]$ i) $(1-\frac{1}{2}x)^3$ $[x^2]$

Expansion of $(a + x)^n$

Consider these expansions:
$$(a+x)^1 = a + x$$
$$(a+x)^2 = a^2 + 2ax + x^2$$
$$(a+x)^3 = a^3 + 3a^2x + 3ax^2 + x^3$$

Notice that the coefficients are the Pascal coefficients.

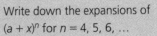

Write down the expansions of $(a + x)^n$ for $n = 4, 5, 6, \ldots$

Example 23

Expand these expressions in powers of x.

a) $(3 + x)^4$ b) $(2 - x)^6$ c) $(2 + 5x)^3$ d) $\left(1 - \dfrac{x}{3}\right)^5$

a) Using Pascal coefficients 1, 4, 6, 4, 1 gives:

$$(3 + x)^4 = 3^4 + 4(3^3 x) + 6(3^2 x^2) + 4(3x^3) + x^4$$

$$\therefore \ (3 + x)^4 = 81 + 108x + 54x^2 + 12x^3 + x^4$$

> $a = 3, n = 4$

b) Using Pascal coefficients 1, 6, 15, 20, 15, 6, 1 gives:

$$(2 - x)^6 = 2^6 + 6(2^5(-x)) + 15(2^4(-x)^2)$$
$$+ 20(2^3(-x)^3) + 15(2^2(-x)^4)$$
$$+ 6(2(-x)^5) + (-x)^6$$

$$\therefore \ (2 - x)^6 = 64 - 192x + 240x^2 - 160x^3 + 60x^4 - 12x^5 + x^6$$

> $a = 2, n = 6, \ 'x' = -x$

c) Using Pascal coefficients 1, 3, 3, 1 gives:

$$(2 + 5x)^3 = 2^3 + 3[2^2(5x)] + 3[2(5x)^2] + (5x)^3$$

$$\therefore \ (2 + 5x)^3 = 8 + 60x + 150x^2 + 125x^3$$

> $a = 2, n = 3, \ 'x' = 5x$

d) Using Pascal coefficients 1, 5, 10, 10, 5, 1 gives:

$$\left(1 - \frac{x}{3}\right)^5 = 1 + 5\left(-\frac{x}{3}\right) + 10\left(-\frac{x}{3}\right)^2 + 10\left(-\frac{x}{3}\right)^3$$
$$+ 5\left(-\frac{x}{3}\right)^4 + \left(-\frac{x}{3}\right)^5$$

$$= 1 - \tfrac{5}{3}x + \tfrac{10}{9}x^2 - \tfrac{10}{27}x^3 + \tfrac{5}{81}x^4 - \tfrac{1}{243}x^5$$

> $a = 1, n = 5, \ 'x' = -\dfrac{x}{3}$

C2

You can find particular terms in a binomial expansion without working out the whole expansion.

Example 24

Find the coefficient of the x^4 term in the expansion of $(3 - 2x)^{10}$.

Rather than expand the whole expression, the x^4 term is given by the Pascal coefficient $\begin{pmatrix} 10 \\ 4 \end{pmatrix}$ multiplied by the term $3^6(-2x)^4$.

This gives:

$$\begin{pmatrix} 10 \\ 4 \end{pmatrix} 3^6(-2x)^4 = 210 \times 729 \times 16x^4$$
$$= 2\,449\,440x^4$$

So the coefficient of the x^4 term is 2 449 440.

> The index 6 in this term comes from $(10 - 4)$.

Example 25

Calculate the value of the constant a if the coefficient of the x^3
term in the expansion of $(a + 2x)^4$ is 160.

The x^3 term in the expansion of $(a + 2x)^4$ is

$$\binom{4}{3} a(2x)^3 = 32ax^3$$

$$\therefore \quad 32a = 160$$

$$\therefore \quad a = 5$$

Remember:

$$\binom{4}{3} = \frac{4!}{3! \times 1!} = 4$$

Exercise 7I

1 Expand each of these expressions.
   a) $(2 + x)^3$ b) $(3 + x)^4$ c) $(6 - 5x)^3$ d) $(2 + \frac{1}{2}x)^4$
   e) $(3x + 2y)^3$ f) $(2x - y)^5$ g) $(2x + 5y)^3$ h) $(3x - 4y)^4$

2 Find the coefficient of the term indicated in square brackets in
the expansion of each of these expressions.
   a) $(2 + 3x)^5$ $[x^3]$ b) $(5 + 2x)^8$ $[x^6]$ c) $(3 + 2x)^7$ $[x^5]$
   d) $(7 - 4x)^5$ $[x^4]$ e) $(2 - 7x)^4$ $[x]$ f) $(5 + 2x)^6$ $[x^3]$
   g) $\left(\frac{1}{3} + \frac{3}{2}x\right)^6$ $[x^3]$ h) $\left(\frac{2}{3} - \frac{2}{5}x\right)^3$ $[x]$

3 Expand each of the following in ascending powers of x, up to and
including the term in x^3.
   a) $(1 - 3x)^5$ b) $(1 + 2x)^{10}$ c) $(1 - 5x)^7$ d) $(2 - 3x)^5$
   e) $(4 - x)^5$ f) $(2 + 3x)^6$ g) $\left(1 + \frac{1}{3}x\right)^9$ h) $\left(4 + \frac{1}{4}x\right)^6$

Try to expand only as far as you
need to.

4 Expand each of the following in ascending powers of x, up to and
including the term in x^2.
   a) $(2 + x)(1 + x)^5$ b) $(5 - x)(1 + x)^6$
   c) $(5 + 4x)(1 - 2x)^7$ d) $(6 + 5x)(3 + 4x)^4$
   e) $(5 + x^2)(1 - 3x)^6$ f) $(7 - 2x^2)(3 - x)^4$
   g) $(2 + 3x + 7x^2)(1 + x)^6$ h) $(1 + x + x^2)(2 + x)^5$

5 Expand each of the expressions.
   a) $(1 + x^3)^4$ b) $(1 + 3x^2)^3$ c) $(3 - 2x^3)^3$
   d) $(1 + x + x^2)^2$ e) $(2 + 3x - x^2)^2$ f) $(2 + x - 4x^2)^2$

6 Find the coefficient of the term indicated in square brackets in
the expansion of each of these expressions.
   a) $\left(3x - \frac{2}{x}\right)^5$ $[x^3]$ b) $\left(2x + \frac{5}{x}\right)^6$ $[x^4]$
   c) $\left(x^2 - \frac{2}{x}\right)^6$ [constant]   d) $\left(x^3 + \frac{3}{x}\right)^4$ $[x^4]$
   e) $\left(2x^3 - \frac{3}{x^2}\right)^4$ $[x^2]$ f) $\left(x^3 + \frac{7}{x}\right)^5$ $[x^7]$
   g) $\left(\frac{3}{x^2} - 5x\right)^4$ $\left[\frac{1}{x^2}\right]$ h) $\left(\frac{4}{x} + x^4\right)^{10}$ [constant]

C2

7 a) Expand each of these in ascending powers of x up to and including the term in x^2.
   i) $(1+x)^4$ ii) $(1-2x)^4$

b) By first factorising the quadratic $1-x-2x^2$, deduce the first three terms in the binomial expansion of $(1-x-2x^2)^4$.

8 a) Expand each of these in ascending powers of x up to and including the term in x^2.
   i) $(1+3x)^6$ ii) $(1-4x)^6$

b) By first factorising the quadratic $1-x-12x^2$, deduce the first three terms in the binomial expansion of $(1-x-12x^2)^6$.

Summary

You should know how to ...	Check out
1 Generate sequences using a recurrence relationship.	**1** Given $u_1 = 2$ and $u_{r+1} = 2u_r - 1$, find the first five terms of the sequence, up to u_5
2 Find a formula for the nth term of an arithmetic and geometric sequence.	**2** Find a formula for the nth term of each of these sequences. a) $5, 8, 11, 14, \ldots$ b) $5, 2.5, 1.25, \ldots$
3 Find the sum of n terms of an arithmetic and geometric series.	**3** a) For the progression $5, 8, 11, 14, \ldots$ find i) the 21st term ii) the sum of the first 21 terms. b) For the series $5 + 2.5 + 1.25 + \ldots$ find i) the 11th term ii) the sum of the first 11 terms.
4 Find the sum to infinity of a geometric series.	**4** For the sequence $6, 4, 2\frac{2}{3}, \ldots$ find a) the 5th term, b) the sum of the first 10 terms, c) the sum to infinity.
5 Expand the binomial expressions $(1+x)^n$ and $(a+bx)^n$ for positive integers n.	**5** Expand each of these expressions. a) $(1+x)^4$ b) $(1-\frac{1}{2}x)^5$ c) $(3+2x)^3$

C2

Revision exercise 7

1 The second term of a geometric series is 24 and the fifth term is 3.

a) Show that the common ratio of the series is $\frac{1}{2}$.

b) Find the first term of the series.

c) Find the sum to infinity of the series. *(AQA, 2002)*

2 An arithmetic series has first term a and common difference d.
The sum of the first 19 terms is 266.

a) Show that $a + 9d = 14$

b) The sum of the fifth and eighth terms is 7.
Find the values of a and d.   (*AQA, 2003*)

3 The first four terms of a geometric sequence are 10, 9, 8.1, 7.29.

a) Show that the common ratio of the sequence is 0.9.

b) Find the nth term.

c) Show that the sum of the first 25 terms is approximately 92.8.

d) Find the sum to infinity.   (*AQA, 2003*)

4 a) Find the sum of the 16 terms of the arithmetic series
$2 + 5 + 8 + \dots + 47$.

b) An arithmetic series $u_1, u_2, u_3 \dots$ has rth term u_r, where
$u_r = 50 - 3r$.

i) Write down the values of u_1, u_2, u_3 and u_4.

ii) Show that the sequence has exactly 16 positive terms.   (*AQA, 2002*)

5 A geometric series has first term 1200 and common ratio r.
Write down the second and third terms of the series in terms of r.   (*AQA, 2002*)

6 An arithmetic series has sixth term 28 and tenth term 44.

a) Find the first term and the common difference.

b) Find the sum of the first terms of the series.   (*AQA, 2003*)

7 An infinite geometric sequence has common ratio r.
The second term of the series is -12. The sum to infinity of the
series is 16.

a) i) Show that r satisfies the equation $4r^2 - 4r - 3 = 0$

ii) Hence find the value of r.

b) Find, in terms of k, an expression for the $(2k)$th term of the series.   (*AQA, 2002*)

8 The ninth term of an arithmetic series is 17 and the sum of the first
five terms is 10.
Determine the first term and the common difference of the series.   (*AQA/AEB, 1998*)

9 The first term of an arithmetic series is 6 and the common
difference of the series is $1\frac{1}{3}$

a) Find the 10th term.

b) Show that the sum of the first 400 terms of the series is 108 800.   (*AQA, 2002*)

10 The sum of the first five terms of an arithmetic series is 5, and the sum of the next five terms is 105.
Find the first term and the common difference.   *(AQA/AEB, 2000)*

11 The third term of a geometric series is 81 and the sixth term is 24.

a) Show that the common ratio of the series is $\frac{2}{3}$.

b) Find the sum to infinity of the series.   *(AQA, 2003)*

12 Find the binomial expansion of $(1 + \frac{1}{2}x)^8$ in ascending powers of x up to and including the term x^3. Simplify the coefficients as much as possible.   *(AQA/AEB, 2001)*

13 Write down the binomial expansion of $(1 + x)^5$.
Hence, or otherwise, express $(1 - \sqrt{3})^5$ in the form $p + q\sqrt{3}$ where p and q are integers.   *(AQA/AEB, 1998)*

14 The cost of a life insurance policy is £55.89 in the first year. Subsequently the cost in each year is 3% more than the cost in the previous year.

a) Find the cost of the policy in the twentieth year.

b) Find the total of all the payments made by the end of the twentieth year.   *(AQA/NEAB, 2001)*

C2

8 Trigonometry

This chapter will show you how to

✦ Use the sine and cosine rules
✦ Find the area of a triangle using its sides and angles
✦ Find the length of an arc and the area of a sector of a circle
✦ Use the graphs of the sine, cosine and tangent functions
✦ Solve trigonometric equations

Before you start

You should know how to ...	Check in
1 Use a calculator to find the sine, cosine and tangent of a given angle.	**1** Find the value of a) $\sin 37°$ b) $\cos 7°$ c) $\tan 60°$ Give your answers to 4 decimal places.
2 Use a calculator to find an angle from a given value of a sine, cosine or tangent.	**2** Find the value of x $(0 < x < 90)$ giving your answer to 1 decimal place if appropriate. a) $\sin x° = 0.5$ b) $\cos x° = 0.3$ c) $\tan x° = 1$
3 Use trigonometry in a right-angled triangle to find its angles.	**3** Find the angles indicated, giving your answers to 1 decimal place. a) b) c) *(continued)*

C2

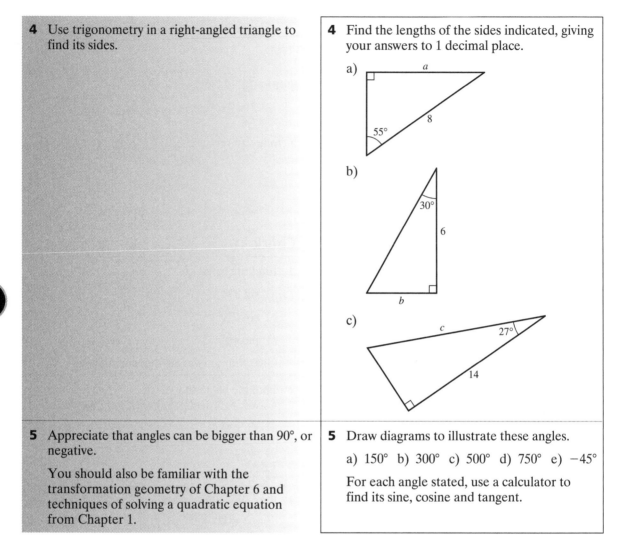

4 Use trigonometry in a right-angled triangle to find its sides.

4 Find the lengths of the sides indicated, giving your answers to 1 decimal place.

a)

b)

c)

5 Appreciate that angles can be bigger than 90°, or negative.

You should also be familiar with the transformation geometry of Chapter 6 and techniques of solving a quadratic equation from Chapter 1.

5 Draw diagrams to illustrate these angles.

a) 150°   b) 300°   c) 500°   d) 750°   e) −45°

For each angle stated, use a calculator to find its sine, cosine and tangent.

8.1 Trigonometric ratios

Trigonometry literally means 'triangle measure'. However, its uses in real life extend far beyond triangles. For example, waves are often described by trigonometric functions.

First you should recap these important facts.

In the right-angled triangle ABC:

+ side AB is called the **hypotenuse**
+ side BC is called the **adjacent** since it is adjacent to (next to) the angle ABC (θ)
+ side AC is called the **opposite** (relative to the angle ABC), since it is opposite the angle ABC.

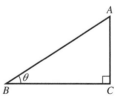

The trigonometric ratios are

$$\sin \theta = \frac{\text{opposite}}{\text{hypotenuse}} \qquad \cos \theta = \frac{\text{adjacent}}{\text{hypotenuse}} \qquad \tan \theta = \frac{\text{opposite}}{\text{adjacent}}$$

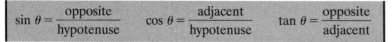

8.2 Sine and cosine rules

You have used trigonometry to calculate lengths and angles in right-angled triangles. In this section you will learn two useful rules that extend to triangles without a right angle.

The sine rule

Consider triangle ABC, with lengths a, b and c.

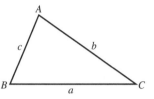

a is the side opposite angle A.

In any triangle ABC,

$$\frac{a}{\sin A} = \frac{b}{\sin B} = \frac{c}{\sin C}$$

To prove this rule, you need to consider two cases:

◆ when triangle ABC is an acute-angled triangle
◆ when triangle ABC is not an acute-angled triangle.

Triangle ABC is acute-angled
Let the perpendicular from A meet BC at D. In triangle ABD:

$$\sin B = \frac{AD}{c}$$

$$\therefore \quad AD = c \sin B \qquad [1]$$

In triangle ADC:

$$\sin C = \frac{AD}{b}$$

$$\therefore \quad AD = b \sin C \qquad [2]$$

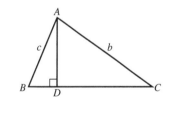

Eliminating AD from [1] and [2] gives:

$$c \sin B = b \sin C$$

$$\therefore \quad \frac{b}{\sin B} = \frac{c}{\sin C} \qquad [3]$$

You will not be required to learn these proofs for your examination.

Similarly, if you draw a perpendicular from B to meet AC:

$$\frac{c}{\sin C} = \frac{a}{\sin A} \qquad [4]$$

Therefore, from [3] and [4],

$$\frac{a}{\sin A} = \frac{b}{\sin B} = \frac{c}{\sin C}$$

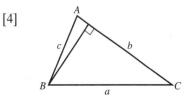

Triangle *ABC* is not acute-angled

Let the perpendicular from *A* meet *CB* extended at *D*.

In triangle *ABD*:

$$\sin A\hat{B}D = \frac{AD}{c}$$

$$\therefore \quad AD = c \sin A\hat{B}D$$

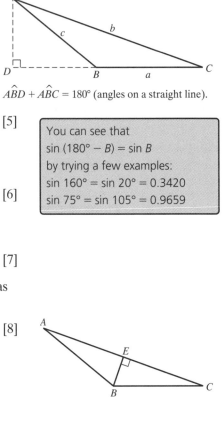

$A\hat{B}D + A\hat{B}C = 180°$ (angles on a straight line).

Now $\angle ABD = (180° - B)$ and $\sin(180° - B) = \sin B$. So:

$$AD = c \sin B \qquad\qquad [5]$$

In triangle *ACD*:

$$\sin C = \frac{AD}{b}$$

$$\therefore \quad AD = b \sin C \qquad\qquad [6]$$

Eliminating *AD* from [5] and [6] gives

$$c \sin B = b \sin C$$

$$\therefore \quad \frac{c}{\sin C} = \frac{b}{\sin B} \qquad\qquad [7]$$

You can see that
$\sin(180° - B) = \sin B$
by trying a few examples:
$\sin 160° = \sin 20° = 0.3420$
$\sin 75° = \sin 105° = 0.9659$

If you draw a perpendicular from *B* to meet *AC* at *E* and proceed as in case (i), you obtain:

$$\frac{a}{\sin A} = \frac{c}{\sin C} \qquad\qquad [8]$$

Therefore, from [7] and [8],

$$\frac{a}{\sin A} = \frac{b}{\sin B} = \frac{c}{\sin C}$$

as required.

Example 1

In triangle ABC, $\hat{A} = 40°$, $\hat{B} = 75°$ and $AB = 6$ cm. Calculate

a) the length *AC* b) the length *BC*.

....

a) $\hat{C} = 180° - (40° + 75°) = 65°$

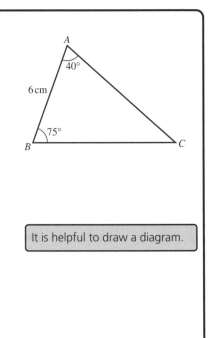

By the sine rule:

$$\frac{AC}{\sin 75°} = \frac{6}{\sin 65°}$$

$$\therefore \quad AC = \frac{6 \sin 75°}{\sin 65°} = 6.4 \ (1 \text{ d.p.})$$

The length of *AC* is 6.4 cm.

b) Applying the sine rule again gives

$$\frac{BC}{\sin 40°} = \frac{6}{\sin 65°}$$

$$\therefore \quad BC = \frac{6 \sin 40°}{\sin 65°} = 4.3$$

It is helpful to draw a diagram.

The length of *BC* is 4.3 cm (1 d.p.).

The ambiguous case

Suppose you are given triangle ABC such that $AC = 7$ cm, $BC = 12$ cm and $\hat{B} = 30°$. Constructing this triangle with ruler and compasses gives the diagram shown.

Since triangle A_1CA_2 is isosceles, $A_1\hat{A}_2C = A_2\hat{A}_1C$. Angles BA_1C and A_2A_1C are supplementary (their sum is $180°$).

In other words, there are two possible positions for vertex A, namely A_1 and A_2.

This is known as the **ambiguous case**. This situation arises when you are given two sides and a non-included angle.

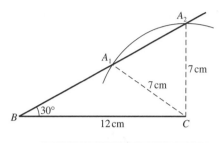

A non-included angle is one that is not the angle between the two given sides.

C2

Example 2

In triangle ABC, $AB = 8$ cm, $BC = 10$ cm and angle $ACB = 42°$.
Calculate the length of AC.

· ·

The diagram shows the two possible triangles which can be drawn from this information.

Applying the sine rule to triangle ABC gives

$$\frac{10}{\sin A} = \frac{8}{\sin 42°}$$

$$\therefore \quad \sin A = \frac{10 \sin 42°}{8}$$

$$\therefore \quad A = 56.8°$$

Therefore, $B\hat{A}'C = 180° - 56.8° = 123.2°$.

The two possible cases are shown in the diagrams.

In case (i), $A\hat{B}C = 180° - (42° + 56.8°) = 81.2°$

Applying the sine rule to triangle ABC gives

$$\frac{AC}{\sin 81.2°} = \frac{8}{\sin 42°}$$

$$\therefore \quad AC = \frac{8 \sin 81.2°}{\sin 42°} = 11.8$$

In case (ii), $A'\hat{B}C = 180° - (42° + 123.2°) = 14.8°$

Applying the sine rule to triangle $A'BC$ gives

$$\frac{A'C}{\sin 14.8°} = \frac{8}{\sin 42°}$$

$$\therefore \quad A'C = \frac{8 \sin 14.8°}{\sin 42°} = 3.1$$

The two possible lengths of AC are 11.8 cm and 3.1 cm (1 d.p.).

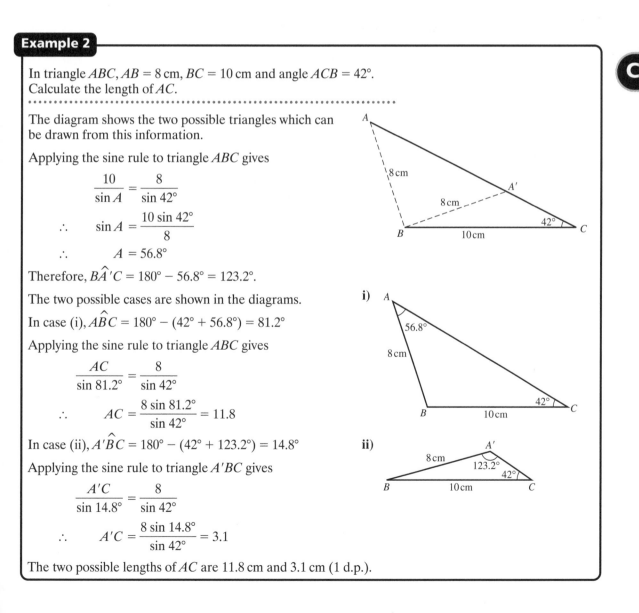

Exercise 8A

State your answers **correct to three significant figures** throughout this exercise.

1 Use the sine rule to find each of the unknown labelled sides or angles. In any ambiguous cases, give both alternatives.

Note that the sine rule can be inverted:

$$\frac{\sin A}{a} = \frac{\sin B}{b} = \frac{\sin C}{c}$$

This form is much easier to use if you are finding angles.

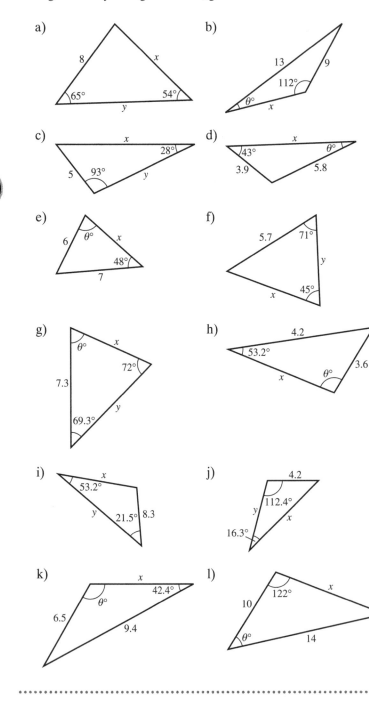

C2

The cosine rule

> In any triangle ABC,
> $$c^2 = a^2 + b^2 - 2ab \cos C$$
> and similarly,
> $$a^2 = b^2 + c^2 - 2bc \cos A$$
> and $b^2 = a^2 + c^2 - 2ac \cos B$

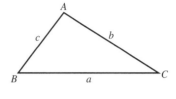

To prove this rule, you need to consider two cases:

✦ when triangle ABC is an acute-angled triangle
✦ when triangle ABC is not an acute-angled triangle.

Triangle ABC is acute-angled
Let the perpendicular from A meet BC at D.

Let $DC = x$, then $BD = a - x$.

In triangle ABD,
$$AD^2 = c^2 - (a - x)^2$$
$$= c^2 - a^2 + 2ax - x^2 \qquad [1]$$

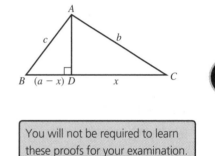

In triangle ADC,
$$AD^2 = b^2 - x^2 \qquad [2]$$

> You will not be required to learn these proofs for your examination.

Eliminating AD^2 from [1] and [2] gives,
$$b^2 - x^2 = c^2 - a^2 + 2ax - x^2$$
$$\therefore \quad b^2 = c^2 - a^2 + 2ax$$
$$\therefore \quad c^2 = a^2 + b^2 - 2ax \qquad [3]$$

In triangle ADC,
$$\cos C = \frac{x}{b}$$
$$\therefore \quad x = b \cos C$$

Substituting $x = b \cos C$ into [3] gives
$$c^2 = a^2 + b^2 - 2a(b \cos C)$$
$$\therefore \quad c^2 = a^2 + b^2 - 2ab \cos C$$

as required.

Triangle ABC is not acute-angled
Let the perpendicular from A meet CB extended at D.

Let $DB = x$.

In triangle ABD,
$$AD^2 = c^2 - x^2 \qquad [4]$$

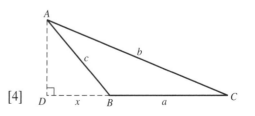

In triangle ADC,
$$AD^2 = b^2 - (a + x)^2$$
$$= b^2 - a^2 - 2ax - x^2 \qquad [5]$$

Eliminating AD^2 from [4] and [5] gives

$$c^2 - x^2 = b^2 - a^2 - 2ax - x^2$$
$$c^2 = b^2 - a^2 - 2ax$$
$$\therefore \quad b^2 = a^2 + c^2 + 2ax \qquad\qquad [6]$$

In triangle ADB,

$$\cos A\hat{B}D = \frac{x}{c}$$
$$\therefore \quad x = c \cos A\hat{B}D$$

Now $A\hat{B}D = 180° - B$ and $\cos(180° - B) = -\cos B$. So:

$$x = -c \cos B$$

Substituting $x = -c \cos B$ into [6] gives

$$b^2 = a^2 + c^2 + 2a(-c \cos B)$$
$$\therefore \quad b^2 = a^2 + c^2 - 2ac \cos B$$

> You can see that
> $\cos(180° - B) = -\cos B$
> by trying a few examples.
> $\cos 40° = -\cos 140° = 0.7660$
> $\cos 131° = -\cos 49° = -0.6561$

C2

as required.

Example 3

In triangle ABC, $AC = 20$ cm, $BC = 11$ cm and angle $A\hat{C}B = 20°$.

Calculate:
a) the length AB
b) the angle $A\hat{B}C$

. . . .

a) Apply the cosine rule to triangle ABC:

$$AB^2 = 11^2 + 20^2 - 2 \times 11 \times 20 \cos 20°$$
$$= 121 + 400 - 413.46 = 107.54$$
$$\therefore \quad AB = \sqrt{107.54} = 10.37$$

The length AB is 10.37 cm.

b) To find angle ABC, rearrange the cosine formula for $\cos B$.

$$b^2 = a^2 + c^2 - 2ac \cos B$$
$$\therefore \quad \cos B = \frac{a^2 + c^2 - b^2}{2ac}$$

Applying this formula to triangle ABC gives

$$\cos B = \frac{11^2 + 10.37^2 - 20^2}{2(11)(10.37)} = -0.7516$$
$$\therefore \quad \angle ABC = 138.7°$$

> You should use the cosine rule
> here because you are given
> 2 sides and the included angle.
> Generally use the cosine rule
> when:
> ✦ you have 2 sides and the
>   included angle
> ✦ you have all 3 sides.
> Otherwise use the sine rule.

Exercise 8B

1 Use the cosine rule where appropriate to find each of the unknown labelled sides or angles.

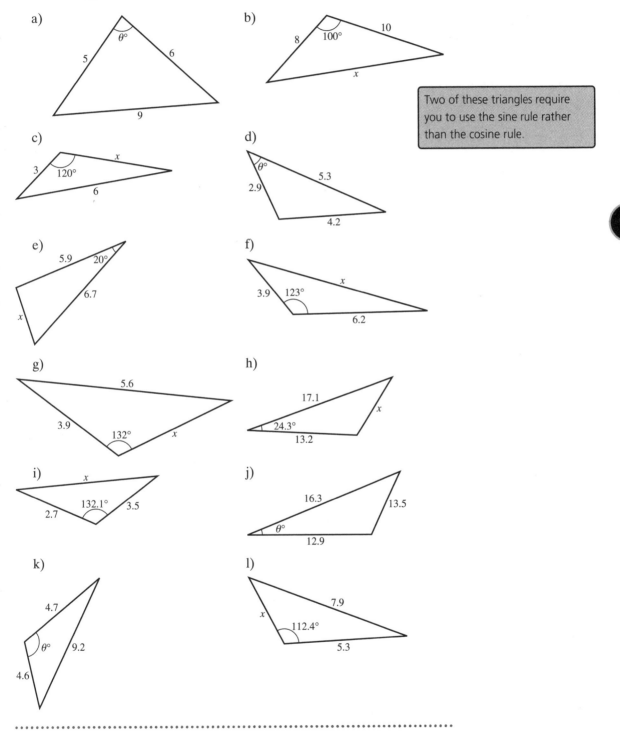

a)

b)

Two of these triangles require you to use the sine rule rather than the cosine rule.

c)

d)

C2

e)

f)

g)

h)

i)

j)

k)

l)

Bearings

You can use the sine and cosine rules to solve problems involving bearings.

Example 4

A ship sails 6 km from S to T on a bearing of 063° and then 9 km from T to U on a bearing of 148°. Calculate:

a) the distance SU b) the bearing of U from S

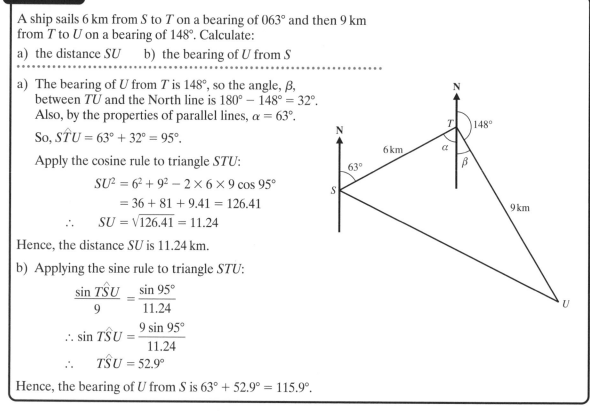

a) The bearing of U from T is 148°, so the angle, β, between TU and the North line is $180° - 148° = 32°$. Also, by the properties of parallel lines, $\alpha = 63°$.

So, $S\hat{T}U = 63° + 32° = 95°$.

Apply the cosine rule to triangle STU:

$$SU^2 = 6^2 + 9^2 - 2 \times 6 \times 9 \cos 95°$$
$$= 36 + 81 + 9.41 = 126.41$$
$$\therefore \quad SU = \sqrt{126.41} = 11.24$$

Hence, the distance SU is 11.24 km.

b) Applying the sine rule to triangle STU:

$$\frac{\sin T\hat{S}U}{9} = \frac{\sin 95°}{11.24}$$
$$\therefore \sin T\hat{S}U = \frac{9 \sin 95°}{11.24}$$
$$\therefore \quad T\hat{S}U = 52.9°$$

Hence, the bearing of U from S is $63° + 52.9° = 115.9°$.

Exercise 8C

1 In triangle ABC, $AB = 6$ cm, $BC = 8$ cm and angle $B = 50°$.
  a) Find the length of AC.   b) Find the size of angle A.

2 In triangle PQR, $PQ = 12$ cm, $QR = 14$ cm and $PR = 11$ cm.
  a) Find the size of angle P.   b) Find the size of angle Q.

3 In triangle LMN, $LM = 5$ cm, $MN = 8$ cm and angle $N = 20°$. Given that L is obtuse,
  a) calculate the size of angle L b) calculate the length of LN.

4 Given that PQR is a triangle in which $PQ = 5$ cm, $QR = 8$ cm and angle $R = 30°$, calculate the two possible values of the length of PR.

5 A ship leaves a harbour, H, and sails for 32 km on a bearing of 025° to a point X. At X it changes course and then sails for 45 km on a bearing of 280° to a port P.
  a) Sketch a diagram showing H, X and P.
  b) Calculate the direct distance from H to P.
  c) Calculate the bearing of P from H.

6 A bird leaves a nest, N, and flies 800 m on a bearing of 132° to a tree T. It then leaves T and flies 650 m on a bearing of 209° to a pylon P. Assuming that N, T and P are the same height above the ground, calculate the distance and bearing on which the bird must fly in order to return directly from P to N.

7 An army cadet is involved in a compass exercise. He leaves a point O and walks 50 m due west to a point A. He then walks 80 m due north to a point B, and finally 60 m, on a bearing of 320°, to a point C.

  a) Illustrate this information on a sketch.
  b) Calculate the distance and bearing of B from O.
  c) Calculate the distance and bearing on which he must walk in order to return from C to O.

8 A ship travelling south-west with constant speed observes the flash of a lighthouse on a bearing of 240°. 8 km further on the ship observes the flash of the same lighthouse, due west.

  a) How far is the ship from the lighthouse at this time?
  b) How close to the lighthouse will it pass?

9 In the cuboid $ABCDEFGH$ calculate the lengths

  a) BD b) BG
  c) DG d) $\angle BGD$.

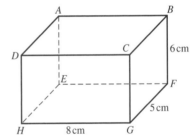

C2

8.3 Area of a triangle

The area of a triangle ABC is given by

$$A = \tfrac{1}{2} \times a \times h$$

where a is the length of the base and h is the perpendicular height. That is,

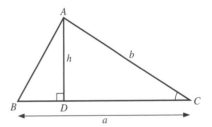

$A = \tfrac{1}{2}ah$

in the usual notation.

In triangle ADC,

$$\sin C = \frac{AD}{AC}$$

$$\therefore \quad \sin C = \frac{h}{b}$$

$$\therefore \quad\quad h = b \sin C$$

Substituting $h = b \sin C$ into $A = \tfrac{1}{2}ah$ gives

$$A = \tfrac{1}{2}ab \sin C$$

Hence, the area of triangle ABC is also given by

$A = \tfrac{1}{2}ab \sin C$

where C is the included angle between sides a and b.

Example 5

In the triangle ABC, $AC = 6$ cm, $BC = 9$ cm and $A\hat{C}B = 30°$.
Calculate the area of triangle ABC.

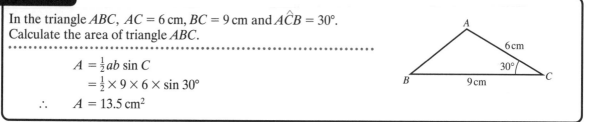

$$A = \tfrac{1}{2}ab \sin C$$
$$= \tfrac{1}{2} \times 9 \times 6 \times \sin 30°$$
$$\therefore \quad A = 13.5 \text{ cm}^2$$

Exercise 8D

State your answers **correct to three significant figures** throughout this exercise.

1 Find the area of each of these triangles.

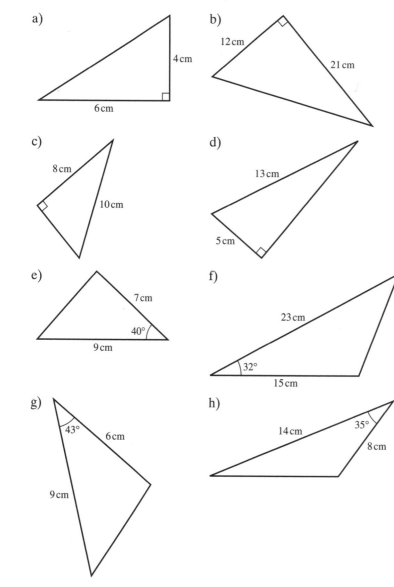

a)

4 cm

6 cm

b)

12 cm

21 cm

c)

8 cm

10 cm

d)

13 cm

5 cm

e)

7 cm

40°

9 cm

f)

23 cm

32°

15 cm

g)

43°

6 cm

9 cm

h)

14 cm

35°

8 cm

C2

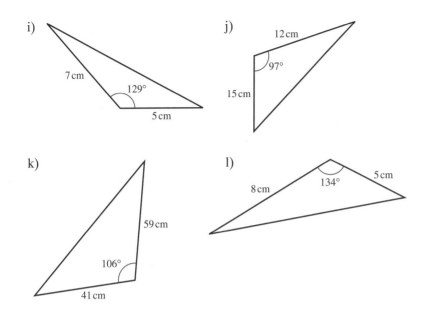

i)

7 cm
129°
5 cm

j)

12 cm
97°
15 cm

k)

59 cm
106°
41 cm

l)

8 cm
134°
5 cm

C2

2 In the triangle ABC, $AB = 9.2$ cm, $BC = 7.8$ cm and $A\hat{B}C = 48°$.
Calculate the area of the triangle.

3 In the triangle PQR, $PQ = 5.9$ cm, $QR = 7.6$ cm and $P\hat{Q}R = 142°$.
Calculate the area of the triangle.

4 KLM is a triangle in which $KL = 7$ cm, $LM = 8$ cm and $MK = 5$ cm.

a) Calculate the size of the angle $K\hat{L}M$.

b) Hence calculate the area of the triangle KLM.

5 In the triangle ABC, $AB = 6.2$ cm, $BC = 8.7$ cm and $C\hat{A}B = 93°$.

a) Calculate the size of the angle $A\hat{B}C$.

b) Hence calculate the area of the triangle ABC.

6 An item of jewellery consists of two identical pyramids,
$PABCD$ and $QABCD$, joined at their common rectangular base.

$AB = 8$ mm, $BC = 12$ mm and $PQ = 30$ mm.

The line PQ passes through the centre of the rectangle $ABCD$.

a) Calculate the area of triangle ABP.

b) Calculate the area of triangle ADP.

The item is to be dipped in silver at cost of 0.4p per mm².

c) Calculate the cost of the dipping.

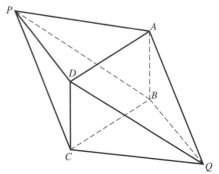

8.4 Radian measure

Consider an arc of length 1 unit of a circle of radius 1 unit.

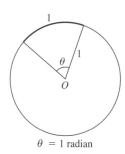

$\theta = 1$ radian

> The angle θ subtended at the centre of the circle by the arc of length 1 unit is called 1 **radian**, written as 1 rad.

The circumference of the circle is given by

$$C = 2\pi r$$

Substituting $r = 1$ gives

$$C = 2\pi(1)$$
$$\therefore \quad C = 2\pi$$

An arc of length 1 subtends an angle of 1 radian $\therefore$ the circumference of length 2π subtends an angle of 2π radians. That is, there are 2π radians at the centre O of the circle. In other words, 2π radians are equivalent to 360°.

C2

Since 2π radians $= 360°$,

$$\pi \text{ radians} = 180° \text{ and } \frac{\pi}{2} \text{ radians} = 90°$$

> 1 radian $\approx 57.3°$.

◆ To convert degrees to radians, multiply by $\dfrac{\pi}{180}$.

◆ To convert radians to degrees, multiply by $\dfrac{180}{\pi}$.

> 1 rad is sometimes written as 1ᶜ.

Example 6

Express each of these angles in radians.
a) 45°   b) 60°   c) 260°
....

a) $45° = 45 \times \dfrac{\pi}{180} = \dfrac{\pi}{4}$ rad   b) $60° = 60 \times \dfrac{\pi}{180} = \dfrac{\pi}{3}$ rad

c) $260° = 260 \times \dfrac{\pi}{180} = 4.54$ rad (to 2 d.p.)

Example 7

Express each of these angles in degrees.

a) $\dfrac{\pi}{6}$ rad   b) $\dfrac{5\pi}{6}$ rad   c) $\dfrac{4\pi}{3}$ rad
....

a) $\dfrac{\pi}{6}$ rad $= \dfrac{\pi}{6} \times \dfrac{180}{\pi} = 30°$ b) $\dfrac{5\pi}{6}$ rad $= \dfrac{5\pi}{6} \times \dfrac{180}{\pi} = 150°$

c) $\dfrac{4\pi}{3}$ rad $= \dfrac{4\pi}{3} \times \dfrac{180}{\pi} = 240°$

Sectors and segments

Consider the sector of a circle, of radius r, which subtends an angle of θ at the centre.

The length, L, of the arc is given by

$$L = \frac{\theta}{2\pi} \times 2\pi r = r\theta$$

where θ is measured in radians.

L is also given by

$$L = \frac{\theta}{360} \times 2\pi r = \frac{\theta \pi r}{180}$$

where θ is measured in degrees.

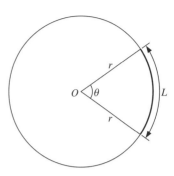

> The length, L, of an arc that subtends an angle θ at the centre of a circle is given by $L = r\theta$, where θ is measured in radians.
>
> Alternatively, $L = \frac{\theta \pi r}{180}$ where θ is measured in degrees.

The area, A, of the sector is given by

$$A = \frac{\theta}{2\pi} \times \pi r^2 = \frac{r^2 \theta}{2}$$

where θ is measured in radians.

A is also given by

$$A = \frac{\theta}{360} \times \pi r^2 = \frac{\theta \pi r^2}{360}$$

where θ is measured in degrees.

> The area, A, of a sector of a circle with angle θ is given by $A = \frac{1}{2}r^2\theta$, where θ is measured in radians.
>
> Alternatively, $A = \frac{\theta \pi r^2}{360}$ where θ is measured in degrees.

Example 8

The sector of a circle of radius 3 cm subtends an angle of $\frac{5\pi}{18}$ rad at the centre. Giving your answers to 1 d.p., find:

a) the length of the arc of the sector
b) the area of the sector of the circle.

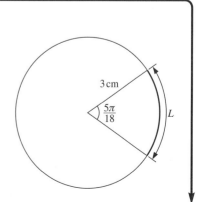

a) The length, L, of the arc is given by

$$L = r\theta$$
$$= \left(\frac{5\pi}{18}\right)(3) = \frac{5\pi}{6} = 2.618$$

The length of the arc is 2.6 cm (to 1 d.p.).

b) The area, A, of the sector is given by

$$A = \frac{r^2\theta}{2}$$

$$= \frac{\left(\frac{5\pi}{18}\right)(3)^2}{2} = \frac{5\pi}{4} = 3.927$$

The area of the sector is 3.9 cm² (1 d.p.).

Example 9

The shaded area in the diagram is a segment of a circle of radius r. Show that the area of the segment is given by

$$\frac{r^2(\pi - 3)}{12}$$

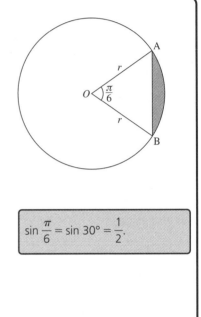

C2

The area, A_s, of the sector of the circle, is given by

$$A_s = \frac{r^2\theta}{2} = \frac{\left(\frac{\pi}{6}\right)r^2}{2}$$

$$= \frac{\pi r^2}{12}$$

The area of triangle OAB, A_t, is given by

$$A_t = \tfrac{1}{2}ab \sin A\hat{O}B = \tfrac{1}{2}(r)(r) \sin \frac{\pi}{6}$$

$$A_t = \frac{r^2}{4}$$

> $\sin \dfrac{\pi}{6} = \sin 30° = \dfrac{1}{2}$.

The area, A, of the shaded segment, is given by

$$A = A_s - A_t = \frac{\pi r^2}{12} - \frac{3r^2}{12}$$

$$\therefore \ \ A = \frac{r^2(\pi - 3)}{12}$$

> Numerical answers are often required to be given in terms of π. Like surd form, it gives an accurate answer.

as required.

Exercise 8E

In this exercise, give your answers to 3 significant figures where appropriate and unless otherwise stated.

1 Express each of these angles in radians, giving your answers in terms of π.

    a) 30°   b) 90°   c) 120°   d) 10°

    e) 80°   f) 300°   g) 36°   h) 240°

    i) 72°   j) 360°   k) 342°   l) 1°

2 Express each of these angles in degrees.

a) π rad
b) $\dfrac{\pi}{4}$ rad
c) 3π rad
d) $\dfrac{\pi}{6}$ rad

e) $\dfrac{4\pi}{5}$ rad
f) $\dfrac{\pi}{12}$ rad
g) $\dfrac{5\pi}{3}$ rad
h) π rad

i) $\dfrac{5\pi}{12}$ rad
j) $\dfrac{\pi}{90}$ rad
k) $\dfrac{3\pi}{2}$ rad
l) $\dfrac{7\pi}{6}$ rad

3 Express each of these angles in degrees correct to 1 decimal place.

a) 4 rad
b) 0.2 rad
c) 4.3 rad
d) 0.5 rad

e) 0.7 rad
f) 3 rad
g) 5.2 rad
h) 2.1 rad

i) 5 rad
j) 0.04 rad
k) 16 rad
l) 1 rad

4 A sector of a circle of radius 5 cm subtends an angle of $\dfrac{3\pi}{10}$ rad at the centre. Calculate

a) the length of the arc of the sector

b) the area of the sector.

C2

5 A circle of radius 9 cm is divided into three equal sectors. Calculate

a) the length of the arc of each sector

b) the area of each sector.

6 A sector of angle $\dfrac{5\pi}{12}$ rad is cut from a circle of radius 6 cm. Calculate

a) the perimeter of the sector

b) the area of the sector.

7 OAB is a sector of a circle, centre O, and is such that $OA = OB = 7$ cm and $A\hat{O}B = \dfrac{5\pi}{14}$ rad. Calculate

a) the perimeter of the sector OAB

b) the area of the sector OAB.

8 The sector of a circle of radius 8 cm subtends an angle of 30° at the centre. Calculate

a) the length of the arc of the sector

b) the area of the sector.

9 OPQ is a sector of a circle, centre O, and is such that $OP = OQ = 12$ cm and $P\hat{O}Q = 45°$. Calculate

a) the perimeter of the sector POQ

b) the area of the sector POQ.

10 Calculate the area of a segment of angle $\dfrac{\pi}{2}$ rad cut from a circle of radius 5 cm.

11 Calculate the area of a segment of angle $\dfrac{\pi}{3}$ rad cut from a circle of radius 10 cm.

12 *OMN* is a sector of a circle, centre *O*, and is such that
OM = *ON* = 12 cm, and *MÔN* = $\frac{\pi}{2}$ rad. *S* is the segment
bounded by the chord *MN* and the arc *MN*. Calculate
a) the area of *S*   b) the perimeter of *S*.

13 *OAB* is a sector of a circle, centre *O*, and is such that
OA = *OB* = 8 cm, and *AÔB* = $\frac{\pi}{5}$ rad. *S* is the segment bounded
by the chord *AB* and the arc *AB*. Calculate
a) the area of *S*   b) the perimeter of *S*.

14 The shaded region in the diagram shows a component for a
machine, which is to be cut from a square piece of metal, *PQRS*,
of centre *O* and side 8 cm. The outer edge of the component is
the regular octagon *ABCEDFGH*, and the inner edge is the
circle centre *O* and radius 3 cm. Calculate
a) the area of the component
b) the outer perimeter of the component.

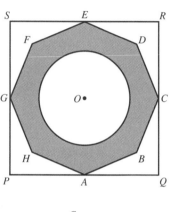

C2

15 The diagram shows a pennant *ABC*, which has a triangular hole
in the middle. The hole is an equilateral triangle *ABC* of side
8 cm. *AB*, *BC* and *CA* are circular arcs with centres at *C*, *A* and
B respectively. Calculate
a) the area of the triangle *ABC*
b) the area of the sector *ABC*
c) the area of the shaded region.

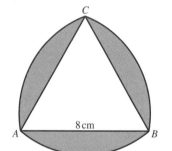

16 An ornamental mirror, *CPQ*, is to be cut from a triangle *ABC* in
which *AB* = 6 m and *AB̂C* = *CÂB* = $\frac{\pi}{4}$ rad. The circular arcs *CP*
and *CQ* have centres *B* and *A* respectively. Calculate
a) the area of the sector *BCP*   b) the area of the triangle *ABC*
c) the area of the mirror *CPQ*   d) the length of the arc *CP*
e) the length of *PQ*   f) the perimeter of the mirror.

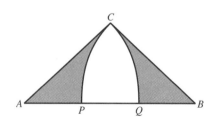

17 The diagram shows two circles, each of radius *r* and such that
the centre of one circle is on the circumference of the other
circle. Prove that the shaded area enclosed by the two circles is
given by the formula $\frac{r^2}{6}(4\pi - 3\sqrt{3})$.

(Hint: You will need to know that $\sin\frac{2\pi}{3} = \frac{\sqrt{3}}{2}$)

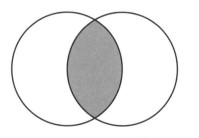

8.5 The functions sin θ, cos θ, tan θ

Graphs of $y = \sin \theta$, $y = \cos \theta$, $y = \tan \theta$

You have seen that the sine, cosine and tangent functions exist for angles outside the range $0 \leqslant \theta \leqslant 90°$.

If you plot values of y against θ you get the graphs shown. There is no restriction on the size of angle θ but for convenience you can use $-360° \leqslant \theta \leqslant 360°$ or $-2\pi \leqslant \theta \leqslant 2\pi$ to show the main features of the graphs.

> You can use degrees or radians on the x-axis.

Properties of the sine function

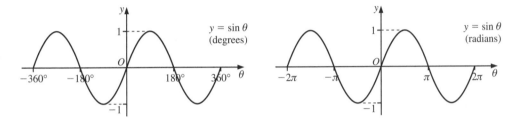

◆ The function $\mathrm{f}(\theta) = \sin \theta$ is periodic, of period 360° or 2π rad. That is:

$$\sin (\theta + 360°) = \sin \theta \text{ or } \sin (\theta + 2\pi) = \sin \theta$$

> The **period** of a function is the smallest interval after which the function repeats the same values.

◆ The graph of $\mathrm{f}(\theta) = \sin \theta$ has rotational symmetry about the origin of order 2.
◆ The maximum value of $\mathrm{f}(\theta)$ is 1 and its minimum value is -1. In other words $-1 \leqslant \sin \theta \leqslant 1$.

Properties of the cosine function

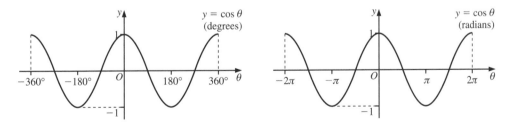

◆ The function $\mathrm{f}(\theta) = \cos \theta$ is periodic, of period 360° or 2π rad. That is:

$$\cos (\theta + 360°) = \cos \theta \text{ or } \cos (\theta + 2\pi) = \cos \theta$$

> Try plotting accurate graphs of $\sin \theta$, $\cos \theta$ and $\tan \theta$ for $-360° \leqslant \theta \leqslant 360°$ using a graphics calculator.

◆ The graph of $\mathrm{f}(\theta) = \cos \theta$ is symmetrical about the y-axis.
◆ The maximum value of $\mathrm{f}(\theta)$ is 1 and its minimum value is -1. In other words $-1 \leqslant \cos \theta \leqslant 1$.

C2

Properties of the tangent function

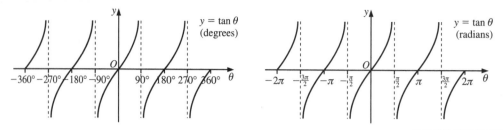

- ◆ The function $f(\theta) = \tan \theta$ is periodic, of period $180°$ or π rad. That is:

  $$\tan (\theta + 180°) = \tan \theta \text{ or } \tan (\theta + \pi) = \tan \theta$$

- ◆ The graph of $f(\theta) = \tan \theta$ has rotational symmetry about the origin of order 2.

- ◆ The function $f(\theta) = \tan \theta$ is not defined when $\theta = \pm 90°, \pm 270°, \ldots,$ or, in radians, $\theta = \pm \dfrac{\pi}{2}, \pm \dfrac{3\pi}{2}, \ldots$

> $\tan \theta \to \infty$ at $90°, 270°, \ldots$
> The lines $y = 90°, y = 270°, \ldots$
> are **asymptotes** to the curve:
> the curve gets nearer and nearer
> to these lines but never actually
> reaches them. $y = \tan \theta$ has no
> maximum or minimum value.

C2

Example 10

Express each of these in terms of an acute angle, using the same trigonometric function as given in the question.

a) $\sin 150°$ b) $\sin 300°$ c) $\cos (-350°)$ d) $\tan 150°$

a) If you look at the graph of $\sin \theta$, you can see that

$$\sin 150° = \sin 30°$$

b)

You can see from the graph of $\sin \theta$ that $\sin 300° = \sin (-60°) = -\sin 60°$ since sine θ has rotational symmetry about the origin. Therefore, $\sin 300° = -60°$.

c)

$$-(360° - 10°) = -350°$$

You can see that $\cos (-350°) = \cos 10°$.

d)

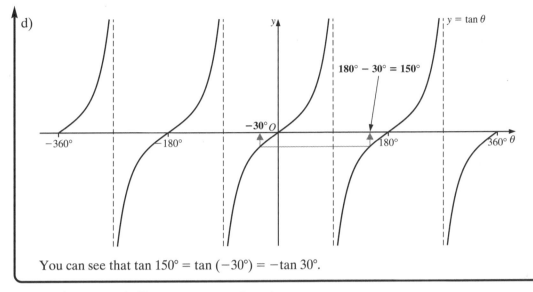

You can see that tan 150° = tan (−30°) = −tan 30°.

C2

The previous example illustrates a general result:

> For any angle θ,
> ✦ $\sin(-\theta) = -\sin\theta$
> ✦ $\cos(-\theta) = \cos\theta$
> ✦ $\tan(-\theta) = -\tan\theta$

Example 11

Express each of these as the trigonometric ratio of an acute angle, using the same trigonometric function as given in the question.

a) $\cos\dfrac{11\pi}{6}$ b) $\tan\left(-\dfrac{\pi}{3}\right)$

....

a)

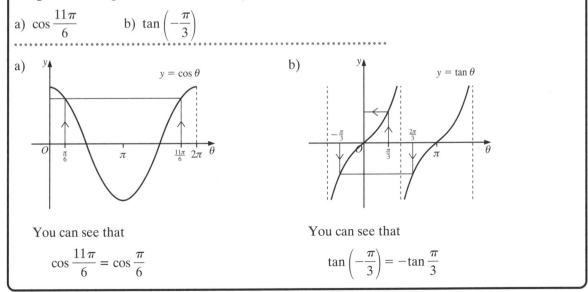

b)

You can see that

$$\cos\frac{11\pi}{6} = \cos\frac{\pi}{6}$$

You can see that

$$\tan\left(-\frac{\pi}{3}\right) = -\tan\frac{\pi}{3}$$

Exercise 8F

By considering the appropriate trigonometric graph, express each part of questions 1 to 3 in terms of an acute angle.

Use the same trigonometric function as in the question.

1 a) $\sin 210°$ b) $\cos 130°$ c) $\tan 160°$ d) $\sin 310°$

   e) $\tan 120°$ f) $\cos 290°$ g) $\tan 260°$ h) $\sin 234°$

   i) $\tan 173°$ j) $\cos 108°$ k) $\sin 126°$ l) $\cos 239°$

2 a) $\cos 420°$ b) $\sin(-60°)$ c) $\tan 390°$ d) $\sin 590°$

   e) $\tan(-154°)$ f) $\cos 620°$ g) $\sin(-425°)$ h) $\cos(-159°)$

   i) $\tan 507°$ j) $\cos 749°$ k) $\tan(-265°)$ l) $\sin 3610°$

3 a) $\sin\left(\dfrac{2\pi}{3}\right)$ b) $\cos\left(\dfrac{7\pi}{6}\right)$ c) $\tan\left(\dfrac{7\pi}{8}\right)$ d) $\tan\left(\dfrac{9\pi}{5}\right)$

   e) $\cos\left(\dfrac{8\pi}{3}\right)$ f) $\sin\left(-\dfrac{2\pi}{9}\right)$ g) $\cos\left(\dfrac{12\pi}{13}\right)$ h) $\tan\left(-\dfrac{7\pi}{4}\right)$

   i) $\cos\left(-\dfrac{6\pi}{19}\right)$ j) $\sin\left(\dfrac{16\pi}{5}\right)$ k) $\tan\left(-\dfrac{9\pi}{7}\right)$ l) $\sin\left(-\dfrac{11\pi}{2}\right)$

C2

Curve sketching

In this section you will be using the results on the transformation of graphs which you studied in Chapter 6.

Example 12

Sketch the graphs of each of these functions for $-360° \leqslant \theta \leqslant 360°$.

a) $f(\theta) = 1 + \sin\theta$ b) $f(\theta) = \tan(\theta + 90°)$

c) $f(\theta) = 2\sin\theta$ d) $f(\theta) = \sin 2\theta$

In each case state the period of the function.

a) To obtain the graph of $f(\theta) = 1 + \sin\theta$, translate the graph of $\sin\theta$ by 1 unit parallel to the y-axis.

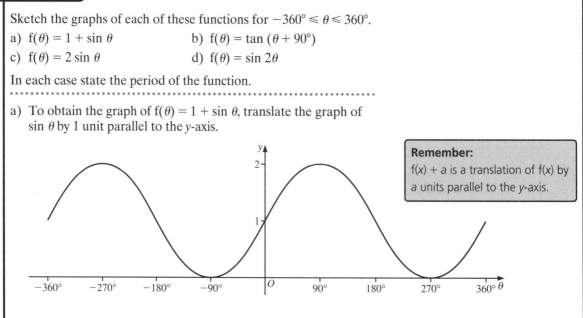

Remember:
$f(x) + a$ is a translation of $f(x)$ by a units parallel to the y-axis.

The period is 360°, which is no change from that of $\sin\theta$.

b) To obtain the graph of f(θ) = tan (θ + 90°), translate the graph of tan θ by −90° parallel to the θ-axis.

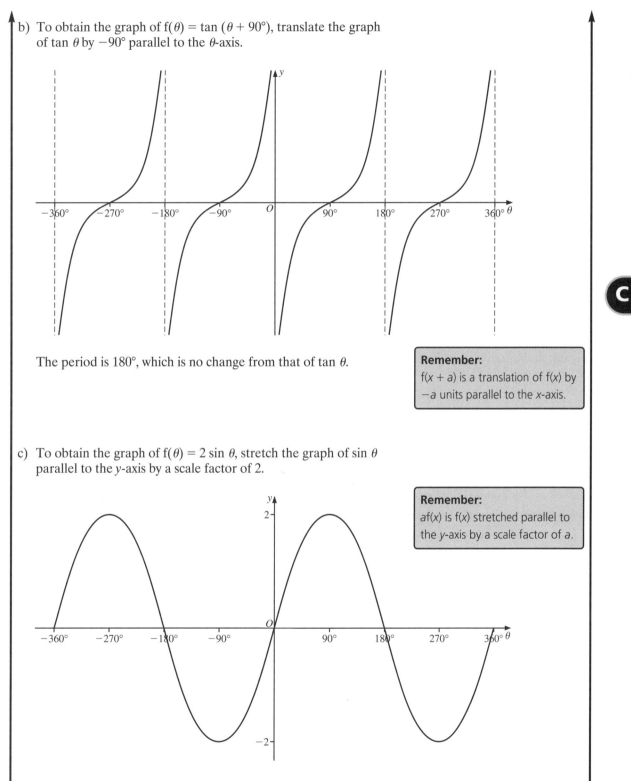

The period is 180°, which is no change from that of tan θ.

> **Remember:**
> f(x + a) is a translation of f(x) by −a units parallel to the x-axis.

c) To obtain the graph of f(θ) = 2 sin θ, stretch the graph of sin θ parallel to the y-axis by a scale factor of 2.

> **Remember:**
> af(x) is f(x) stretched parallel to the y-axis by a scale factor of a.

The period is 360°, which is no change from that of sin θ.

d) To obtain the graph of $f(\theta) = \sin 2\theta$, stretch the graph of $y = \sin \theta$ parallel to the θ-axis by a scale factor of $\frac{1}{2}$.

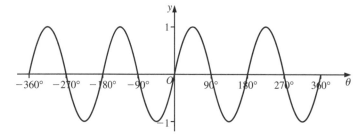

The period is 180° (the graph repeats every 180°).
This is half the period of the $\sin \theta$ function.

Exercise 8G

1 Sketch the graphs of each of these functions for $-360° \leqslant \theta \leqslant 360°$.

   a) $y = 1 + \cos \theta$ b) $y = \sin (\theta + 30°)$ c) $y = \tan 2\theta$
   d) $y = 3 \sin \theta$ e) $y = -\tan \theta$ f) $y = \cos (\theta - 50°)$

2 Sketch the graphs of each of these functions for $0 \leqslant \theta \leqslant 2\pi$.

   a) $y = \cos 2\theta$ b) $y = \tan\left(\theta + \dfrac{\pi}{3}\right)$ c) $y = 2 - \sin \theta$

   d) $y = 2 \cos \theta$ e) $y = \tan\left(\dfrac{\theta}{2}\right)$ f) $y = \sin\left(\theta - \dfrac{\pi}{6}\right)$

3 Sketch the graph of $y = 2 + \sin (\theta - 30°)$, for $0 \leqslant \theta \leqslant 360°$.

✸8.6 Trigonometric ratios of 30°, 45° and 60°

Consider the right-angled isosceles triangle ABC.

Using Pythagoras' theorem gives

$$AB^2 = BC^2 + AC^2$$
$$= 1^2 + 1^2$$
$$\therefore \quad AB = \sqrt{2}$$

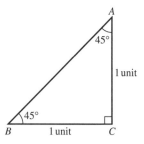

The trigonometric ratios are:

$$\sin 45° = \frac{AC}{AB} = \frac{1}{\sqrt{2}}$$

$$\cos 45° = \frac{BC}{AB} = \frac{1}{\sqrt{2}}$$

$$\tan 45° = \frac{AC}{BC} = 1$$

$$\sin 45° = \frac{1}{\sqrt{2}} \qquad \cos 45° = \frac{1}{\sqrt{2}} \qquad \tan 45° = 1$$

You do not need to memorise these ratios.

Consider the equilateral triangle *ABC* with sides of length 2 units.

Let *D* be the point where the perpendicular from *A* meets the base *BC*.

From Pythagoras' theorem:

$$AD^2 = AB^2 - BD^2$$
$$= 2^2 - 1^2$$
$$\therefore \quad AD = \sqrt{3}$$

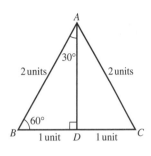

The trigonometric ratios are:

$$\sin 30° = \frac{BD}{AB} \quad \text{and} \quad \sin 60° = \frac{AD}{AB}$$

$$= \frac{1}{2} \qquad\qquad = \frac{\sqrt{3}}{2}$$

$$\sin 30° = \frac{1}{2} \quad \text{and} \quad \sin 60° = \frac{\sqrt{3}}{2}$$

$$\cos 30° = \frac{AD}{AB} \quad \text{and} \quad \cos 60° = \frac{BD}{AB}$$

$$= \frac{\sqrt{3}}{2} \qquad\qquad = \frac{1}{2}$$

> You do not need to memorise these ratios.

$$\cos 30° = \frac{\sqrt{3}}{2} \quad \text{and} \quad \cos 60° = \frac{1}{2}$$

$$\tan 30° = \frac{BD}{AD} \quad \text{and} \quad \tan 60° = \frac{AD}{BD}$$

$$= \frac{1}{\sqrt{3}} \qquad\qquad = \sqrt{3}$$

$$\tan 30° = \frac{1}{\sqrt{3}} \quad \text{and} \quad \tan 60° = \sqrt{3}$$

The trigonometric ratios of 30°, 45° and 60° are summarised in the table.

Ratio	$\theta = 30°$	$\theta = 45°$	$\theta = 60°$
$\sin \theta$	$\frac{1}{2}$	$\frac{1}{\sqrt{2}}$	$\frac{\sqrt{3}}{2}$
$\cos \theta$	$\frac{\sqrt{3}}{2}$	$\frac{1}{\sqrt{2}}$	$\frac{1}{2}$
$\tan \theta$	$\frac{1}{\sqrt{3}}$	1	$\sqrt{3}$

C2

Example 13

Find the perimeter of triangle ABC shown, expressing your answer in the form $a + b\sqrt{c}$, where a, b and c are integers.

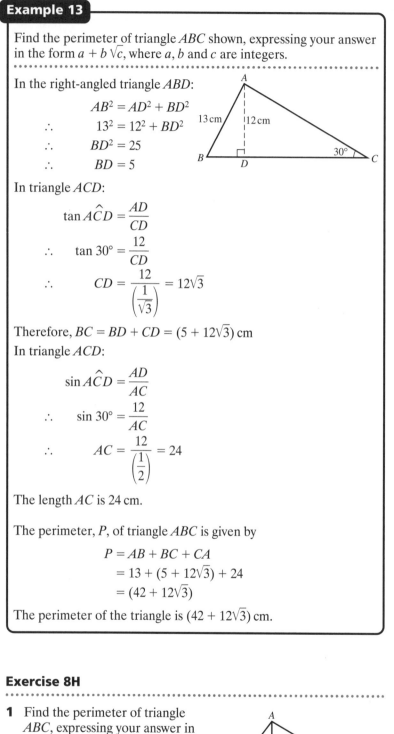

In the right-angled triangle ABD:

$$AB^2 = AD^2 + BD^2$$

$\therefore \qquad 13^2 = 12^2 + BD^2$

$\therefore \qquad BD^2 = 25$

$\therefore \qquad BD = 5$

In triangle ACD:

$$\tan A\hat{C}D = \frac{AD}{CD}$$

$\therefore \qquad \tan 30° = \dfrac{12}{CD}$

$\therefore \qquad CD = \dfrac{12}{\left(\dfrac{1}{\sqrt{3}}\right)} = 12\sqrt{3}$

Therefore, $BC = BD + CD = (5 + 12\sqrt{3})$ cm

In triangle ACD:

$$\sin A\hat{C}D = \frac{AD}{AC}$$

$\therefore \qquad \sin 30° = \dfrac{12}{AC}$

$\therefore \qquad AC = \dfrac{12}{\left(\dfrac{1}{2}\right)} = 24$

The length AC is 24 cm.

The perimeter, P, of triangle ABC is given by

$$P = AB + BC + CA$$
$$= 13 + (5 + 12\sqrt{3}) + 24$$
$$= (42 + 12\sqrt{3})$$

The perimeter of the triangle is $(42 + 12\sqrt{3})$ cm.

> You need to find the lengths BC and AC.

Exercise 8H

1 Find the perimeter of triangle ABC, expressing your answer in the form $a + b\sqrt{3}$ where a and b are integers.

2 Find the perimeter of triangle PQR, expressing your answer in the form $a + b\sqrt{c}$ where a, b and c are integers.

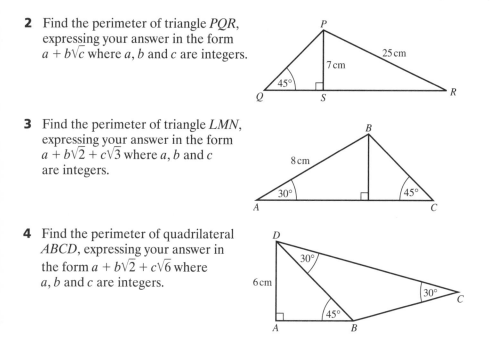

3 Find the perimeter of triangle LMN, expressing your answer in the form $a + b\sqrt{2} + c\sqrt{3}$ where a, b and c are integers.

4 Find the perimeter of quadrilateral $ABCD$, expressing your answer in the form $a + b\sqrt{2} + c\sqrt{6}$ where a, b and c are integers.

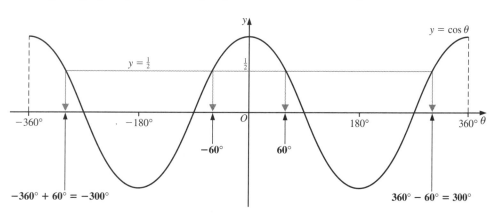

C2

8.7 Trigonometric equations

You will have met trigonometric equations before. For example, $\cos \theta = \frac{1}{2}$ is a trigonometric equation in which the unknown is θ. In this particular case, the acute angle θ which would satisfy this equation is 60°. However, because the cosine graph is periodic, you know there are other solutions to this equation.

> You have met this type of equation when solving triangles.

Drawing the graph of $y = \cos \theta$ and $y = \frac{1}{2}$ on the same set of axes gives:

This shows that in the range $-360° \leqslant \theta \leqslant 360°$ there are actually *four* solutions to the equation $\cos \theta = \frac{1}{2}$. These are $\theta = \pm 60°, \pm 300°$.

If no range for θ is stated, there is an infinite number of solutions to this equation. For this reason, trigonometric equations are usually accompanied by a range for θ.

Example 14

Solve the following equations for θ, where $-360° \leqslant \theta \leqslant 360°$.

a) $\sin \theta = \dfrac{\sqrt{3}}{2}$ b) $\cos \theta = \dfrac{1}{3}$ c) $\tan \theta = -\dfrac{1}{4}$

....

a) Drawing the graphs of $y = \sin \theta$ and $y = \dfrac{\sqrt{3}}{2}$ on the same set of
   axes for $-360° \leqslant \theta \leqslant 360°$ gives:

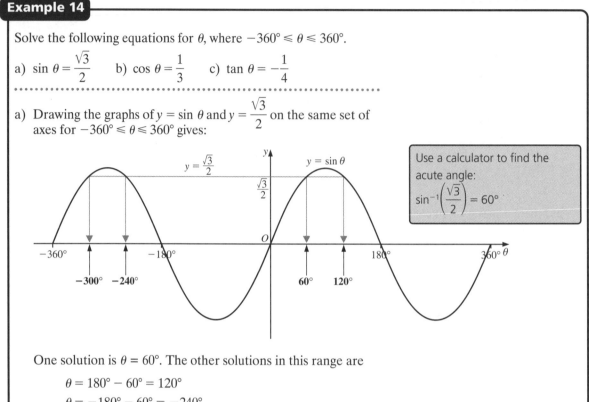

> Use a calculator to find the acute angle:
> $\sin^{-1}\!\left(\dfrac{\sqrt{3}}{2}\right) = 60°$

One solution is $\theta = 60°$. The other solutions in this range are

$$\theta = 180° - 60° = 120°$$
$$\theta = -180° - 60° = -240°$$
$$\theta = -360° + 60° = -300°$$

The solutions are $\theta = 60°$, $120°$, $-240°$ and $-300°$.

b) Drawing the graphs of $y = \cos \theta$ and $y = \frac{1}{3}$ on the same set of
   axes for $-360° \leqslant \theta \leqslant 360°$ gives:

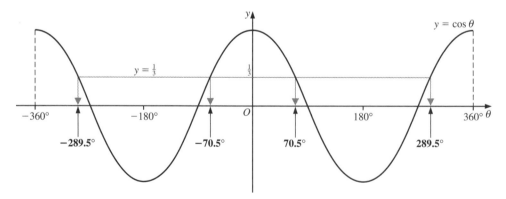

The calculator gives the value of θ as $\cos^{-1}(\frac{1}{3}) = 70.5°$, to one
decimal place. The other positive solution in this range is
$\theta = 360° - 70.5° = 289.5°$. Since the cosine graph is symmetrical
about the y-axis the other solutions in this range are $\theta = -70.5°$
and $\theta = -289.5°$.

Therefore $\theta = \pm 70.5°$, $\pm 289.5°$.

c) Drawing the graphs of $y = \tan \theta$ and $y = -\frac{1}{4}$ on the same set of axes for $-360° \leqslant \theta \leqslant 360°$ gives:

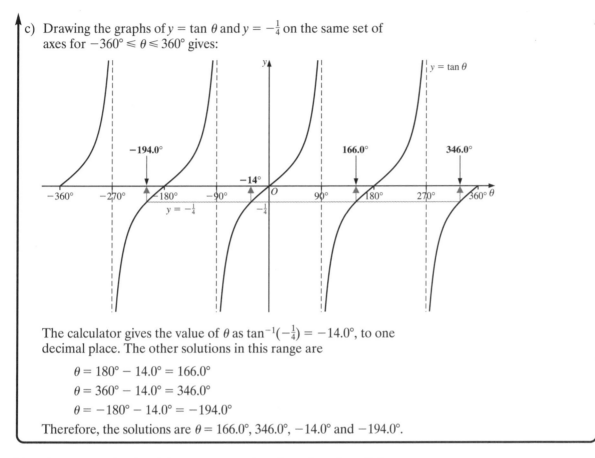

The calculator gives the value of θ as $\tan^{-1}(-\frac{1}{4}) = -14.0°$, to one decimal place. The other solutions in this range are

$$\theta = 180° - 14.0° = 166.0°$$
$$\theta = 360° - 14.0° = 346.0°$$
$$\theta = -180° - 14.0° = -194.0°$$

Therefore, the solutions are $\theta = 166.0°, 346.0°, -14.0°$ and $-194.0°$.

To solve an equation involving a compound angle such as $(\theta + x°)$ it is helpful to change the range.

Example 15

Solve each of these equations for θ, for the given range.

a) $\sin(\theta + 30°) = 0.2, \quad 0° \leqslant \theta \leqslant 360°$

b) $\cos\left(\theta - \dfrac{\pi}{3}\right) = 0.5, \quad 0 \leqslant \theta \leqslant 2\pi$

· ·

a) Changing the range to $\theta + 30°$ gives $30° \leqslant \theta + 30° \leqslant 390°$.

$$\sin(\theta + 30°) = 0.2$$
$$\therefore \quad \theta + 30° = 11.5° \text{ to one decimal place.}$$

This solution is outside the range. The solutions in the range are

$$180° - 11.5° = 168.5° \text{ and } 360° + 11.5° = 371.5°$$

Therefore

$$\theta + 30° = 168.5°, 371.5°$$
$$\therefore \quad \theta = 138.5°, 341.5°$$

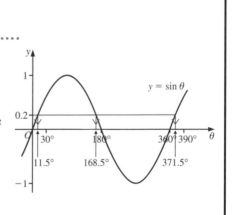

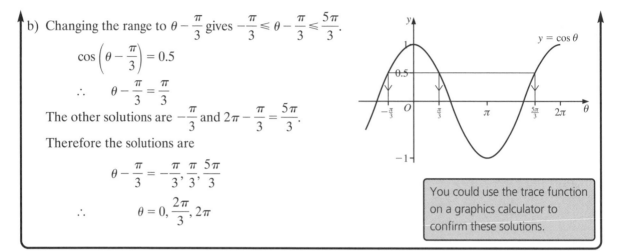

b) Changing the range to $\theta - \dfrac{\pi}{3}$ gives $-\dfrac{\pi}{3} \leqslant \theta - \dfrac{\pi}{3} \leqslant \dfrac{5\pi}{3}$.

$$\cos\left(\theta - \dfrac{\pi}{3}\right) = 0.5$$

$$\therefore \qquad \theta - \dfrac{\pi}{3} = \dfrac{\pi}{3}$$

The other solutions are $-\dfrac{\pi}{3}$ and $2\pi - \dfrac{\pi}{3} = \dfrac{5\pi}{3}$.

Therefore the solutions are

$$\theta - \dfrac{\pi}{3} = -\dfrac{\pi}{3}, \dfrac{\pi}{3}, \dfrac{5\pi}{3}$$

$$\therefore \qquad \theta = 0, \dfrac{2\pi}{3}, 2\pi$$

> You could use the trace function on a graphics calculator to confirm these solutions.

C2

An equation may involve powers of trigonometric functions.

Example 16

Solve each of these equations for θ, where $0 \leqslant \theta \leqslant 2\pi$.

a) $\sin^2 \theta = \dfrac{1}{4}$ b) $\cos^2 \theta = \dfrac{1}{2}$

....

a) $\sin^2 \theta = \dfrac{1}{4}$ $\therefore$ $\sin \theta = \pm\sqrt{\dfrac{1}{4}} = \pm\dfrac{1}{2}$

When $\sin \theta = \dfrac{1}{2}$, one solution is $\theta = \dfrac{\pi}{6}$.

In the range $0 \leqslant \theta \leqslant 2\pi$, the other solution is $\theta = \pi - \dfrac{\pi}{6} = \dfrac{5\pi}{6}$.

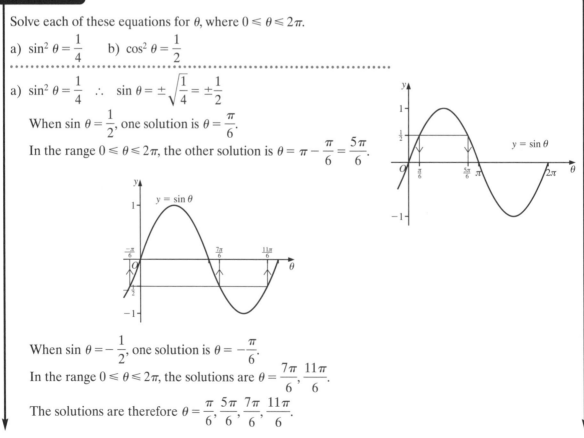

When $\sin \theta = -\dfrac{1}{2}$, one solution is $\theta = -\dfrac{\pi}{6}$.

In the range $0 \leqslant \theta \leqslant 2\pi$, the solutions are $\theta = \dfrac{7\pi}{6}, \dfrac{11\pi}{6}$.

The solutions are therefore $\theta = \dfrac{\pi}{6}, \dfrac{5\pi}{6}, \dfrac{7\pi}{6}, \dfrac{11\pi}{6}$.

b) $\cos^2 \theta = \dfrac{1}{2}$ $\therefore$ $\cos \theta = \pm\sqrt{\dfrac{1}{2}} = \pm\dfrac{1}{\sqrt{2}}$

When $\cos \theta = \dfrac{1}{\sqrt{2}}$, one solution is $\theta = \dfrac{\pi}{4}$.

In the range $0 \le \theta \le 2\pi$, the other solution is $\theta = 2\pi - \dfrac{\pi}{4} = \dfrac{7\pi}{4}$.

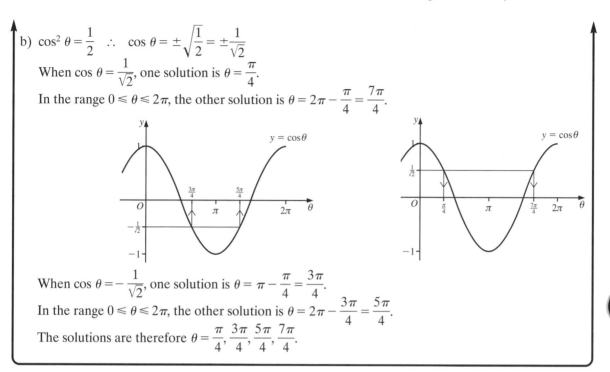

When $\cos \theta = -\dfrac{1}{\sqrt{2}}$, one solution is $\theta = \pi - \dfrac{\pi}{4} = \dfrac{3\pi}{4}$.

In the range $0 \le \theta \le 2\pi$, the other solution is $\theta = 2\pi - \dfrac{3\pi}{4} = \dfrac{5\pi}{4}$.

The solutions are therefore $\theta = \dfrac{\pi}{4}, \dfrac{3\pi}{4}, \dfrac{5\pi}{4}, \dfrac{7\pi}{4}$.

C2

More complicated trigonometric equations can be treated like algebraic equations.

Example 17

Solve each of these equations for θ, where $-180° \le \theta \le 180°$.

a) $\tan^2 \theta - \tan \theta = 0$ b) $2\cos^2 \theta - \cos \theta - 1 = 0$

a) Notice that $\tan^2 \theta - \tan \theta = 0$ is a quadratic equation in $\tan \theta$. Factorising gives:

$$\tan \theta \, (\tan \theta - 1) = 0$$

$\therefore$ $\tan \theta = 0$ or $\tan \theta = 1$

When $\tan \theta = 0$, $\theta = -180°, 0°$ and $180°$ in the required range.

When $\tan \theta = 1$, one solution is $\theta = 45°$. The other solution is $\theta = -180° + 45° = -135°$.

The solutions are $\theta = -180°, -135°, 0°, 45°$ and $180°$.

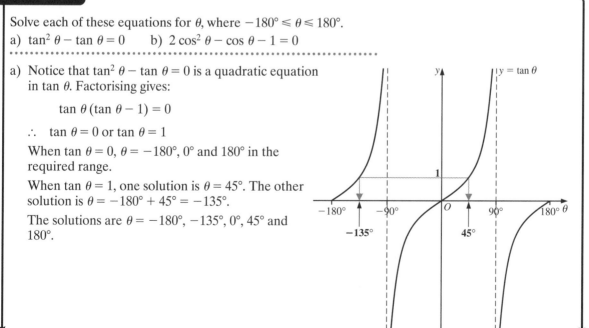

b) Notice that $2\cos^2\theta - \cos\theta - 1 = 0$ is a quadratic equation in $\cos\theta$. Factorising gives:

$$(2\cos\theta + 1)(\cos\theta - 1) = 0$$

$\therefore \quad \cos\theta = -\tfrac{1}{2}$ or $\cos\theta = 1$

When $\cos\theta = -\tfrac{1}{2}$, one solution is $\theta = -120°$. The other solution in the required range is $\theta = 120°$,

When $\cos\theta = 1$, the only solution in the required range is $0°$.

The solutions are $\theta = -120°$, $0°$ and $120°$.

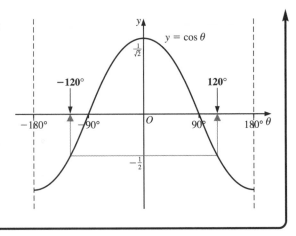

Exercise 8I

1. Solve each of the following equations for $0 \leqslant \theta \leqslant 360°$, giving your answers correct to one decimal place.

   a) $\sin\theta = 0.3$

   b) $\cos\theta = 0.7$

   c) $\tan\theta = 2$

   d) $\cos\theta = -0.5$

   e) $\sin\theta = -0.35$

   f) $\tan\theta = -7$

   g) $\cos\theta = 0.4$

   h) $\sin\theta = -1$

   > When solving a trigonometric equation, ensure that your calculator is in the correct mode – either DEGREES or RADIANS.

2. Solve each of the following equations for $0 \leqslant \theta \leqslant 2\pi$, giving your answers correct to two decimal places.

   a) $\sin\theta = 0.8$

   b) $\cos\theta = 0.2$

   c) $\tan\theta = 3$

   d) $\cos\theta = -0.6$

   e) $\sin\theta = -0.75$

   f) $\tan\theta = -6$

   g) $\cos\theta = 0.9$

   h) $\sin\theta = 0.3$

3. Solve each of the following equations for $0 \leqslant \theta \leqslant 360°$, giving your answers correct to one decimal place.

   a) $\sin(\theta - 40°) = 0.8$

   b) $\cos(\theta + 20°) = 0.2$

   c) $\tan(x - 50°) = 4$

   d) $\sin(\theta - 30°) = -0.7$

   e) $\tan(\theta + 23°) = -8$

   f) $\cos(\theta + 46°) = 0.25$

   g) $\sin(x + 15°) = -0.9$

   h) $\tan(\theta - 76°) = 0.4$

4. Solve each of the following equations for $-\pi \leqslant \theta \leqslant \pi$, giving your answers correct to two decimal places.

   a) $\cos^2\theta = 0.4$

   b) $\tan^2\theta = 9$

   c) $\sin^2\theta = 0.2$

   d) $2\sin^2\theta - \sin\theta = 0$

   e) $3\cos^2\theta = \cos\theta$

   f) $5\sin\theta\cos\theta - \sin\theta = 0$

   g) $\tan^2\theta + 4\tan\theta = 0$

   h) $6\sin^2\theta - 5\sin\theta + 1 = 0$

Multiple angles

The trigonometric equations described so far have involved solving
$\sin\theta = k$, $\cos\theta = k$ or $\tan\theta = k$, for some number k.
Now consider equations that involve 2θ, 3θ, ...

Consider the equation $\sin 2\theta = \frac{1}{2}$, where $-180° \leqslant \theta \leqslant 180°$.

If you solve $\sin x = \frac{1}{2}$ in the range $-180° \leqslant x \leqslant 180°$, you get $x = 30°$
and $x = 150°$.

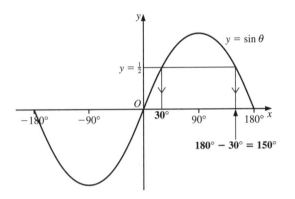

$x = 2\theta$ $\therefore$ $\theta = 15°$ and $\theta = 75°$.

However you have lost two other solutions to the equation
$\sin 2\theta = \frac{1}{2}$: $\theta = -105°$ and $\theta = -165°$. These solutions have been
missed because the range in which you have been working is for θ
and not 2θ.

To completely solve this equation, you must change the range to
match the multiple angle. That is:

$\sin 2\theta = \frac{1}{2}$ $-360° \leqslant 2\theta \leqslant 360°$

Now you have:

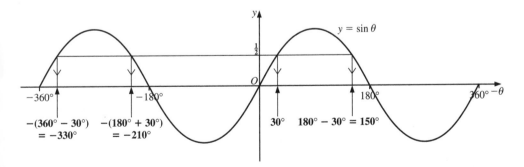

Therefore,

$$2\theta = -330°, -210°, 30° \text{ and } 150°$$
$$\therefore \qquad \theta = -165°, -105°, 15° \text{ and } 75°$$

C2

Example 18

Solve each of these equations in the stated range.
a) $\cos^2 2\theta - 1 = 0$, $-180° \leqslant \theta \leqslant 180°$
b) $\tan(2\theta + 45°) = \sqrt{3}$, $-90° \leqslant \theta \leqslant 90°$

a) Change the range to 2θ ∴ $-360° \leqslant 2\theta \leqslant 360°$.

$$\cos^2 2\theta - 1 = 0$$
$$\cos^2 2\theta = 1$$
$$∴\quad \cos 2\theta = \pm 1$$

When $\cos 2\theta = 1$: $2\theta = -360°, 0°$ and $360°$
                            ∴ $\theta = -180°, 0°$ and $180°$
When $\cos 2\theta = -1$: $2\theta = -180°$ and $180°$
                            ∴ $\theta = -90°$ and $90°$

The solutions are $\theta = -180°, -90°, 0°, 90°$ and $180°$.

> To see this, look at the graph of $\cos\theta$ on page 195.

b) Change the range to $(2\theta + 45°)$:
$$-90° \leqslant \theta \leqslant 90°$$
$$-180° \leqslant 2\theta \leqslant 180°$$
$$-180° + 45° \leqslant 2\theta + 45° \leqslant 180° + 45°$$
$$∴\quad -135° \leqslant 2\theta + 45° \leqslant 225°$$

One solution of $\tan(2\theta + 45°) = \sqrt{3}$ is
$$2\theta + 45° = 60° \quad ∴\quad 2\theta = 15° \quad \text{giving}\quad \theta = 7.5°$$
In the required range, the other solution is
$$2\theta + 45° = -120° \quad ∴\quad 2\theta = -165° \quad \text{giving}\quad \theta = -82.5°$$
The solutions are $\theta = 7.5°$ and $-82.5°$.

> To see this, look at the graph of $\tan\theta$ on page 196.

Standard trigonometric identities

Here are two trigonometric identities that you should learn.

For any angle θ,

✦ $\tan\theta \equiv \dfrac{\sin\theta}{\cos\theta}$

✦ $\sin^2\theta + \cos^2\theta \equiv 1$

> These two identities are very useful in solving trigonometric equations. You should memorise them.

To demonstrate these two results for an acute angle θ, consider the right-angled triangle shown here.

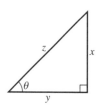

◆ You know that $\sin \theta = \dfrac{x}{z}$ and $\cos \theta = \dfrac{y}{z}$. Therefore,

$$\frac{\sin \theta}{\cos \theta} = \frac{\left(\dfrac{x}{z}\right)}{\left(\dfrac{y}{z}\right)} = \frac{x}{y} = \tan \theta$$

as required.

> You will not be required to prove these results in the C2 examination.

◆ $\sin^2 \theta + \cos^2 \theta = \left(\dfrac{x}{z}\right)^2 + \left(\dfrac{y}{z}\right)^2$

$$= \frac{x^2 + y^2}{z^2}$$

By Pythagoras' theorem, $x^2 + y^2 = z^2$. Therefore,

$$\sin^2 \theta + \cos^2 \theta = \frac{z^2}{z^2} = 1$$

as required.

Further trigonometric equations

To solve trigonometric equations such as

$$2 \sin \theta - \cos \theta = 0 \quad \text{and} \quad 4 \cos^2 \theta + 3 \sin \theta = 4$$

you must reduce them to one or more of the forms $\sin \theta = k$, $\cos \theta = k$ or $\tan \theta = k$ (where k is a constant).

Example 19

Solve $2 \sin \theta - \cos \theta = 0, 0° \leqslant \theta \leqslant 180°$.

$2 \sin \theta - \cos \theta = 0$

∴ $\quad 2 \sin \theta = \cos \theta$

Divide by $\cos \theta$ to obtain

$$2 \frac{\sin \theta}{\cos \theta} = \frac{\cos \theta}{\cos \theta}$$

$$2 \tan \theta = 1$$

∴ $\quad \tan \theta = \frac{1}{2}$

When $\tan \theta = \frac{1}{2}$, $\theta = 26.6°$, in the range $0° \leqslant \theta \leqslant 180°$.

> You divide by $\cos \theta$ because
> $$\tan \theta = \frac{\sin \theta}{\cos \theta}$$

Example 20

Solve the equation $4 \cos^2 \theta + 3 \sin \theta = 4, 0 \leqslant \theta \leqslant 2\pi$.

Notice that if you replace $\cos^2 \theta$ with an expression in terms of $\sin^2 \theta$, the original equation becomes a quadratic in $\sin \theta$.

$$\sin^2 \theta + \cos^2 \theta = 1$$

∴ $\quad \cos^2 \theta = 1 - \sin^2 \theta$

Substituting this into the equation gives

$$4(1 - \sin^2 \theta) + 3 \sin \theta = 4$$

$$4 - 4\sin^2 \theta + 3 \sin \theta = 4$$

$$3 \sin \theta - 4 \sin^2 \theta = 0$$

$$\therefore \quad \sin \theta (3 - 4 \sin \theta) = 0$$

Solving gives $\sin \theta = 0$ or $\sin \theta = \frac{3}{4}$.

When $\sin \theta = 0$, $\theta = 0$, π and 2π in the range $0 \leqslant \theta \leqslant 2\pi$.

When $\sin \theta = \frac{3}{4}$, $\theta = 0.85$ rad to two decimal places. The other solution is $\theta = \pi - 0.85 = 2.29$ rad.

The solutions are $\theta = 0, 0.85, 2.29, \pi, 2\pi$.

> To see this, look at the graph of $\sin \theta$ on page 195.

> Use your calculator in RAD mode.

Exercise 8J

C2

1 Solve each of the following equations for $0 \leqslant \theta \leqslant \pi$, giving your answers correct to two decimal places.

a) $\sin 2\theta = 0.6$

b) $\tan 3\theta = -5$

c) $\cos 2\theta = 0.4$

d) $\sin 3\theta = 0.8$

2 Solve each of the following equations for $0 \leqslant \theta \leqslant 2\pi$, giving your answers in radians correct to one decimal place.

a) $\sin \theta = 3 \cos \theta$

b) $5 \cos \theta = 3 \sin \theta$

c) $\sin \theta + \cos \theta = 0$

d) $2 \cos \theta - 3 \sin \theta = 0$

e) $\sin \theta = 2 \cos \theta$

f) $3 \cos \theta + 5 \sin \theta = 0$

g) $\sin \theta - 5 \cos \theta = 0$

h) $3 \cos \theta = 7 \sin \theta$

3 Solve each of the following equations for $-180° \leqslant \theta \leqslant 180°$, giving your answers correct to one decimal place.

a) $6 \cos^2 \theta - \sin \theta - 5 = 0$

b) $2 \sin^2 \theta + 3 \cos \theta - 3 = 0$

c) $6 \sin^2 \theta = 5 \cos \theta + 7$

d) $4 \cos^2 \theta = 4 \sin \theta - 5$

e) $2 \cos^2 \theta + 3 \sin \theta = 3$

f) $3 \sin^2 \theta + 5 \cos \theta - 1 = 0$

g) $8 \sin^2 \theta = 11 - 10 \cos \theta$

h) $\sin^2 \theta - 2 = 2 \cos^2 \theta - 4 \sin \theta$

4 a) Factorise the expression $6x^3 + 5x^2 - 2x - 1$.

b) Hence solve the equation $6 \sin^3 \theta + 5 \sin^2 \theta - 2 \sin \theta - 1 = 0$, for $-180° \leqslant \theta \leqslant 180°$.

Summary

You should know how to ...	Check out
1 Use the sine rule and cosine rule to find the angles and/or sides of any triangle.	**1 a)** Find the lengths of the sides a and b. **b)** Find the size of the angles $\hat{Q}$ and $\hat{R}$.
2 Find the area of any triangle using the formula $A = \frac{1}{2}ab \sin C$.	**2** Find the areas of the triangles in question 1.
3 Convert between degrees and radians as measures of the size of any angle.	**3 a)** Convert these angles to radians: i) $42°$ ii) $217°$ **b)** Express these angles as multiples of π^c. i) $120°$ ii) $315°$ **c)** Convert to degrees: i) 0.75^c ii) 2.5^c **d)** Express in degrees: i) $\dfrac{\pi^c}{6}$ ii) $\dfrac{7\pi^c}{4}$
4 Find the length of an arc and area of a sector of a circle	**4 a)** i) Find the arc length. ii) Find the area. **b)** i) Find the angle θ. ii) Calculate the area of the sector.

C2

5 Recognise the graphs of the trigonometric functions sin x, cos x and tan x and transformations of these graphs.

5   Give an equation for each of these graphs.

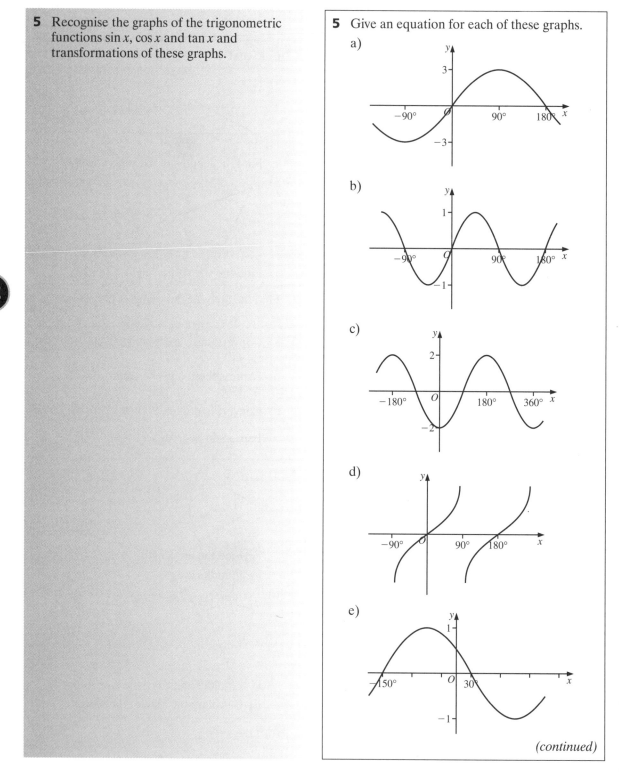

a)

b)

c)

d)

e)

(continued)

C2

5 (*continued*)

f)

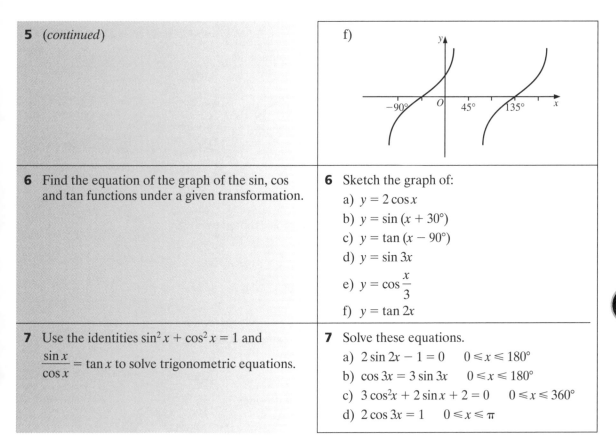

6 Find the equation of the graph of the sin, cos and tan functions under a given transformation.

6 Sketch the graph of:
a) $y = 2\cos x$
b) $y = \sin(x + 30°)$
c) $y = \tan(x - 90°)$
d) $y = \sin 3x$
e) $y = \cos\dfrac{x}{3}$
f) $y = \tan 2x$

C2

7 Use the identities $\sin^2 x + \cos^2 x = 1$ and $\dfrac{\sin x}{\cos x} = \tan x$ to solve trigonometric equations.

7 Solve these equations.
a) $2\sin 2x - 1 = 0$ $0 \leqslant x \leqslant 180°$
b) $\cos 3x = 3\sin 3x$ $0 \leqslant x \leqslant 180°$
c) $3\cos^2 x + 2\sin x + 2 = 0$ $0 \leqslant x \leqslant 360°$
d) $2\cos 3x = 1$ $0 \leqslant x \leqslant \pi$

Revision exercise 8

1 The points A, B and C have coordinates $(3, 2)$, $(4, -1)$ and $(-7, -3)$ respectively.

a) Calculate the lengths of AB, BC and CA in surd form. Deduce that triangle ABC is isosceles and show that $\cos C\hat{A}B = \dfrac{\sqrt{2}}{10}$.

> To remind yourself of the distance between two points, look at page 59.

b) Calculate the area of the triangle ABC and hence, or otherwise, show that the perpendicular from A to BC has length $\dfrac{7}{\sqrt{5}}$.

c) Find the equation of the circle with centre A and which touches the line BC.   (*AQA/AEB, 1996*)

2 The triangle ABC has $AB = 5$ cm, $BC = 3$ cm, $CA = 7$ cm.

a) Use the cosine rule to find the size of angle ABC giving your answer in radians in terms of π.

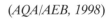

b) The circular sector centre B and radius r cm is removed from the triangle. The area of the sector, shaded in the diagram, is equal to one tenth of the area of the original triangle. Calculate the value of r, giving your answer to three significant figures.   (*AQA/AEB, 1998*)

3 A wire of length 10 cm is cut into two pieces. One of these pieces is bent to form an equilateral triangle of side x cm and the other piece is bent to form a sector of a circle of angle θ radians and radius x cm, as shown.

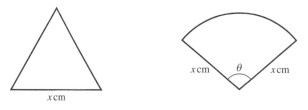

a) Show that $5x + x\theta = 10$.

b) The sum of the area of the triangle and the sector is denoted by A cm².

   i) Show that $A = \dfrac{\sqrt{3}}{4}x^2 - \dfrac{5}{2}x + 5x$

   ii) Find $\dfrac{\mathrm{d}A}{\mathrm{d}x}$ and hence find the value of x for which A has a stationary value.

   iii) Find $\dfrac{\mathrm{d}^2A}{\mathrm{d}x^2}$ and hence determine whether this stationary value is a maximum or a minimum.

   (AQA, 2002)

4 a) The diagram shows an equilateral triangle ABC with sides of length 6 cm and an arc BC of a circle with centre A.

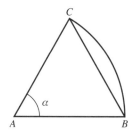

   i) Write down, in radians, the value of the angle α.

   ii) Find the length of the arc BC.

   iii) Show that the area of the triangle ABC is $9\sqrt{3}$ cm².

   iv) Show that the area of the sector ABC is 6π cm².

b) The diagram shows an ornament made from a flat sheet of metal.

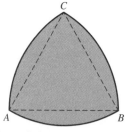

Its boundary consists of three arcs of circles. The straight lines AB, AC and BC are each of length 6 cm. The arcs BC, AC and AB have centres A, B and C respectively.

   i) The boundary of the ornament is decorated with gilt edging. Find the total length of the boundary, giving your answer to the nearest centimetre.

   ii) Find the area of one side of the ornament, giving your answer to the nearest square centimetre.

   (AQA, 2002)

5 The diagram shows a sketch of the graph $y = \cos 2x$ with a line of symmetry L.

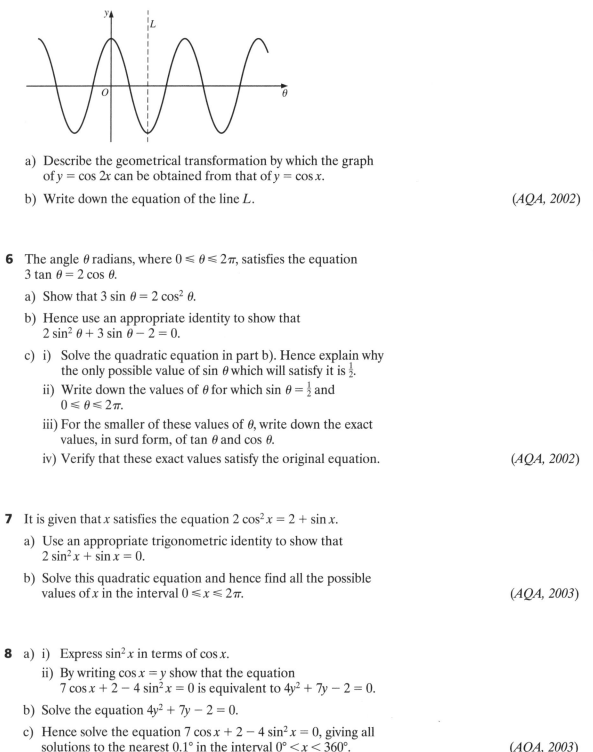

a) Describe the geometrical transformation by which the graph of $y = \cos 2x$ can be obtained from that of $y = \cos x$.

b) Write down the equation of the line L.   *(AQA, 2002)*

C2

6 The angle θ radians, where $0 \leqslant \theta \leqslant 2\pi$, satisfies the equation $3 \tan \theta = 2 \cos \theta$.

a) Show that $3 \sin \theta = 2 \cos^2 \theta$.

b) Hence use an appropriate identity to show that $2 \sin^2 \theta + 3 \sin \theta - 2 = 0$.

c) i) Solve the quadratic equation in part b). Hence explain why the only possible value of $\sin \theta$ which will satisfy it is $\frac{1}{2}$.

ii) Write down the values of θ for which $\sin \theta = \frac{1}{2}$ and $0 \leqslant \theta \leqslant 2\pi$.

iii) For the smaller of these values of θ, write down the exact values, in surd form, of $\tan \theta$ and $\cos \theta$.

iv) Verify that these exact values satisfy the original equation.   *(AQA, 2002)*

7 It is given that x satisfies the equation $2 \cos^2 x = 2 + \sin x$.

a) Use an appropriate trigonometric identity to show that $2 \sin^2 x + \sin x = 0$.

b) Solve this quadratic equation and hence find all the possible values of x in the interval $0 \leqslant x \leqslant 2\pi$.   *(AQA, 2003)*

8 a) i) Express $\sin^2 x$ in terms of $\cos x$.

ii) By writing $\cos x = y$ show that the equation $7 \cos x + 2 - 4 \sin^2 x = 0$ is equivalent to $4y^2 + 7y - 2 = 0$.

b) Solve the equation $4y^2 + 7y - 2 = 0$.

c) Hence solve the equation $7 \cos x + 2 - 4 \sin^2 x = 0$, giving all solutions to the nearest $0.1°$ in the interval $0° < x < 360°$.   *(AQA, 2003)*

9 a) Express the equation $5 \sin 2x - 4 \cos 2x = 0$ in the form $\tan 2x = k$
where k is a constant.

   b) Hence find all solutions of the equation $5 \sin 2x - 4 \cos 2x = 0$
in the interval $0° < x < 180°$ giving your answers to the nearest 0.1°.   *(AQA, 2004)*

10 The area of a sector of a circle of radius 10 cm is 75 cm².
Find the arc length of this sector.   *(AQA, 2003)*

11 The diagram shows a circle with centre O and radius 3 cm. The points
A and B on the circle are such that the angle AOB is 1.5 radians.

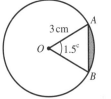

C2

   a) Find the length of the minor arc AB.

   b) Find the the area of the minor sector OAB.

   c) Show the area of the shaded segment is approximately 2.3 cm².   *(AQA, 2001)*

12 The diagram shows a sector A of a circle with centre O and radius
5 cm. OP and OQ are the radii forming part of the boundary
of A, and the angle POQ is 2θ radians.

The tangents to the circle at P and Q intersect at T, and the shaded
region outside the circle is B.

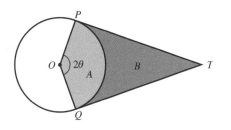

   a) Write down the area of the sector A in terms of θ.

   b) Find the area of the triangle OPT in terms of θ.

   c) Deduce that the area of the region B is $25(\tan \theta - \theta)$ cm².

   d) Given that the regions A and B have equal areas, show that
$\tan \theta - 2\theta = 0$.   *(AQA, 2002)*

13 The diagram shows a square of side 6 cm and a sector of a circle of radius 6 cm and angle θ radians.

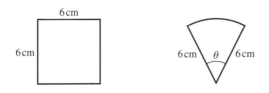

The area of the square is three times the area of the sector.

a) Show that $\theta = \dfrac{2}{3}$.

b) Show that the perimeter of the square is $1\frac{1}{2}$ times the perimeter of the sector.

(AQA, 2002)

14 The acute angle θ radians is such that $\sin \theta = \dfrac{5}{13}$.

a) i) Show that $\cos \theta = \dfrac{12}{13}$.

ii) Find the value of $\tan \theta$, giving your value as a fraction.

b) Use your calculator to find the value of θ, giving your answer to three decimal places.

c) The diagram shows a sector of a circle of radius r cm and angle θ radians. The length of the arc which forms part of the boundary of the sector is 5 cm.

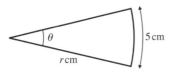

i) Show that $r \approx 12.7$.

ii) Find the area of the sector, giving your answer to the nearest square centimetre.

(AQA, 2003)

15 Solve the equation $\cos(3x - 20°) = -0.2$ giving all solutions to the nearest $0.1°$ in the interval $0° < x < 180°$.

(AQA, 2003)

16 a) Write down the exact values of $\sin \dfrac{\pi}{6}$, $\cos \dfrac{\pi}{6}$ and $\tan \dfrac{\pi}{6}$.

b) It is given that x satisfies the equation $3\sin^2 x = \cos^2 x$

By first using an appropriate trigonometrical identity to simplify this equation, find all the solutions of the equation in the interval $0° \leqslant x \leqslant 2\pi$.

(AQA, 2004)

C2

17 Solve the equation $\cos\left(x + \dfrac{\pi}{6}\right) = -0.5$ in the interval $0 \leqslant x \leqslant 2\pi$ leaving your answer in terms of π.

(AQA, 2002)

18 Solve the equation $\tan 3x = 1$ in the interval $0 \leqslant x \leqslant 2\pi$ leaving your answer in terms of π.

(AQA, 2002)

19 A student models the evening lighting-up time by the equation

$L = 6.125 - 2.25 \cos\left(\dfrac{\pi t}{6}\right)$ where the time, L hours pm, is always

in GMT (Greenwich Mean Time) and t is in months, starting in mid-December. The model assumes that all months are equally long.

a) Calculate the value of L for mid-January and for mid-May.

b) Find, by solving an appropriate equation, the two months in the year when the lighting up time will be 5 pm (GMT).

c) Write down an equation for L if t were to be in months starting in mid-March.

(AQA/NEAB, 1996)

C2

9 Indices and logarithms

This chapter will show you how to

+ Work with negative and fractional indices
+ Find logarithms to any base
+ Use the laws of logarithms to simplify expressions
+ Solve equations of the form $a^x = b$

Before you start

You should know how to ...	Check in
1 Raise numbers to a power.	**1** Find the value of: a) 2^4 b) 6^3 c) 13^0 d) 5^{-1} e) 4^{-2}

2 Use the rules of indices.	**2** a) Write these expressions using a single power.
	    i) $p^2 \times p^5$ ii) $\dfrac{q^5}{q^3}$ iii) $(r^4)^3$ iv) $\dfrac{s^2}{s^3}$
	    b) Simplify as far as possible:
	      i) $2p \times 3p^2 \times 4q$ ii) $\dfrac{12x^3y^2}{3xy}$
	      iii) $\dfrac{6xy^3}{12x^2y}$ iv) $\dfrac{(x^3)^2}{(x^2)^3}$

You should know some basic rules relating to indices.

For positive integers m and n:	For example
1 $x^m \times x^n = x^{m+n}$	$2^3 \times 2^6 = 2^9$
2 $x^m \div x^n = x^{m-n}$	$3^5 \div 3^2 = 3^3$
3 $(x^m)^n = x^{mn}$	$(5^3)^2 = 5^6$

9.1 Negative and fractional indices

You know that $3 \div 3 = 1$. The second law of indices tells you that:

$$3^1 \div 3^1 = 3^0$$
$$\therefore \qquad 3^0 = 1$$

Generally; $\quad x^m \div x^m = x^{m-m} = x^0$

and $\qquad x^m \div x^m = \dfrac{x^m}{x^m} = 1$

so:

$$x^0 = 1 \quad (x \neq 0)$$

You also know that $3^0 \div 3^1 = 1 \div 3 = \frac{1}{3}$. From the second law of indices,

$$3^0 \div 3^1 = 3^{-1}$$
$$\therefore \qquad 3^{-1} = \tfrac{1}{3}$$

Generally:

$$x^{-1} = \frac{1}{x} \quad (x \neq 0)$$

Now

$$(x^{-1})^m = \left(\frac{1}{x}\right)^m = \frac{1}{x^m}$$

and by the third law of indices:

$$(x^{-1})^m = x^{-m}$$

Therefore,

$$x^{-m} = \frac{1}{x^m}$$

By the first law of indices:

$$5^{\frac{1}{2}} \times 5^{\frac{1}{2}} = 5^1 = 5$$

Therefore, $5^{\frac{1}{2}} = \sqrt{5}$.

Similarly,

$$5^{\frac{1}{3}} \times 5^{\frac{1}{3}} \times 5^{\frac{1}{3}} = 5^1$$

Therefore, $5^{\frac{1}{3}} = \sqrt[3]{5}$. Generally,

$$x^{\frac{1}{n}} = \sqrt[n]{x}$$

To interpret $x^{\frac{m}{n}}$ consider

$$x^{\frac{m}{n}} = (x^{\frac{1}{n}})^m \quad \text{or} \quad x^{\frac{m}{n}} = (x^m)^{\frac{1}{n}}$$
$$= (\sqrt[n]{x})^m \qquad\qquad = \sqrt[n]{x^m}$$

Usually we write:

$$x^{\frac{m}{n}} = \sqrt[n]{x^m}$$

Example 1

Without using a calculator, write each of these as a fraction or whole number.

a) 5^{-2} b) $49^{\frac{1}{2}}$ c) $25^{-\frac{1}{2}}$

a) Rewrite this in a form that has no negative indices:

$$5^{-2} = \frac{1}{5^2} = \frac{1}{25}$$

b) You know that $x^{\frac{1}{2}} = \sqrt{x}$, therefore

$$49^{\frac{1}{2}} = \sqrt{49} = 7$$

c) Again, rewrite in a form that has no negative indices:

$$25^{-\frac{1}{2}} = \frac{1}{25^{\frac{1}{2}}} = \frac{1}{\sqrt{25}} = \frac{1}{5}$$

$$x^{-m} = \frac{1}{x^m}$$

Example 2

Without using a calculator, write each of these as a fraction or whole number.

a) $4^{\frac{3}{2}}$ b) $\left(\frac{2}{3}\right)^{-3}$ c) $\left(\frac{1}{8}\right)^{-\frac{4}{3}}$

a) Rewriting $4^{\frac{3}{2}}$ gives

$$4^{\frac{3}{2}} = \left(4^{\frac{1}{2}}\right)^3 = 2^3 = 8$$

b) Again, rewrite in a form which has no negative indices:

$$\left(\frac{2}{3}\right)^{-3} = \frac{1}{\left(\frac{2}{3}\right)^3} = \left(\frac{3}{2}\right)^3 = \frac{27}{8}$$

c) Rewriting gives:

$$\left(\frac{1}{8}\right)^{-\frac{4}{3}} = \frac{1}{\left(\frac{1}{8}\right)^{\frac{4}{3}}} = 8^{\frac{4}{3}} = (\sqrt[3]{8})^4 = 2^4 = 16$$

$$4^{\frac{1}{2}} = \sqrt{4} = 2$$

C2

You should be able to solve equations involving negative and fractional indices.

Example 3

Solve each of these.

a) $x^{\frac{1}{5}} = 3$ b) $x^{\frac{4}{3}} = 81$ c) $x^{\frac{1}{3}} = 4x^{-\frac{1}{3}}$

a) $x^{\frac{1}{5}} = 3$ $\left(x^{\frac{1}{5}}\right)^5 = 3^5$

$$\therefore\ x = 243$$

b) $x^{\frac{4}{3}} = 81$ $\left(x^{\frac{4}{3}}\right)^{\frac{1}{4}} = 81^{\frac{1}{4}}$

$$x^{\frac{1}{3}} = 3$$

$$\left(x^{\frac{1}{3}}\right)^3 = 3^3$$

$$\therefore\ x = 27$$

$$\left(x^{\frac{1}{5}}\right)^5 = x^{\frac{1}{5} \times 5}$$
$$= x^1$$

c) $x^{\frac{1}{3}} = 4x^{-\frac{1}{3}}$ $\qquad$ $x^{\frac{1}{3}} \times x^{\frac{1}{3}} = 4x^{-\frac{1}{3}} \times x^{\frac{1}{3}}$

$$x^{\frac{2}{3}} = 4x^0$$

$$\therefore \quad x^{\frac{2}{3}} = 4$$

So:

$$\left(x^{\frac{2}{3}}\right)^{\frac{1}{2}} = 4^{\frac{1}{2}}$$

$$x^{\frac{1}{3}} = \pm 2$$

$$\left(x^{\frac{1}{3}}\right)^3 = (\pm 2)^3$$

$$\therefore \qquad x = (\pm 2)^3$$

Now $2^3 = 8$ and $(-2)^3 = -8$. The solutions are $x = \pm 8$.

> Multiply throughout by $x^{\frac{1}{3}}$ to make all the indices positive.

> $\left(x^{\frac{2}{3}}\right)^{\frac{1}{2}} = x^{\frac{2}{3} \times \frac{1}{2}}$
> $= x^{\frac{1}{3}}$

Exercise 9A

1 Simplify each of these.
   a) $x^5 \times x^4$ $\qquad\qquad$ b) $p^3 \times p^{-1}$
   c) $(3k^3)^2$ $\qquad\qquad$ d) $y^{\frac{1}{2}} \times y^{\frac{1}{3}}$
   e) $c^7 \div c^3$ $\qquad\qquad$ f) $9h^2 \div 6h^{-4}$
   g) $(4d^2)^2 \div (2d)^3$ $\qquad\quad$ h) $(6p^{-3})^4 \div (9p^{-4})^2$

2 Evaluate each of these.
   a) $4^{\frac{1}{2}}$ $\qquad$ b) $27^{\frac{1}{3}}$ $\qquad$ c) $9^{\frac{3}{2}}$ $\qquad$ d) $8^{\frac{5}{3}}$
   e) $125^{\frac{2}{3}}$ $\qquad$ f) $49^{\frac{3}{2}}$ $\qquad$ g) $\left(\frac{1}{25}\right)^{\frac{1}{2}}$ $\qquad$ h) $\left(\frac{8}{27}\right)^{\frac{2}{3}}$

3 Evaluate each of these.
   a) 7^{-1} $\qquad$ b) 3^{-2} $\qquad$ c) $4^{-\frac{1}{2}}$ $\qquad$ d) $25^{-\frac{3}{2}}$
   e) $\left(\frac{2}{3}\right)^{-1}$ $\qquad$ f) $27^{-\frac{2}{3}}$ $\qquad$ g) $\left(\frac{9}{4}\right)^{-\frac{1}{2}}$ $\qquad$ h) $\left(\frac{125}{8}\right)^{-\frac{1}{3}}$

4 Solve each of these equations for x.
   a) $3x^3 = 375$ $\qquad\qquad$ b) $98x^2 = 2$
   c) $x^3 + 343 = 0$ $\qquad\quad$ d) $9x^{-1} = 5$
   e) $x^{-3} = 8$ $\qquad\qquad$ f) $x^{-2} = 25$
   g) $x^{-6} - 64 = 0$ $\qquad\quad$ h) $25x^{-2} = 9$

5 Solve each of these equations for x.
   a) $x^{\frac{1}{2}} = 3$ $\qquad\qquad$ b) $x^{\frac{1}{5}} = 2$
   c) $7x^{\frac{1}{2}} + 2 = 0$ $\qquad\quad$ d) $x^{-\frac{1}{4}} = 4$
   e) $4x^{\frac{1}{2}} = x^{-\frac{3}{2}}$ $\qquad\quad$ f) $5x^{\frac{2}{3}} = x^{-\frac{1}{3}}$
   g) $7x^{\frac{1}{6}} = x^{-\frac{5}{6}}$ $\qquad\quad$ h) $9x^{\frac{2}{3}} - 4x^{-\frac{4}{3}} = 0$

6 Solve each of these equations for x.
   a) $x^{\frac{2}{3}} = 9$ $\qquad\qquad$ b) $x^{\frac{3}{2}} = 64$
   c) $5x^{\frac{3}{4}} + 40 = 0$ $\qquad\quad$ d) $x^{-\frac{2}{3}} = 81$
   e) $x^{-\frac{1}{2}} = 5$ $\qquad\qquad$ f) $x^{\frac{3}{4}} = 27$
   g) $6x^{\frac{1}{3}} + 1 = 0$ $\qquad\quad$ h) $x^{\frac{3}{5}} + 8 = 0$

7 Solve these equations for x.
   a) $x^{\frac{2}{3}} - x^{\frac{1}{3}} - 2 = 0$ $\qquad\quad$ b) $2x^{\frac{1}{4}} = 9 - 4x^{-\frac{1}{4}}$

9.2 Logarithms

A **logarithm** (log for short) is an index. To see this, consider the result

$$10^2 = 100$$

You can write this using log notation as

$$\log_{10} 100 = 2$$

The number 10 is called the **base** of the logarithm. Similarly,

logarithm   number   number

$$2^3 = 8 \text{ can be written as } \log_2 8 = 3 \text{ —logarithm}$$

base   base

In this case the base is 2.

Generally,

$x = m^n$ is written as $\log_m x = n$

A special case occurs when $n = \log_m m$. In this case you have to find the value of n such that

$$m^n = m$$

It is clear that $n = 1$. Therefore $\log_m m = 1$. In other words, the log of any number to the same base equals 1.

Example 4

Write each of these equations using logarithm notation.

a) $5^2 = 25$ b) $6^3 = 216$

a) Using the general form gives

$$\log_5 25 = 2$$

b) Using the general form gives

$$\log_6 216 = 3$$

Example 5

Write $\log_8 64 = 2$ in the form $a^b = c$. Hence find $\log_2 64$.

Using index notation gives

$$8^2 = 64, \text{ which is in the required form.}$$

Writing $8 = 2^3$ gives

$$(2^3)^2 = 64$$
$$\therefore \quad 2^6 = 64$$

Using the general form to re-write this gives

$$\log_2 64 = 6$$

Laws of logarithms

You should learn these three laws of logarithms:

1 $\log ab = \log a + \log b$

2 $\log\left(\dfrac{a}{b}\right) = \log a - \log b$

3 $\log a^n = n\log a$

> These three results are true for any base. If you are using logs to the same base then you usually leave the base out and simply write $\log x$.

To prove these laws, let $x = \log_m a$ and $y = \log_m b$. Then

$$m^x = a \text{ and } m^y = b \qquad [1]$$

1) From [1]:

$$ab = m^x m^y = m^{x+y}$$

and by definition of log,

$$\log_m(ab) = x + y$$
$$= \log_m a + \log_m b$$

as required.

2) Using [1] again,

$$\frac{a}{b} = \frac{m^x}{m^y} = m^{x-y}$$

$$\therefore \quad \log_m\left(\frac{a}{b}\right) = x - y$$
$$= \log_m a - \log_m b$$

as required.

> You will not be required to prove the laws of logarithms in your C2 examination.

3) Using [1] again,

$$a^n = (m^x)^n = m^{xn}$$
$$\therefore \quad \log_m a^n = xn$$
$$= n\log_m a$$

as required.

Example 6

Evaluate each of these

a) $\log_3 81$ b) $\log_5\left(\frac{1}{25}\right)$

a) Writing $81 = 3^4$ gives

$$\log_3 81 = \log_3 3^4$$
$$= 4\log_3 3$$
$$= 4 \times 1$$
$$\therefore \quad \log_3 81 = 4$$

> Using $\log a^n = n\log a$

> Using $\log_m m = 1$

b) Writing $\frac{1}{25} = 25^{-1} = (5^2)^{-1} = 5^{-2}$ gives

$$\log_5\left(\frac{1}{25}\right) = \log_5 5^{-2}$$
$$= -2\log_5 5$$
$$= -2 \times 1$$
$$\therefore \quad \log_5\left(\frac{1}{25}\right) = -2$$

> Using $\log a^n = n\log a$

> Using $\log_m m = 1$

You can use the rules to combine logarithms into a single logarithm.

Example 7

Express each of these as a single logarithm.
a) $\log 3 + \log 5$ b) $\log 27 - \log 9$
c) $3 \log 2 + \log 4 - \log 8$ d) $2 \log x - 3 \log y + 2 \log xy$

a) $\log 3 + \log 5 = \log(3 \times 5)$
$\qquad = \log 15$

b) $\log 27 - \log 9 = \log\left(\dfrac{27}{9}\right)$
$\qquad = \log 3$

c) Notice that $3 \log 2 = \log 2^3 = \log 8$. Therefore:
$\quad 3 \log 2 + \log 4 - \log 8 = \log 8 + \log 4 - \log 8$
$\qquad\qquad\qquad = \log 4$

d) $2 \log x = \log x^2$, $3 \log y = \log y^3$ and $2 \log xy = \log(xy)^2$
Therefore:
$\quad 2 \log x - 3 \log y + 2 \log xy = \log x^2 - \log y^3 + \log(xy)^2$
$\qquad\qquad\qquad = \log\left(\dfrac{x^2}{y^3}\right) + \log(xy)^2$
$\qquad\qquad\qquad = \log\left(\dfrac{x^2}{y^3} \times x^2y^2\right)$
$\qquad\qquad\qquad = \log\left(\dfrac{x^4}{y}\right)$

Using $\log ab = \log a + \log b$

Using $\log\left(\dfrac{a}{b}\right) = \log a - \log b$

Using $\log a^n = n \log a$

You may be asked to expand a logarithm.

Example 8

Express each of these in terms of $\log a$, $\log b$, $\log c$.
a) $\log\left(\dfrac{1}{a^2}\right)$
b) $\log\left(\dfrac{ab}{c}\right)$
c) $\log\sqrt{\dfrac{a}{bc^2}}$

a) $\log\left(\dfrac{1}{a^2}\right) = \log a^{-2}$
$\qquad = -2 \log a$
b) $\log\left(\dfrac{ab}{c}\right) = \log(ab) - \log c$
$\qquad = \log a + \log b - \log c$

Using $\log a^n = n \log a$

Using $\log\left(\dfrac{a}{b}\right) = \log a - \log b$
and $\log ab = \log a + \log b$

c)
$$\log \sqrt{\frac{a}{bc^2}} = \log\left(\frac{a}{bc^2}\right)^{\frac{1}{2}}$$
$$= \frac{1}{2}\log\left(\frac{a}{bc^2}\right)$$
$$= \frac{1}{2}(\log a - \log bc^2)$$
$$= \frac{1}{2}[(\log a - (\log b + 2\log c)]$$
$$\therefore \quad \log\sqrt{\frac{a}{bc^2}} = \frac{1}{2}(\log a - \log b - 2\log c)$$

Exercise 9B

1 Write each of these in terms of logarithms.

a) $2^5 = 32$ b) $3^4 = 81$ c) $4^{-2} = \frac{1}{16}$

d) $9^3 = 729$ e) $6^2 = 36$ f) $7^{-3} = \frac{1}{343}$

g) $12^0 = 1$ h) $10^6 = 1\,000\,000$ i) $2^{-9} = \frac{1}{512}$

j) $16^{\frac{1}{2}} = 4$ k) $1000^{\frac{1}{3}} = 10$ l) $\left(\frac{1}{2}\right)^3 = \frac{1}{8}$

2 Evaluate each of these logarithms.

a) $\log_3 27$ b) $\log_2 32$ c) $\log_{10} 100$

d) $\log_5 125$ e) $\log_4 4$ f) $\log_7 49$

g) $\log_3\left(\frac{1}{9}\right)$ h) $\log_4\left(\frac{1}{256}\right)$ i) $\log_{10}(0.0001)$

j) $\log_6 1$ k) $\log_2 1024$ l) $\log_3\left(\frac{1}{243}\right)$

3 Express each of these in terms of $\log a$ and $\log b$.

a) $\log(ab)$ b) $\log\left(\frac{a}{b}\right)$ c) $\log(a^2b)$

d) $\log(\sqrt{a})$ e) $\log\left(\frac{1}{a^2}\right)$ f) $\log(a\sqrt{b})$

g) $\log\left(\frac{a^3}{b}\right)$ h) $\log\left(\frac{a^2}{b^3}\right)$ i) $\log\left(\sqrt{\frac{a}{b}}\right)$

j) $\log\left(\frac{1}{ab^4}\right)$ k) $\log\left(\frac{1}{\sqrt{ab}}\right)$ l) $\log(\sqrt[6]{a^2b})$

4 Express each of the following as a single logarithm.

a) $\log 3 + \log 4$ b) $\log 2 + \log 7$

c) $\log 15 - \log 3$ d) $\log 24 - \log 4$

e) $\log 2 + \log 3 + \log 5$ f) $\log 6 + \log 3 - \log 9$

g) $2\log 3 + \log 4 - \log 12$ h) $3\log 2 + 2\log 5 - \log 20$

i) $\frac{1}{2}\log 80 - \frac{1}{2}\log 5$ j) $\log 15 - \frac{1}{2}\log 9$

k) $2\log a - \log b - \log c$ l) $\log a + \frac{1}{2}\log b - 3\log c$

5 Given x and y are both positive, solve the simultaneous equations

$$\log(xy) = 7 \quad \log\left(\frac{x}{y}\right) = 1$$

9.3 Using logarithms to solve equations

You can use logarithms to solve equations where x appears in the power.

Consider the equation $y = a^x$.

Take logarithms of both sides:

$$\log_a y = \log_a a^x$$
$$\log_a y = x \log_a a$$
$$\therefore \qquad \log_a y = x$$

This key point relates indices and logarithms:

$$y = a^x \iff x = \log_a y$$

> Taking logarithms of both sides is a useful technique for solving some equations.

> The symbol $\iff$ means that both statements imply each other.

Example 9

Solve these equations for x.

a) $3^x = 10$ b) $5^{2x} = 8$ c) $2^{-3x} = 5$

a)
$$3^x = 10$$
$$\log 3^x = \log 10$$
$$x \log 3 = \log 10$$
$$\therefore \qquad x = \frac{\log 10}{\log 3} = 2.10$$

b)
$$5^{2x} = 8$$
$$\log 5^{2x} = \log 8$$
$$2x \log 5 = \log 8$$
$$\therefore \qquad x = \frac{\log 8}{2 \log 5} = 0.65$$

c)
$$2^{-3x} = 5$$
$$\log 2^{-3x} = \log 5$$
$$-3x \log 2 = \log 5$$
$$\therefore \qquad x = \frac{\log 5}{-3 \log 2} = -0.77$$

> Your calculator will probably allow you to calculate logs either to base 10 or to a base known as e. Both will lead to the same solution.
> Using base 10,
> $$\frac{\log 10}{\log 3} = \frac{1}{0.4771} = 2.0959$$
> Using base e,
> $$\frac{\log 10}{\log 3} = \frac{2.3026}{1.0986} = 2.0959$$

If the unknown, x, appears on both sides of the equation, you should rearrange it to get x on the LHS only.

Example 10

Solve the equation $5 \times 2^x = 3 \times 7^x$ for x.

$$5 \times 2^x = 3 \times 7^x$$
$$\log(5 \times 2^x) = \log(3 \times 7^x)$$
$$\log 5 + \log 2^x = \log 3 + \log 7^x$$
$$\log 5 + x \log 2 = \log 3 + x \log 7$$
$$x \log 2 - x \log 7 = \log 3 - \log 5$$
$$x(\log 2 - \log 7) = \log 3 - \log 5$$
$$\therefore \qquad x = \frac{\log 3 - \log 5}{\log 2 - \log 7} = 0.41, \text{ to 2 decimal places}$$

> $\log ab = \log a + \log b$

> $\log a^n = n \log a$

Exercise 9C

Throughout this exercise answers should be given correct to two decimal places.

1 Solve these equations for x.

a) $2^x = 5$ b) $3^x = 7$

c) $9^x = 28$ d) $12^x = 5$

e) $4^x = 212$ f) $5^x = 63$

g) $7^x = 4$ h) $19^x = 2$

2 Solve these equations for x.

a) $4^{2x} = 9$ b) $5^{3x} = 29$

c) $3^{5x} = 40$ d) $2^{x+1} = 15$

e) $6^{x-2} = 4$ f) $9^{x+3} = 78$

g) $2^{3x-2} = 53$ h) $5^{2x+1} = 10$

3 Solve these equations for x.

a) $3 \times 2^x = 7$ b) $5 \times 3^x = 2$

c) $7 \times 4^x = 20$ d) $9 \times 5^x = 4$

4 Solve these equations for x.

a) $2^{x-1} = 3^{x+1}$ b) $5^{x-2} = 2^{x+3}$

c) $3^{2x-1} = 5^x$ d) $6^{1-x} = 2^{3x+1}$

5 a) Factorise the quadratic expression $2u^2 - 11u + 5$.

    b) Hence solve the equation $2 \times 2^{2x} - 11 \times 2^x + 5 = 0$.

9.4 Graph of $y = a^x$

Consider the function $y = 2^x$.

The table shows a selection of values for this function.

x	-3	-2	-1	0	1	2	3
$y = 2^x$	$\frac{1}{8}$	$\frac{1}{4}$	$\frac{1}{2}$	1	2	4	8

$$2^{-3} = \frac{1}{2^3} = \frac{1}{8}$$

Note that as x increases by 1, the value of the function doubles.

Using the table, you can sketch the graph of $y = 2^x$.

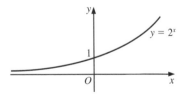

$y = 2^x$ is an example of an exponential function.

The value of y is doubling for each unit increase in x. Note that y is positive for all values of x.

A function of the form $y = a^x$ is called an exponential function.

Now consider the function $y = \left(\dfrac{1}{2}\right)^x$, or $y = 2^{-x}$

First compile a table of values:

x	-3	-2	-1	0	1	2	3
$y = 2^{-x}$	8	4	2	1	$\frac{1}{2}$	$\frac{1}{4}$	$\frac{1}{8}$

Note that as x increases by 1, the value of the function halves.

Here is the graph of $y = 2^{-x}$, with $y = 2^x$ for comparison.

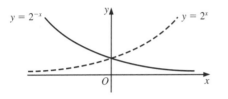

Generally, for a function $y = a^x$, the graph takes one of two forms.

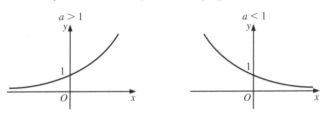

In both cases, the y-intercept is 1 and the x-axis is an asymptote.

> $\left(\dfrac{1}{2}\right)^x = (2^{-1})^x = 2^{-x}$

> $2^{-(-3)} = 2^3 = 8$

> You can obtain the graph of $y = 2^{-x}$ by reflecting the graph of $y = 2^x$ in the y-axis.

C2

> You may like to consider what happens when $a = 1$.

Exercise 9D

1 Use a table of values or a graphics calculator to sketch the functions:

a) $y = 3^x$ b) $y = 4^x$ c) $y = 5^x$

Describe any patterns that you notice.

2 Use a table of values or a graphics calculator to sketch the functions:

a) $y = \left(\dfrac{1}{3}\right)^x$ b) $y = \left(\dfrac{1}{4}\right)^x$ c) $y = \left(\dfrac{1}{5}\right)^x$

Describe any patterns that you notice.

Summary

You should know how to ...	Check out
1 Simplify expressions involving indices that are rational numbers.	**1** a) Write as a power of 3: i) $9\sqrt{3}$ ii) $\frac{1}{27}$ b) Write as a power of 2: i) $\frac{\sqrt{2}}{8}$ ii) $\frac{4}{\sqrt{2}}$ c) Write as a fraction: i) $64^{-\frac{1}{3}}$ ii) $\frac{8^2 \times 8^{-3}}{2^3}$
2 Find the value of a logarithm to any base.	**2** Find the value of: a) $\log_3 81$ b) $\log_5 \frac{1}{125}$ c) $\log_{10} 0.001$
3 Use the laws of logarithms to simplify logarithmic expressions.	**3** Express as a single logarithm: a) $\log_a 3 + \log_a 4 - 21 \log_a 6$ b) $2\log_2 4 + \log_4 8 - \frac{1}{2}\log_2 16$
4 Recognise the graph of the exponential function $y = a^x$	**4** Sketch the graph of: a) $y = 3^x$ b) $y = 0.5^x$
5 Solve equations of the form $a^x = b$.	**5** Solve: a) $5^x = 100$ b) $4 \times 3^x - 2 = 0$

Revision exercise 9

1 a) Express each of the following as a power of 3.

   i) $\sqrt{3}$ ii) $\frac{3^x}{\sqrt{3}}$

   b) Hence, or otherwise, solve the equation $\frac{3^x}{\sqrt{3}} = \frac{1}{3}$. *(AQA, 2003)*

2 It is given that $p = 8^{\frac{1}{2}}$ and $q = 4^{\frac{3}{4}}$.

   a) Show that $p = 2^{\frac{3}{2}}$.

   b) Similarly express q as a power of 2.

   c) Hence express pq as a power of 2. *(AQA, 2003)*

3 In a light rain shower, the proportion P of the area of a pavement that remains dry t seconds after the rain starts is given by $P = 0.98^t$.

   a) Express t in terms of P.

   b) Find how long it will take before only 10% of the pavement remains dry. Give your answer to the nearest second. *(AQA/NEAB, 1996)*

4 The value, £I, of an investment in a fixed rate savings scheme after t years is given by

$$I = 2000 \times 1.055^t$$

Find the value of t when the value of the investment reaches £2500. Give your answer to 3 significant figures.   *(AQA/NEAB, 2000)*

5 A formula connecting the brightness, B, of a star and its magnitude, M, is

$$B = 0.3981^{(M-1)}$$

Obtain a formula for the magnitude, M, of a star in terms of its brightness, B.   *(AQA/NEAB, 1999)*

6 Write $\log x^3 + \log xy - \log y^2$ as a single term.
Hence obtain an expression for y in terms of x if
$\log x^3 + \log xy - \log y^2 = 0$.   *(AQA/NEAB, 1996)*

C2

7 a) Write down the value of $\log_2 8$.

b) Express $\log_2 9$ in the form $n \log_2 3$.

c) Hence show that $\log_2 72 = m + n \log_2 3$, where m and n are integers.   *(AQA, 2002)*

8 a) Given that $\log_a x = \log_a 5 + 2 \log_a 3$ where a is a positive constant, show that $x = 45$.

b) i) Write down the value of $\log_2 2$.
   ii) Given that $\log_2 y = \log_4 2$ find the value of y.   *(AQA, 2002)*

9 a) Given that $\log_a x = 2(\log_a k - \log_a 2)$ where a is a positive constant, show that

$$k^2 = 4x$$

b) Given that $\log_3 y = \log_9 27$ find the value of y.   *(AQA, 2003)*

10 a) Explain briefly why $\log_5 125 = 3$.

b) Find the value of   i) $\log_5 (125^2)$ ii) $\log_5 \sqrt{125}$ iii) $\log_5 \left(\dfrac{1}{\sqrt{125}} \right)$

c) Solve the equation $\log_5 (125x) = 4$.   *(AQA, 2003)*

11 The third term of a geometric series is 81 and the sixth term is 24.

a) Show that the common ratio of the series is $\frac{2}{3}$.

b) i) The first term of the series is a. Show that $\log a = 6 \log 3 - 2 \log 2$
   ii) The hundredth term of the series is u. Write down an expression for u and hence show that

$$\log u = p \log 2 - q \log 3,$$

where p and q are positive integers to be found.   *(AQA, 2003)*

12 Write $\log(6x) - \frac{1}{2}\log\left(\frac{x^2}{16}\right)$ in the form $\log a$, stating the value of the constant a.

(AQA/NEAB, 2001)

13 The value of an investment £I, after t years with a fixed annual interest rate of 4% is given by

$$I = 4000 \times 1.04^t$$

Find how many complete years it takes for the investment to be worth at least £15 000.

(AQA/NEAB, 1998)

14 According to a report, the number of mobile phones in use in the UK increased from approximately 44 000 in 1985 to 9 million in 1998.

a) Show that the average annual growth factor from 1985 to 1998 was approximately 1.506.

b) Hence write down an expression for the number of mobile phones in use in the UK t years after 1985 and estimate when the number of mobile phones in use in the UK first reached 1 million.

(AQA/NEAB, 1999)

C2

10 Further differentiation

This chapter will show you how to

- Differentiate $y = ax^n$ for any rational number n
- Differentiate sums and differences of functions
- Extend the work you did in Chapter 4

Before you start

C2

You should know how to ...	Check in
1 Find the gradient of a curve at a given point.	**1** For the following functions, find $\dfrac{dy}{dx}$ and the gradient at the given value of x. a) $y = 3x^2 - 2$; $x = 1$ b) $y = x^3 - 4x$; $x = -1$ c) $y = 2x^3 + 3x^2$; $x = 2$
2 Find the derivative of a polynomial function.	**2** For the following functions, find the value of the derivative indicated. a) $f(x) = 5 + 2x - x^2$; $f'(3)$ b) $f(x) = x - x^3$; $f'(-2)$
3 Find the second derivative and use it to determine the nature of a stationary point on a curve.	**3** For the curves given in question 1, find the coordinates of the stationary points and use the second derivative to identify the stationary points as maxima or minima.
4 Use the first derivative to determine if a function is increasing or decreasing.	**4** For the curves and functions given in questions 1 and 2, determine whether the function is increasing or decreasing at the given value of x.
5 Manipulate algebraic expressions with indices. and fractions.	**5** Write the following as a single power of x. a) $\dfrac{x^2}{\sqrt{x}}$ b) $x^3\sqrt{x}$ c) $x(x^{\frac{1}{3}})^4$ d) $\dfrac{\sqrt[4]{x}}{x^2}$ Write the following algebraic functions as the sum or differences of two fractions, simplifying as far as possible. e) $\dfrac{x^3 - x^2}{x^5}$ f) $\dfrac{x\sqrt{x} + x}{x^2}$ g) $\dfrac{\sqrt[3]{x} - \sqrt{x}}{x}$
You should also be familiar with the content of Chapter 4.	

In Chapter 4 you learned that if $y = ax^n$ then $\dfrac{dy}{dx} = anx^{n-1}$, where n is a positive integer. In fact, this is true for all rational numbers n.

Example 1

Find $\dfrac{dy}{dx}$ for each of these.

a) $y = x^3$ b) $y = 6x^4$ c) $y = \dfrac{1}{x^5}$

d) $y = \dfrac{3}{4x^2}$ e) $y = x^{\frac{1}{3}}$ f) $y = \dfrac{1}{x\sqrt{x}}$

a) When $y = x^3$,
$$\dfrac{dy}{dx} = 3x^{3-1}$$
$$\therefore \dfrac{dy}{dx} = 3x^2$$

b) When $y = 6x^4$,
$$\dfrac{dy}{dx} = 6 \times (4x^{4-1})$$
$$\therefore \dfrac{dy}{dx} = 24x^3$$

c) When $y = \dfrac{1}{x^5} = x^{-5}$,
$$\dfrac{dy}{dx} = -5x^{-5-1}$$
$$= -5x^{-6}$$
$$\therefore \dfrac{dy}{dx} = -\dfrac{5}{x^6}$$

d) When $y = \dfrac{3}{4x^2} = \dfrac{3}{4}x^{-2}$,
$$\dfrac{dy}{dx} = \dfrac{3}{4} \times -2x^{-2-1}$$
$$= -\dfrac{3}{2}x^{-3}$$
$$\therefore \dfrac{dy}{dx} = -\dfrac{3}{2x^3}$$

e) When $y = x^{\frac{1}{3}}$,
$$\dfrac{dy}{dx} = \dfrac{1}{3}x^{\frac{1}{3}-1}$$
$$\therefore \dfrac{dy}{dx} = \dfrac{1}{3}x^{-\frac{2}{3}}$$
$$= \dfrac{1}{3x^{\frac{2}{3}}}$$

f) When $y = \dfrac{1}{x\sqrt{x}} = \dfrac{1}{x^{\frac{3}{2}}} = x^{-\frac{3}{2}}$,
$$\dfrac{dy}{dx} = -\dfrac{3}{2}x^{-\frac{3}{2}-1}$$
$$= -\dfrac{3}{2}x^{-\frac{5}{2}}$$
$$\therefore \dfrac{dy}{dx} = -\dfrac{3}{2x^{\frac{5}{2}}}\left(= -\dfrac{3}{2\sqrt{x^5}}\right)$$

10.1 Sum or difference of two functions

When y is made up of more than one function, to find the first derivative you differentiate each function in turn.

$$y = f(x) \pm g(x) \quad \therefore \quad \dfrac{dy}{dx} = f'(x) \pm g'(x)$$

This applies to the sum or difference of any number of functions.

Example 2

Find $f'(x)$ for each of these functions.

a) $f(x) = 4x^2 + 1$ b) $f(x) = 2x^3 + \sqrt{x}$ c) $f(x) = x + \dfrac{1}{x}$

d) $f(x) = x^2 + 6x^{\frac{1}{3}} - 3$ e) $f(x) = \dfrac{2}{\sqrt{x}} + \dfrac{3}{x^2} - 1$

....

a) When $f(x) = 4x^2 + 1$,

$\qquad f'(x) = 8x$

b) When $f(x) = 2x^3 + \sqrt{x} = 2x^3 + x^{\frac{1}{2}}$,

$\qquad\qquad f'(x) = 6x^2 + \dfrac{1}{2}x^{-\frac{1}{2}}$

$\qquad\qquad\qquad = 6x^2 + \dfrac{1}{2x^{\frac{1}{2}}}$

$\qquad \therefore\quad f'(x) = 6x^2 + \dfrac{1}{2\sqrt{x}}$

c) When $f(x) = x + \dfrac{1}{x} = x + x^{-1}$,

$\qquad\qquad f'(x) = 1 - x^{-2}$

$\qquad \therefore\quad f'(x) = 1 - \dfrac{1}{x^2}$

d) When $f(x) = x^2 + 6x^{\frac{1}{3}} - 3$,

$\qquad\qquad f'(x) = 2x + 2x^{-\frac{2}{3}}$

$\qquad\qquad\qquad = 2x + \dfrac{2}{\sqrt[3]{x^2}}$

e) When $f(x) = \dfrac{2}{\sqrt{x}} + \dfrac{3}{x^2} - 1 = 2x^{-\frac{1}{2}} + 3x^{-2} - 1$,

$\qquad\qquad f'(x) = -x^{-\frac{3}{2}} - 6x^{-3}$

$\qquad\qquad\qquad = -\dfrac{1}{x} - \dfrac{6}{x^3}$

$\qquad \therefore\quad f'(x) = -\dfrac{1}{\sqrt{x^3}} - \dfrac{6}{x^3}$

C2

A function may not be given in the form ax^n. In this case, you need to manipulate the expression for y and write it as a sum of functions, each in the form ax^n.

Example 3

Find $\dfrac{dy}{dx}$ for each of the these functions.

a) $y = (x + 3)^2$ b) $y = \sqrt{x}(x^2 - 1)$ c) $y = \dfrac{x^3 + 6}{x}$

....

a) $y = (x + 3)^2$,

$\qquad \therefore\qquad y = (x + 3)(x + 3)$

$\qquad\qquad\qquad = x^2 + 6x + 9$

$$\therefore \quad \frac{dy}{dx} = 2x + 6$$

b) $y = \sqrt{x}(x^2 - 1) = x^{\frac{1}{2}}(x^2 - 1)$

Expand the bracket.

$$y = x^{\frac{5}{2}} - x^{\frac{1}{2}}$$

$$\therefore \quad \frac{dy}{dx} = \frac{5}{2}x^{\frac{3}{2}} - \frac{1}{2}x^{-\frac{1}{2}}$$

You can simplify this expression by factorising it. Take out $\frac{1}{2}x^{-\frac{1}{2}}$ (the lowest power of x in the expression). This gives:

$$\frac{dy}{dx} = \frac{1}{2}x^{-\frac{1}{2}}(5x^2 - 1)$$

$$= \frac{1}{2x^{\frac{1}{2}}}(5x^2 - 1)$$

$$= \frac{1}{2x}(5x^2 - 1)$$

$$\therefore \quad \frac{dy}{dx} = \frac{1}{2\sqrt{x}}(5x^2 - 1)$$

Examples b) and c) show how you can manipulate the derivative to obtain a more mathematically tidy result. Note that any form of the correct derivative is acceptable. However, it is useful to understand such manipulation since many examination questions ask for the derivative in a particular form.

c) $y = \dfrac{x^3 + 6}{x} = \dfrac{x^3}{x} + \dfrac{6}{x} = x^2 + \dfrac{6}{x} = x^2 + 6x^{-1}$

$$\frac{dy}{dx} = 2x - 6x^{-2}$$

$$= 2x^{-2}(x^3 - 3)$$

$$\therefore \quad \frac{dy}{dx} = \frac{2(x^3 - 3)}{x^2}$$

Exercise 10A

1 Differentiate each of these with respect to x.

a) x^{-2} b) x^{-4} c) $2x^{-3}$ d) $4x^{-1}$ e) $\dfrac{1}{x^3}$

f) $-\dfrac{1}{x^2}$ g) $\dfrac{3}{x^3}$ h) $-\dfrac{2}{x}$ i) $\dfrac{3}{2x^2}$ j) $\dfrac{9}{2x^3}$

2 Find $f'(x)$ for each of these functions.

a) $f(x) = x^{\frac{1}{2}}$ b) $f(x) = 9x^{\frac{1}{3}}$ c) $f(x) = x^{-\frac{2}{3}}$

d) $f(x) = -10x^{-\frac{1}{5}}$ e) $f(x) = 7\sqrt{x}$ f) $f(x) = \sqrt[3]{x}$

g) $f(x) = \dfrac{4}{5\sqrt{x}}$ h) $f(x) = -\dfrac{15}{\sqrt[5]{x}}$ i) $f(x) = \sqrt{x^5}$

3 Find $\dfrac{dy}{dx}$ for each of these functions.

a) $y = x^2 + 2x$ b) $y = 3x^2 - 5x$ c) $y = 5 - 4x^3$

d) $y = x^2 + 2x + 3$ e) $y = x^7 + 3x^4$ f) $y = x^4 - 3x^2 + 2$

g) $y = 5x^2 - \dfrac{2}{x^3}$ h) $y = x^2 - 2x^4$ i) $y = \dfrac{3}{x} - 1 + 4x^3$

4 Differentiate each of these with respect to x.

a) $2\sqrt{x} + 1$

b) $\sqrt{x} + \dfrac{1}{x}$

c) $4x^{-2} - 3x$

d) $3x^{\frac{1}{3}} - 4x^{-\frac{1}{3}}$

e) $4x^{\frac{1}{2}} + 2x - 1$

f) $6x^{\frac{2}{3}} - 4x^{\frac{5}{2}}$

g) $\dfrac{9}{\sqrt[3]{x}} - \dfrac{8}{\sqrt[4]{x}}$

h) $\dfrac{6}{\sqrt{x}} - 4\sqrt{x}$

i) $\sqrt{x} + 1 + \dfrac{1}{\sqrt{x}}$

5 Find $f'(x)$ for each of these functions.

a) $f(x) = 4x - 7$

b) $f(x) = 2\sqrt{x} + \dfrac{5}{2x}$

c) $f(x) = 4x^2 + 7x - 3$

d) $f(x) = (\sqrt[6]{x})^5$

e) $f(x) = 6\sqrt{x} - \dfrac{3}{2x^2}$

f) $f(x) = 2x^{-7} - 5x^{-3} + x$

g) $f(x) = \dfrac{3}{\sqrt[6]{x}} - \dfrac{2}{\sqrt[4]{x}}$

h) $f(x) = \dfrac{5}{x^2} - \dfrac{2}{x} + 3$

i) $f(x) = 9x^{\frac{4}{3}} + 3$

j) $f(x) = 2x^{-4} - 4x^{-2}$

6 Find $\dfrac{dy}{dx}$ for each of these functions.

a) $y = x^2(x + 3)$

b) $y = x^3(4 - x^2)$

c) $y = \sqrt{x}(5 + x)$

d) $y = 6\sqrt{x}(x^3 - 2x + 1)$

e) $y = 2x^{\frac{1}{4}}(x^2 - 2)$

f) $y = (x + 3)(x - 4)$

g) $y = (x + 4)^2$

h) $y = 2(x - 3)^2$

i) $y = (x + 8)(x - 2)$

j) $y = (x + 5)(2x - 1)$

7 Differentiate each of these with respect to x.

a) $x^{-\frac{1}{2}}(x + 1)$

b) $\dfrac{x^2 + 7}{x}$

c) $\dfrac{x + 5}{x^2}$

d) $\dfrac{3x^2 + 2}{x}$

e) $\dfrac{6x^3 - 7}{x^2}$

f) $\dfrac{2x + 3}{5x}$

g) $\dfrac{6x^2 - 7x^3}{3\sqrt{x}}$

h) $x^2(2 - x)^2$

i) $\dfrac{(x + 5)^2}{x}$

8 Find $f'(x)$ for each of the following.

a) $f(x) = x^3(3x - 1)$

b) $f(x) = 2x^2(x - 1)^2$

c) $f(x) = \dfrac{3x^3 + 5}{x^2}$

d) $f(x) = \dfrac{(2x - 5)(x - 4)}{x^3}$

e) $f(x) = \dfrac{(3x - 1)^2}{2x}$

f) $f(x) = \dfrac{5x + 3}{2\sqrt{x}}$

g) $f(x) = \dfrac{2x^2 - 5}{(3\sqrt{x})^2}$

h) $f(x) = \dfrac{3\sqrt{x} - 7}{2\sqrt{x}}$

10.2 Tangents and normals to a curve

You saw in Chapter 4 that

✦ the gradient of a curve at a point P is the gradient of the tangent to the curve at the point P
✦ the gradient is found by differentiating the function.

This section extends that work to a wider range of functions.

Example 4

Find the gradient of the curve $f(x) = x^2 + \dfrac{1}{x}$ at the point $P(1, 2)$.

To find the gradient of the curve, first find $f'(x)$:

$$f(x) = x^2 + \frac{1}{x}$$

$$= x^2 + x^{-1}$$

$$\therefore \quad f'(x) = 2x - x^{-2}$$

$$= 2x - \frac{1}{x^2}$$

The gradient of the curve at the point $P(1, 2)$ is given by $f'(1)$:

$$f'(1) = 2(1) - \frac{1}{(1)^2} = 1$$

The gradient of the curve at point P is 1.

If you know the gradient of a given curve at any point then you can often work out the coordinates of that point.

Example 5

The gradient of the curve $y = 3x^2 + x - 3$ at the point P is 13. Find the coordinates of point P.

When $y = 3x^2 + x - 3$, then $\dfrac{dy}{dx} = 6x + 1$.

$\dfrac{dy}{dx} = 13$ at point P

$$\therefore \quad 6x + 1 = 13$$

$$\therefore \quad x = 2$$

To find the y-coordinate of point P substitute $x = 2$ into $y = 3x^2 + x - 3$:

$$y = 3(2)^2 + 2 - 3$$

$$\therefore \quad y = 11$$

The coordinates of point P are $(2, 11)$.

In the next example, you can use the information given to set up a pair of simultaneous equations.

Example 6

The curve C is given by $y = ax^2 + b\sqrt{x}$, where a and b are constants. Given that the gradient of C at the point $(1, 1)$ is 5, find a and b.

Rewrite $y = ax^2 + b\sqrt{x}$ as $y = ax^2 + bx^{\frac{1}{2}}$ and then differentiate:

$$\frac{dy}{dx} = 2ax + \frac{b}{2}x^{-\frac{1}{2}} = 2ax + \frac{b}{2x^{\frac{1}{2}}}$$

The point $(1, 1)$ is on the curve C. Therefore,

$$1 = a(1)^2 + b(1)^{\frac{1}{2}} \quad \therefore \quad 1 = a + b \qquad [1]$$

> Substitute $x = 1$ in the equation of the curve.

The gradient of the curve when $x = 1$ is 5. Therefore,

$$2a(1) + \frac{b}{2(1)^{\frac{1}{2}}} = 5 \quad \therefore \quad 4a + b = 10 \qquad [2]$$

> Substitute $x = 1$ in the equation of the derived function.

Solving [1] and [2] simultaneously gives $a = 3$ and $b = -2$.

C2

Example 7

Find the equation of the tangent to the curve $f(x) = \dfrac{1}{x^2}$ at the point $P(-1, 1)$. Find the coordinates of the point where this tangent meets the curve again.

> As is often the case, a sketch helps:

$$f(x) = \frac{1}{x^2} = x^{-2} \quad \therefore \quad f'(x) = -2x^{-3} = -\frac{2}{x^3}$$

The gradient of the tangent to the curve at the point $P(-1, 1)$ is

$$f'(-1) = -\frac{2}{(-1)^3} = 2$$

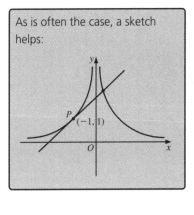

Therefore, the equation of the tangent is $y = 2x + c$.

The tangent passes through $P(-1, 1)$. Therefore,

$$1 = 2(-1) + c \quad \therefore \quad c = 3$$

Therefore, the equation of the tangent to the curve at the point P is $y = 2x + 3$.

The tangent meets the curve again at the points whose x-coordinates satisfy

$$2x + 3 = \frac{1}{x^2}$$

$$\therefore \quad 2x^3 + 3x^2 - 1 = 0$$

$$\therefore \quad (2x - 1)(x^2 + 2x + 1) = 0$$

> You can factorise this cubic equation by inspection.

Solving this equation gives

$$2x - 1 = 0 \quad \text{or} \quad x^2 + 2x + 1 = 0$$
$$\therefore \quad x = \tfrac{1}{2} \quad \text{or} \quad (x + 1)(x + 1) = 0$$
$$\therefore \quad x = -1$$

When $x = \tfrac{1}{2}$, $f(\tfrac{1}{2}) = 4$.

When $x = -1$, $f(-1) = 1$. This is, in fact, just point P.

The tangent meets the curve again at the point with coordinates $(\tfrac{1}{2}, 4)$.

Exercise 10B

1   Find the gradient of each of these curves at the point given.

a) $y = x^2$, at $(3, 9)$
b) $y = 2x^3 - 4$, at $(2, 12)$

c) $y = \sqrt{x} + 2$, at $(9, 5)$
d) $y = \dfrac{1}{x}$, at $(3, \tfrac{1}{3})$

e) $y = 5 - x^2$, at $(-2, 1)$
f) $y = 3 - \dfrac{2}{x}$, at $(4, \tfrac{5}{2})$

g) $y = x + \dfrac{3}{x}$, at $(3, 4)$
h) $y = 2 - \dfrac{4}{x^2}$, at $(-2, 1)$

i) $y = \dfrac{x + 5}{x}$, at $(-1, -4)$
j) $y = 3x + 7$, at $(-3, -2)$

k) $y = 6\sqrt{x} + \dfrac{1}{2\sqrt{x}}$, at $(\tfrac{1}{9}, \tfrac{7}{2})$
l) $y = \dfrac{4 - x^3}{x^2}$, at $(-2, 3)$

2   Find the coordinates of any points on each of these curves where the gradient is as stated.

a) $y = x^3$, grad 12
b) $y = 3x^2$, grad -6

c) $y = x^4 + 1$, grad 32
d) $y = \dfrac{4}{x}$, grad -16

e) $y = \dfrac{16}{x^2}$, grad 4
f) $y = x^3 + 2x - 1$, grad 29

g) $y = x^3 - x^2 + 3$, grad 0
h) $y = 2x^3 - 4x^2 + 3x + 2$, grad 1

i) $y = \sqrt{x} + 5$, grad 1
j) $y = 4\sqrt{x} - x$, grad 5

k) $y = \dfrac{4 - x}{x}$, grad -1
l) $y = \dfrac{x^2 + 3}{2x^2}$, grad 3

3   The curve C is defined by $y = ax^2 + b$, where a and b are constants. Given that the gradient of the curve at the point $(2, -2)$ is 3, find the values of a and b.

4   Given that the curve with equation $y = Ax^2 + Bx$ has gradient 7 at the point $(6, 8)$, find the values of the constants A and B.

5   A curve whose equation is $y = \dfrac{a}{x} + c$ passes through the point $(3, 9)$ with gradient 5. Find the values of the constants a and c.

6   Given that the curve with equation $y = a\sqrt{x} + b$, has gradient 3 at the point $(4, 6)$, find the values of the constants a and b.

7 A curve with equation $y = A\sqrt{x} + \dfrac{B}{\sqrt{x}}$, for constants A and B,

passes through the point $(1, 6)$ with gradient -1. Find A and B.

8 Find the equation of the tangent to each of the following curves at the point indicated by the given value of x.

a) $y = x^2 + 3$, where $x = 2$ b) $y = 2x^3 - 1$, where $x = 1$

c) $y = \dfrac{9}{x}$, where $x = -3$ d) $y = 6x - x^2$, where $x = 4$

e) $y = 5 - \dfrac{8}{x^2}$, where $x = -2$ f) $y = 6\sqrt{x}$, where $x = 4$

g) $y = x^3 - x^2 + 2$, where $x = 1$ h) $y = x^2 - 10x + 30$, where $x = 5$

The normal to a curve at a point P is the straight line through P which is perpendicular to the tangent at P.

Since the tangent and normal are perpendicular to each other, if the gradient of the tangent

is m then the gradient of the normal is $-\dfrac{1}{m}$.

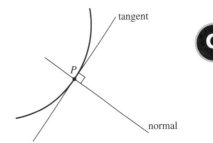

C2

Example 8

Given that $f(x) = \dfrac{1}{x^2}$ and that point $P(-1, 1)$ lies on the curve of $f(x)$, find

a) the equation of the tangent to the curve at the point P
b) the equation of the normal to the curve at the point P.

a) $f(x) = \dfrac{1}{x^2} = x^{-2}$. Therefore,

$$f'(x) = -2x^{-3} = -\dfrac{2}{x^3}$$

The gradient of the tangent to the curve at the point $P(-1, 1)$ is

$$f'(-1) = -\dfrac{2}{(-1)^3} = -2$$

Therefore the equation of the tangent is $y = -2x + c$.
The tangent passes through $P(-1, 1)$. So:

$$1 = -2(-1) + c$$
$$\therefore \quad c = -1$$

Therefore the equation of the tangent to the curve at P is
$y = -2x - 1$.

b) The gradient of the normal to the curve at the point $P(-1, 1)$ is $\frac{1}{2}$.

Therefore the equation of the normal is $y = \frac{1}{2}x + c$.

The normal passes through $P(-1, 1)$. Therefore

$$1 = \frac{1}{2}(-1) + c$$

$$\therefore \quad c = \frac{3}{2}$$

Therefore the equation of the normal to the curve at P is $y = \frac{1}{2}x + \frac{3}{2}$ or $2y - x - 3 = 0$.

Example 9

Find the equations of the normals to the curve $y = x^3 - 3x^2 + 4$ which are perpendicular to the line $y - 24x = 1$.

••

The equation $y - 24x = 1$ can be written as $y = 24x + 1$, giving the gradient of the line as 24.

If the required normals are perpendicular to the line $y = 24x + 1$, they must have a gradient of $-\frac{1}{24}$. Therefore, the gradient of the corresponding tangents to the curve is 24.

> The tangents at the points where the normals intersect the curve must be parallel to the given line.

$$y = x^3 - 3x^2 + 4 \quad \therefore \quad \frac{dy}{dx} = 3x^2 - 6x.$$

Now $\dfrac{dy}{dx} = 24$. Therefore,

$$3x^2 - 6x = 24$$

$$\therefore \quad 3x^2 - 6x - 24 = 0$$

$$\therefore \quad x^2 - 2x - 8 = 0$$

$$\therefore \quad (x + 2)(x - 4) = 0$$

Solving gives $x = -2$ or $x = 4$.

When $x = -2$: $y = (-2)^3 - 3(-2)^2 + 4 = -16$

When $x = 4$: $y = (4)^3 - 3(4)^2 + 4 = 20$

So you want the normals to the curve at the points $P(-2, -16)$ and $Q(4, 20)$.

Both these normals have equations of the form $y = -\frac{1}{24}x + c$. Since one of the normals passes through $P(-2, -16)$, it follows that

$$-16 = -\tfrac{1}{24}(-2) + c$$

$$\therefore \quad c = -\tfrac{193}{12}$$

Therefore, the equation of the normal through $P(-2, -16)$ is

$$y = -\tfrac{1}{24}x - \tfrac{193}{12} \quad \text{or} \quad 24y + x + 386 = 0$$

For the normal at point $Q(4, 20)$,

$$20 = -\tfrac{1}{24}(4) + c$$

$$\therefore \quad c = \tfrac{121}{6}$$

Therefore, the equation of the normal through $Q(4, 20)$ is

$$y = -\tfrac{1}{24}x + \tfrac{121}{6} \quad \text{or} \quad 24y + x - 484 = 0$$

Exercise 10C

1 Find the equation of the normal to each of the following curves at the point indicated by the given value of x.

a) $y = x^2 - 3x$, where $x = 2$

b) $y = x^3 + 4$, where $x = -1$

c) $y = \dfrac{6}{x}$, where $x = 3$

d) $y = 2\sqrt{x}$, where $x = 9$

e) $y = 6 - \dfrac{1}{x^2}$, where $x = 1$

f) $y = x^3 + 2x^2 - 3$, where $x = -2$

g) $y = x^4 - 9x^2$, where $x = 3$

h) $y = \dfrac{x - 3}{x^2}$, where $x = -1$

i) $y = \sqrt{x}(x^2 - 2)$, where $x = 1$

j) $y = 3 - \dfrac{36}{x^2}$, where $x = -3$

k) $y = \dfrac{4 + x^2}{x}$, where $x = -2$

l) $y = 3\sqrt{x} + \dfrac{1}{\sqrt{x}}$, where $x = \dfrac{1}{4}$

2 a) Find the values of x at which the gradient of the curve $y = x^3 - 6x^2 + 9x + 2$ is zero.

b) Hence find the equations of the tangents to the curve which are parallel to the x-axis.

3 a) Find the values of x for which the gradient of the curve $y = x^3 - 3x^2 - 9x + 10$ is 15.

b) Hence find the equations of the tangents to the curve which have gradient 15.

4 Find the equations of the two normals to the curve $y = 8 + 15x + 3x^2 - x^3$ which have gradient $\frac{1}{9}$.

5 Show that the curve $y = 3x^4 - 4x^3 + 6x^2 - 18x + 10$ has just one normal of gradient $\frac{1}{6}$ and find its equation.

6 a) Find the equation of the tangent, t, to the curve $y = x^2 + 5x + 2$, which is perpendicular to the line, l, with equation $3y + x = 5$.

b) Find also the coordinates of the point where t meets l.

7 a) Find the equation of the tangent at the point $(1, 2)$ on the curve $y = x^3 + 3x - 2$.

b) Find also the coordinates of the point where this tangent meets the curve again.

8 Find the coordinates of the point, P, where the tangent to the curve $y = x^3 + x - 3$ at $(2, 7)$ meets the curve again.

C2

9 a) Find the equation of the normal at the point (2, 3) on the curve $y = 2x^3 - 12x^2 + 23x - 11$.

   b) Find also the coordinates of the points where the normal meets the curve again.

10 Find the coordinates of the two points, where the normal to the curve $y = \frac{1}{2}x^3 - x + 3$ at the point (0, 3) meets the curve again.

11 The tangent to the curve $y = ax^2 + 1$ at the point (1, b) has gradient 6. Find the values of the constants a and b.

12 The normal to the curve $y = x^3 + cx$ at the point (2, d) has gradient $\frac{1}{2}$. Find the values of the constants c and d.

13 The tangent to the curve $y = a\sqrt{x} - 5$ at the point (4, b) is parallel to the line $y = 2x + 1$. Find the values of the constants a and b.

C2

10.3 Second derivative

In Chapter 4 you learned how to find the second derivative, denoted by $\frac{d^2y}{dx^2}$ or $f''(x)$. Here are two more examples.

Example 10

Given that $f(x) = x + \dfrac{1}{x}$, find $f'(x)$ and $f''(x)$.

$$f(x) = x + \frac{1}{x} = x + x^{-1}$$
$$\therefore \quad f'(x) = 1 - x^{-2}$$
$$= 1 - \frac{1}{x^2}$$

Given that $f'(x) = 1 - x^{-2}$, then

$$f''(x) = 2x^{-3}$$
$$= \frac{2}{x^3}$$

Equations can involve derivatives.

Example 11

If $y = 4x^3$, find $\dfrac{dy}{dx}$ and $\dfrac{d^2y}{dx^2}$. Hence show that y satisfies

$$3y\frac{d^2y}{dx^2} - 2\left(\frac{dy}{dx}\right)^2 \equiv 0$$

When $y = 4x^3$,

$$\frac{dy}{dx} = 12x^2 \quad \text{and} \quad \frac{d^2y}{dx^2} = 24x$$

Substituting into the LHS of

$$3y\frac{d^2y}{dx^2} - 2\left(\frac{dy}{dx}\right)^2 \equiv 0$$

gives

$$3y\frac{d^2y}{dx^2} - 2\left(\frac{dy}{dx}\right)^2 \equiv 3(4x^3)(24x) - 2(12x^2)^2$$

$$\equiv 288x^4 - 288x^4 \equiv 0$$

as required.

LHS just means 'left-hand side'.

Exercise 10D

1 Find $\dfrac{d^2y}{dx^2}$ for each of these functions.

a) $y = 3x^3 + 5x$

b) $y = x^2 - 4x^6$

c) $y = \dfrac{1}{x}$

d) $y = \dfrac{2}{x^2} - x$

e) $y = \dfrac{1}{\sqrt{x}} - \sqrt{x}$

f) $y = \sqrt[3]{x} - x^3$

g) $y = x^3(x^2 + 5)$

h) $y = (x^2 - 1)(2x + 3)$

i) $y = \dfrac{x^2 - 1}{x}$

j) $y = \dfrac{\sqrt{x} + 5}{\sqrt{x}}$

k) $y = \dfrac{6x - 5}{x^2}$

l) $y = \dfrac{5x - 4}{3\sqrt{x}}$

2 Given that a, b, c and d are constants, find the values of $\dfrac{dy}{dx}$ and $\dfrac{d^2y}{dx^2}$ for each of the following.

a) $y = ax^2 + bx + c$

b) $y = \dfrac{a}{x} + \dfrac{b}{x^2}$

c) $y = a\sqrt{x} + \dfrac{b}{\sqrt{x}}$

d) $y = (ax + b)(cx + d)$

e) $y = \dfrac{ax^3 + bx^2}{cx}$

3 Given that $y = \dfrac{1}{\sqrt{x}}$, show that

$$2x\left(\frac{d^2y}{dx^2}\right) + 3\frac{dy}{dx} \equiv 0$$

4 Given that $y = \dfrac{1}{x^2}$, show that

$$y\left(\frac{d^2y}{dx^2}\right) + \left(\frac{dy}{dx}\right)^2 - 10y^3 \equiv 0$$

5 Given that $y = \dfrac{x + 1}{x^2}$, show that

$$\frac{d^2y}{dx^2} + \frac{4}{x}\left(\frac{dy}{dx}\right) + \frac{2}{x^2}y \equiv 0$$

10.4 Stationary points

In Chapter 4 you saw how you can use the second derivative to determine the nature of stationary points on a graph (see page 103).

> Knowledge of the point of inflection will not be examined in either C1 or C2.

At all stationary points, the gradient of the curve is zero. That is, $\dfrac{dy}{dx} = 0$.

The diagram shows the graph of some function $y = f(x)$ which possesses a maximum, a minimum and a point of inflection. The graph of the derived function is shown below it.

♦ At the maximum point P, the gradient of the derived function is negative. That is,

$$\dfrac{d^2y}{dx^2} < 0 \quad \text{at a maximum}$$

♦ At the point of inflection Q, the gradient of the derived function is zero. That is,

$$\dfrac{d^2y}{dx^2} = 0$$

♦ At the minimum point R, the gradient of the derived function is positive. That is,

$$\dfrac{d^2y}{dx^2} > 0 \quad \text{at a minimum}$$

Example 12

Find the coordinates of the stationary point on the curve $y = x + \dfrac{4}{x^2}$ and determine its nature.

....

$y = x + \dfrac{4}{x^2} = x + 4x^{-2} \quad \therefore \quad \dfrac{dy}{dx} = 1 - 8x^{-3}$

At a stationary point, $\dfrac{dy}{dx} = 0$. So:

$$1 - 8x^{-3} = 0$$

$$1 - \frac{8}{x^3} = 0$$

$$\therefore \qquad x^3 = 8$$

$$\therefore \qquad x = 2$$

When $x = 2$: $\quad y = 2 + \dfrac{4}{(2)^2} = 3$

The coordinates of the stationary point are $(2, 3)$.

To determine the nature of the stationary point, check the sign of $\dfrac{d^2y}{dx^2}$ at the point.

$$\frac{dy}{dx} = 1 - 8x^{-3}$$

$$\therefore \quad \frac{d^2y}{dx^2} = 24x^{-4} = \frac{24}{x^4}$$

For the point $(2, 3)$:

$$\left. \frac{d^2y}{dx^2} \right|_{x=2} = \frac{24}{(2)^4} > 0$$

Therefore the stationary point is a minimum.

> You could use a graphics calculator to check the results of these two examples.

Example 13

Find the coordinates of the stationary point on the curve $y = x - \sqrt{x}$ and determine its nature.

. . . .

$$y = x - \sqrt{x} = x - x^{\frac{1}{2}} \quad \therefore \quad \frac{dy}{dx} = 1 - \tfrac{1}{2}x^{-\frac{1}{2}}$$

At a stationary point, $\dfrac{dy}{dx} = 0$. So:

$$1 - \frac{1}{2x^{\frac{1}{2}}} = 0$$

$$2x^{\frac{1}{2}} = 1$$

$$x^{\frac{1}{2}} = \tfrac{1}{2}$$

$$\therefore \quad x = \tfrac{1}{4}$$

When $x = \tfrac{1}{4} : y = \tfrac{1}{4} - \sqrt{\tfrac{1}{4}} = -\tfrac{1}{4}$

The coordinates of the stationary point are $\left(\tfrac{1}{4}, -\tfrac{1}{4} \right)$.

To determine the nature of the stationary point, check the sign of $\dfrac{d^2y}{dx^2}$ at the point $\left(\tfrac{1}{4}, -\tfrac{1}{4} \right)$:

$$\frac{d^2y}{dx^2} = \tfrac{1}{4}x^{-\frac{3}{2}}$$

$$= \frac{1}{4x^{\frac{3}{2}}}$$

For the point $\left(\tfrac{1}{4}, -\tfrac{1}{4} \right)$,

$$\frac{d^2y}{dx^2} = \frac{1}{4\left(\frac{1}{4}\right)^{\frac{3}{2}}} > 0$$

Therefore the stationary point is a minimum.

Differentiation is useful in practical problems where you want to find the conditions that will give you a maximum or minimum value of, say, an area.

C2

Example 14

A closed, right circular cylinder of base radius r cm and height h cm has a volume of 54π cm³. Show that S, the total surface area of the cylinder, is given by

$$S = \frac{108\pi}{r} + 2\pi r^2$$

Hence find the radius and height which make the surface area a minimum.

· ·

The volume, V, is given by

$$V = \pi r^2 h \qquad\qquad [1]$$

The total surface area, S, is given by

$$S = 2\pi rh + 2\pi r^2 \qquad\qquad [2]$$

$V = 54\pi$, so from [1]:

$$\pi r^2 h = 54\pi$$
$$\therefore \quad h = \frac{54}{r^2}$$

Substituting $h = \dfrac{54}{r^2}$ into [2] gives

$$S = 2\pi r\left(\frac{54}{r^2}\right) + 2\pi r^2$$

$$\therefore \quad S = \frac{108\pi}{r} + 2\pi r^2$$

as required.

Maximum/minimum surface area occurs when $\dfrac{\mathrm{d}S}{\mathrm{d}r} = 0$. Now

$$S = 108\pi r^{-1} + 2\pi r^2$$

$$\therefore \quad \frac{\mathrm{d}S}{\mathrm{d}r} = -108\pi r^{-2} + 4\pi r = -\frac{108\pi}{r^2} + 4\pi r$$

When $\dfrac{\mathrm{d}S}{\mathrm{d}r} = 0$: $\quad -\dfrac{108\pi}{r^2} + 4\pi r = 0$

$$\therefore \quad 4\pi r^3 = 108\pi$$
$$\therefore \quad\quad r^3 = 27$$

Therefore, the radius, r, is 3 cm.

When $r = 3$: $\quad h = \dfrac{54}{(3)^2} = 6$

In other words, the height is 6 cm.

You must check that this value of r corresponds to a minimum, by checking the second derivative.

$$\frac{\mathrm{d}^2 S}{\mathrm{d}r^2} = 216\pi r^{-3} + 4\pi$$

C2

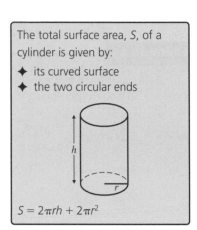

The total surface area, S, of a cylinder is given by:

✦ its curved surface
✦ the two circular ends

$S = 2\pi rh + 2\pi r^2$

When $r = 3$,

$$\frac{d^2S}{dr^2} = \frac{216\pi}{(3)^3} + 4\pi = 12\pi$$

which is positive. That is, $\dfrac{d^2S}{dr^2} > 0$ when $r = 3$, which implies that $r = 3$ corresponds to a minimum S.

So, the surface area is a minimum when the radius is 3 cm and the height is 6 cm.

Exercise 10E

1 Find the coordinates of the stationary points on each of the following curves, and determine their nature.

a) $y = x + \dfrac{1}{x}$ b) $y = 9x + \dfrac{1}{x}$ c) $y = x^2 + \dfrac{16}{x}$

d) $y = x + \dfrac{4}{x^2}$ e) $y = \dfrac{1}{x} - \dfrac{3}{x^2}$ f) $y = \dfrac{2}{x^3} - \dfrac{1}{x^2}$

g) $y = \dfrac{12x^2 - 1}{x^3}$ h) $y = \dfrac{2 - x^3}{x^4}$ i) $y = x - 4\sqrt{x}$

j) $y = x^{\frac{3}{2}} - 6x$ k) $y = \dfrac{1 + x}{\sqrt{x}}$ l) $y = \dfrac{\sqrt{x} - 6}{x^2}$

2 A closed cuboidal box of square base has volume $8\ \text{m}^3$. Given that the square base has sides of length x metres, show that

a) the height of the box is $\dfrac{8}{x^2}$ metres

b) the surface area of the box is $\left(2x^2 + \dfrac{32}{x}\right)\text{m}^2$.

Given also that the surface area of the box is a minimum,

c) find the value of x.

3 An open metal tank of square base has volume $108\ \text{m}^3$. Given that the square base has sides of length x metres, show that

a) the height of the tank is $\dfrac{108}{x^2}$ metres

b) the external surface area of the tank is $\left(x^2 + \dfrac{432}{x}\right)\text{m}^2$.

Given also that the surface area of the tank is a minimum,

c) find the value of x.

4 A silver bar of volume $576\ \text{cm}^3$ is cuboidal in shape, and has a length which is twice its breadth. Given that the breadth of the bar is x cm, show that

a) the height of the bar is $\dfrac{288}{x^2}$ cm

b) the surface area of the bar is $\left(4x^2 + \dfrac{1728}{x}\right)\text{cm}^2$.

Given also that the surface area is a minimum.

c) find the value of x.

5 An open cuboidal tank of rectangular base is to be made with an external surface area of 36 m². The base is to be such that its length is three times its breadth. Given that the breadth of the tank is x metres, show that

a) the height of the tank is $\left(\dfrac{36 - 3x^2}{8x}\right)$ metres

b) the volume of the tank is $\left(\dfrac{27x}{2} - \dfrac{9x^3}{8}\right)$ m³.

Given also that the volume of the tank is a maximum,

c) find the value of x, and the value of that maximum volume.

6 A closed cuboidal plastic box is to be made with an external surface area of 216 cm². The base is to be such that its length is four times its breadth. Given that the breadth of the box is x cm, show that

a) the height of the box is $\left(\dfrac{108 - 4x^2}{5x}\right)$ cm

b) the volume of the box is $\left(\dfrac{432x}{5} - \dfrac{16x^3}{5}\right)$ cm³.

Given also that the volume of the box is a maximum,

c) find the value of x, and the value of that maximum volume.

7 A closed cuboidal box of square base and volume 36 cm³ is to be constructed and silver plated on the outside. Silver plating for the top and the base costs 40p per cm², and silver plating for the sides costs 30p per cm². Given that the length of the sides of the base is to be x cm, find expressions, in terms of x, for

a) the height of the box

b) the cost of plating the top

c) the cost of plating a side

d) the total cost of plating the box.

Given also that this cost is to be a minimum,

e) find the value of x

f) calculate the cost of plating the box.

8 An *open* cuboidal fish tank of rectangular base and volume 2.5 m³ is to be made in such a way that its length is three times its breadth. Glass for the sides costs £4 per m², and glass for the base costs £15 per m². Given that the base has breadth x m, find expressions, in terms of x, for

a) the height of the tank

b) the cost of all the glass for the sides

c) the cost of glass for the base.

Given also that the cost is to be a minimum,

d) find the value of x

e) calculate the cost of the glass for the tank.

10.5 Increasing and decreasing functions

You have already met the idea of increasing and decreasing functions in section 4.7. For example:

The function f(x) is increasing for $x > 0$.

The function g(x) is decreasing for $x < 0$.

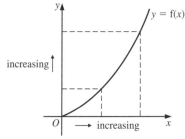
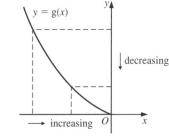

In the case of f(x) the gradient of the curve is positive: f$'(x) > 0$.

In the case of g(x) the gradient of the curve is negative: g$'(x) < 0$.

A function may have both increasing sections and decreasing sections. illustrated by the graph on the right.

The gradient of a curve indicates where the function is increasing or decreasing.

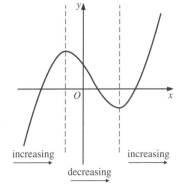

C2

Example 15

Determine the range of values of x for which these functions increase and decrease.

a) $y = \dfrac{1}{x^2}$, $(x \neq 0)$

b) $y = \dfrac{1}{x^3}$, $(x \neq 0)$

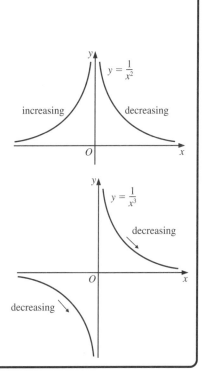

a) $y = \dfrac{1}{x^2} = x^{-2}$ $\therefore$ $\dfrac{dy}{dx} = -2x^{-3} = -\dfrac{2}{x^3}$

You can see that:

$$\frac{dy}{dx} < 0 \text{ when } x > 0 \text{ and } \frac{dy}{dx} > 0 \text{ when } x < 0$$

Therefore the function is decreasing for $x > 0$ and increasing for $x < 0$.

b) If $y = \dfrac{1}{x^3} = x^{-3}$ then $\dfrac{dy}{dx} = -3x^{-4} = -\dfrac{3}{x^4}$. You can see that:

$$\frac{dy}{dx} < 0 \text{ for all values of } x \ (x \neq 0)$$

Therefore the function is decreasing for all values of x $(x \neq 0)$.

Exercise 10F

1 Determine the range of values of x for which these functions increase or decrease.

a) $f(x) = x^2 - 8x + 3$

b) $f(x) = 7 - 2x - x^2$

c) $f(x) = x^3 - 3x^2 - 9x + 4$

d) $f(x) = 5 + 36x - 3x^2 - 2x^3$

e) $f(x) = x^4 + 4x^3 - 8x^2 - 48x + 20$

f) $f(x) = x + \dfrac{4}{x}$

2 Given $f(x) = 2x^3 - 6x^2 + 6x + 5$,

a) show that $f'(x) = 6(x - 1)^2$

b) deduce that $f(x)$ is an increasing function for all values of x.

3 Given $f(x) = 4 - 27x - 9x^2 - x^3$,

a) show that $f'(x) = -3(x + 3)^2$

b) deduce that $f(x)$ is a decreasing function for all values of x.

4 Show that $f(x) = 5 - 6x - x^3$ is a decreasing function for all values of x.

5 Show that $f(x) = 3x^5 + 5x^3 + 15x - 7$ is an increasing function for all values of x.

6 Show that $f(x) = \dfrac{1}{x^3} - x$ is a decreasing function for all values of x.

7 Show that $f(x) = x^3 + 6x^2 + 30x - 5$ is an increasing function for all values of x.

Summary

You should know how to ...	Check out
1 Differentiate $y = ax^n$ for any rational number n.	**1** Differentiate $y = 4x^{\frac{1}{2}}$
2 Differentiate expressions containing sums and differences of the form ax^n.	**2** Differentiate a) $y = 2x^2 + \dfrac{2}{x^2}$ b) $y = x^{\frac{3}{2}} - 6x^{\frac{2}{3}}$
3 Use first and second derivatives in the techniques you learned in Chapter 4.	**3** a) Find the coordinates of the stationary points on the curve $y = x^2 + \dfrac{1}{x^2}$. b) Find the equation of the tangent to the curve $y = 5 - x^2 - \dfrac{1}{x^2}$ at $x = 2$. c) Determine whether the curve $f(x) = x^{\frac{3}{2}} - 6x^{\frac{2}{3}}$ is increasing or decreasing at $x = 1$ and $x = 4$.

Revision exercise 10

Exam questions on calculus in the C2 module tend to contain both differentiation and integration. Therefore, most of the relevant revision questions are contained at the end of the next chapter.

1 A curve has equation $y = x^2 - \dfrac{54}{x}$.

Find $\dfrac{dy}{dx}$ and $\dfrac{d^2y}{dx^2}$ in terms of x.

Calculate the coordinates of the stationary point of the curve and determine whether it is a maximum or minimum point.   *(AQA/AEB, 1996)*

2 The graph of $y = x + 4x^{-2}$ has one stationary point.

a) Find $\dfrac{dy}{dx}$ and $\dfrac{d^2y}{dx^2}$.

b) Find the coordinates of the stationary point.

c) Find the value of $\dfrac{d^2y}{dx^2}$ at the stationary point, and hence determine

whether the stationary point is a maximum or a minimum.   *(AQA, 2003)*

3 a) It is given that $y = 2\pi x^2 + \dfrac{1000}{x}$.

i) Find $\dfrac{dy}{dx}$.

ii) Show that $\dfrac{dy}{dx} = 0$ when $x^3 = \dfrac{250}{\pi}$.

iii) Find $\dfrac{d^2y}{dx^2}$.

iv) Verify that $\dfrac{d^2y}{dx^2} = 12\pi$ when $x^3 = \dfrac{250}{\pi}$.

v) Find, to one decimal place, the value of x for which y has a stationary value and state whether this stationary value is a maximum or minimum.

b) A closed cylindrical tin can contains $500\,cm^3$ of liquid when full. The can has base radius r cm and total external surface area A cm^2.

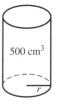

500 cm^3

r

It is given that $A = 2\pi r^2 + \dfrac{1000}{r}$.

Use your results from a) to find the smallest possible value for the total external surface area of the can. Give your answer to the nearest square centimetre.   *(AQA, 2002)*

11 Further integration

This chapter will show you how to

- Integrate ax^n for any rational number n
- Integrate sums and differences of functions
- Extend the work you did in Chapter 5
- Use the trapezium rule to estimate areas

You should know how to ...	Check in
1 Find indefinite integrals.	**1** Find these indefinite integrals. a) $\int 3x^2 - 2 \ dx$ b) $\int 3x + 2x^3 \ dx$ c) $\int 4x^2 - x + 7 \ dx$
2 Evaluate definite integrals.	**2** Evaluate these definite integrals. a) $\int_1^3 3x^2 - 2 \ dx$ b) $\int_{-1}^0 3x + 2x^3 \ dx$ c) $\int_{-2}^2 4x^2 - x + 7 \ dx$
3 Use definite integrals to find the area beneath a curve.	**3** a) Evaluate $\int_1^3 x^2 - 4x + 3 \ dx$ b) Find the area between the x-axis and the curve $y = x^2 - 4x + 3$.
4 Manipulate algebraic expressions with indices and fractions.	**4** See Check in for Chapter 10, point **5**.

11.1 Integrating ax^n

You saw in Chapter 5 that if $\dfrac{dy}{dx} = ax^n$ then

$$y = \frac{ax^{n+1}}{n+1} + c \qquad (n \neq -1)$$

That is

$$\int ax^n \ dx = \frac{ax^{n+1}}{n+1} + c \qquad (n \neq -1)$$

In the examples you have seen so far n has always been a positive integer. However, this result is true for all n (except $n = -1$) and we now consider functions where n is not a positive integer.

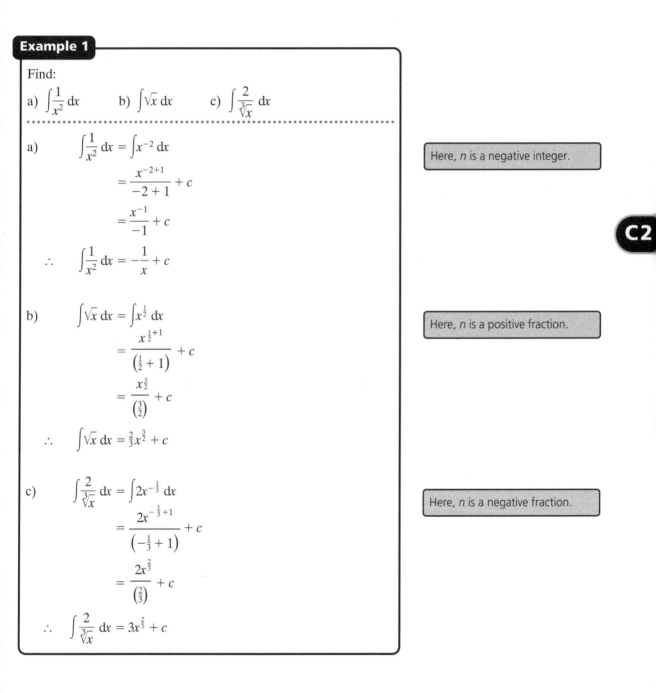

Example 1

Find:

a) $\int \dfrac{1}{x^2}\,dx$ b) $\int \sqrt{x}\,dx$ c) $\int \dfrac{2}{\sqrt[3]{x}}\,dx$

a) $\int \dfrac{1}{x^2}\,dx = \int x^{-2}\,dx$

$\qquad = \dfrac{x^{-2+1}}{-2+1} + c$

$\qquad = \dfrac{x^{-1}}{-1} + c$

∴ $\int \dfrac{1}{x^2}\,dx = -\dfrac{1}{x} + c$

Here, n is a negative integer.

b) $\int \sqrt{x}\,dx = \int x^{\frac{1}{2}}\,dx$

$\qquad = \dfrac{x^{\frac{1}{2}+1}}{\left(\frac{1}{2}+1\right)} + c$

$\qquad = \dfrac{x^{\frac{3}{2}}}{\left(\frac{3}{2}\right)} + c$

∴ $\int \sqrt{x}\,dx = \frac{2}{3}x^{\frac{3}{2}} + c$

Here, n is a positive fraction.

c) $\int \dfrac{2}{\sqrt[3]{x}}\,dx = \int 2x^{-\frac{1}{3}}\,dx$

$\qquad = \dfrac{2x^{-\frac{1}{3}+1}}{\left(-\frac{1}{3}+1\right)} + c$

$\qquad = \dfrac{2x^{\frac{2}{3}}}{\left(\frac{2}{3}\right)} + c$

∴ $\int \dfrac{2}{\sqrt[3]{x}}\,dx = 3x^{\frac{2}{3}} + c$

Here, n is a negative fraction.

C2

You also saw in Chapter 5 that to integrate a function which is a sum of other functions you simply integrate each function in turn. The following example illustrates this technique.

Example 2

Find:

a) $\int \left(2x - \dfrac{1}{x^3}\right) dx$

b) $\int \left(\dfrac{x^3 - 3x}{x}\right) dx$

c) $\int \sqrt{x}(x + 1)\, dx$

···

a) $\int \left(2x - \dfrac{1}{x^3}\right) dx = \int 2x\, dx - \int \dfrac{1}{x^3}\, dx$

Express as the integral of a sum of functions and integrate.

$\qquad = \int 2x\, dx - \int x^{-3}\, dx$

$\qquad = x^2 - \dfrac{x^{-2}}{-2} + c$

You only need one constant of integration.

$\qquad = x^2 + \dfrac{x^{-2}}{2} + c$

$\therefore \quad \int \left(2x - \dfrac{1}{x^3}\right) dx = x^2 + \dfrac{1}{2x^2} + c$

b) $\int \left(\dfrac{3x^3 - x}{x}\right) dx = \int \left(\dfrac{3x^3}{x} - \dfrac{x}{x}\right) dx$

Express as the integral of a sum of functions.

$\qquad = \int 3x^2\, dx - \int 1\, dx$

$\therefore \quad \int \left(\dfrac{x^3 - 3x}{x}\right) dx = x^3 - x + c$

Now integrate.

c) $\int \sqrt{x}(x + 1)\, dx = \int x^{\frac{1}{2}}(x + 1)\, dx$

Express as the integral of a sum of functions.

$\qquad = \int \left(x^{\frac{3}{2}} + x^{\frac{1}{2}}\right) dx$

$\qquad = \int x^{\frac{3}{2}}\, dx + \int x^{\frac{1}{2}}\, dx$

$\therefore \quad \int \sqrt{x}(x + 1)\, dx = \dfrac{x^{\frac{5}{2}}}{\left(\frac{5}{2}\right)} + \dfrac{x^{\frac{3}{2}}}{\left(\frac{3}{2}\right)} + c$

Now integrate.

$\qquad = \dfrac{2x^{\frac{5}{2}}}{5} + \dfrac{2x^{\frac{3}{2}}}{3} + c$

$\therefore \quad \int \sqrt{x}(x + 1)\, dx = \dfrac{2}{5}\sqrt{x^5} + \dfrac{2}{3}\sqrt{x^3} + c$

Example 3

Given that

$$f''(x) = 2 - \frac{2}{\sqrt{x^3}} \quad \text{and} \quad f'(1) = 0$$

find $f'(x)$. Given further that $f(1) = 8$, find $f(x)$.

$$f''(x) = 2 - \frac{2}{\sqrt{x^3}} = 2 - 2x^{-\frac{3}{2}},$$

$$\therefore \quad f'(x) = \int \left(2 - 2x^{-\frac{3}{2}} \right) dx$$

$$= 2x - \frac{2x^{-\frac{1}{2}}}{\left(-\frac{1}{2}\right)} + c_1$$

$$\therefore \quad f'(x) = 2x + 4x^{-\frac{1}{2}} + c_1 \qquad [1]$$

Since $f'(1) = 0$, substituting into [1] gives $c_1 = -6$ and so

$$f'(x) = 2x + \frac{4}{\sqrt{x}} - 6 = 2x + 4x^{-\frac{1}{2}} - 6$$

Therefore,

$$f(x) = \int \left(2x + 4x^{-\frac{1}{2}} - 6 \right) dx = x^2 + 8x^{\frac{1}{2}} - 6x + c_2$$

Since $f(1) = 8$,

$$8 = 1 + 8 - 6 + c_2$$

$$\therefore \quad c_2 = 5$$

Therefore, $f(x) = x^2 + 8\sqrt{x} - 6x + 5$.

Integrate $f''(x)$ to get $f'(x)$.

Integrate $f'(x)$ to get $f(x)$.

C2

Exercise 11A

1 Find each of these integrals.

a) $\int x^{-2} \, dx$ b) $\int x^{-4} \, dx$ c) $\int 2x^{-3} \, dx$ d) $\int -6x^{-4} \, dx$

e) $\int \frac{1}{x^3} \, dx$ f) $\int -\frac{1}{x^5} \, dx$ g) $\int \frac{3}{x^2} \, dx$ h) $\int -\frac{2}{x^3} \, dx$

i) $\int \frac{4}{x^7} \, dx$ j) $\int \frac{3}{2x^4} \, dx$ k) $\int -\frac{5}{3x^2} \, dx$ l) $\int \frac{2}{3x^4} \, dx$

2 Integrate each of these functions with respect to x.

a) $f(x) = x^{\frac{1}{3}}$ b) $f(x) = 3x^{\frac{1}{2}}$ c) $f(x) = x^{-\frac{2}{3}}$

d) $f(x) = -4x^{-\frac{1}{5}}$ e) $f(x) = -3\sqrt{x}$ f) $f(x) = \sqrt[4]{x}$

g) $f(x) = \frac{4}{\sqrt[3]{x}}$ h) $f(x) = -\frac{2}{\sqrt[5]{x}}$ i) $f(x) = \frac{3}{7\sqrt{x}}$

j) $f(x) = \frac{6}{5\sqrt[3]{x}}$ k) $f(x) = \sqrt{x^3}$ l) $f(x) = \sqrt{9x}$

3 Integrate each of these with respect to x.
  a) $x^3 + 2x$
  b) $3x^2 - 4x$
  c) $x^3 - 1$
  d) $6 + 3x^5$
  e) $x^2 - 5x + 3$
  f) $x^8 + 2x^5$
  g) $x^4 - 3x + 2$
  h) $x^2 + \dfrac{1}{x^2}$
  i) $5x^4 - \dfrac{2}{x^3}$
  j) $2x^6 + \dfrac{8}{x^5}$
  k) $x^2 - \dfrac{3}{x^2}$
  l) $\dfrac{5}{x^2} - 2 - 2x^3$

4 Find each of these integrals.
  a) $\int (3\sqrt{x} - 4)\,dx$
  b) $\int \left(\sqrt{x} + \dfrac{1}{\sqrt{x}}\right) dx$
  c) $\int (3x^{\frac{1}{3}} - 2x^{\frac{1}{4}})\,dx$
  d) $\int (5x^{-\frac{1}{2}} + 2x^{-\frac{1}{3}})\,dx$
  e) $\int \left(4\sqrt{x} - \dfrac{2}{3x^2}\right) dx$
  f) $\int \left(2\sqrt[3]{x} - \dfrac{6}{\sqrt{x}}\right) dx$
  g) $\int \left(\dfrac{4}{\sqrt[3]{x}} - 8\sqrt{x}\right) dx$
  h) $\int \left(\sqrt[4]{x} - \dfrac{1}{\sqrt[4]{x}}\right) dx$
  i) $\int \left(\dfrac{4}{3\sqrt[3]{x}} - 2\sqrt[7]{x}\right) dx$
  j) $\int \left(\dfrac{2}{\sqrt[6]{x}} - \dfrac{8}{\sqrt[3]{x}}\right) dx$

5 Find $\int y\,dx$ for each of these.
  a) $y = x(3 - x)$
  b) $y = x^2(x + 5)$
  c) $y = x^3(2 - x^2)$
  d) $y = \sqrt{x}(x + 3)$
  e) $y = 3\sqrt{x}(x^2 - x + 1)$
  f) $y = x^{\frac{1}{3}}(2x + 3)$
  g) $y = 2(x + 5)^2$
  h) $y = x(x - 1)^2$
  i) $y = 3x^{\frac{1}{4}}(x - 2)\,dx$
  j) $y = (\sqrt{x} - 3)(\sqrt{x} + 5)$

6 Integrate each of these functions with respect to x.
  a) $f(x) = 5x(x - 2)$
  b) $f(x) = x^3(6x^2 - 1)$
  c) $f(x) = \sqrt{x}(x^2 + 1)$
  d) $f(x) = x^{-\frac{1}{3}}(2x + 3)$
  e) $f(x) = \dfrac{x^2 + 5}{x^2}$
  f) $f(x) = \dfrac{x - 4}{x^3}$
  g) $f(x) = \dfrac{3x^2 + 5}{x^2}$
  h) $f(x) = \dfrac{4x^3 - 3x^2}{2x}$
  i) $f(x) = \dfrac{5x^2 - 4}{\sqrt{x}}$
  j) $f(x) = \dfrac{6x - 3}{2\sqrt{x}}$

7 Given that a, b, c and d are constants, write down expressions for each of these.
  a) $\int (ax + b)\,dx$
  b) $\int \left(a\sqrt{x} + \dfrac{b}{\sqrt{x}}\right) dx$
  c) $\int (ax + b)(cx + d)\,dx$

8 Show that

$$\int x^{n-1} + x^{2n-1}\, dx = \frac{x^n(2 + x^n)}{2n} + c$$

for any non-zero constant, n.

9 In each part of this question, use the information given to find an expression for y in terms of x.

a) $\dfrac{dy}{dx} = 3x^2 + 1, y = 12$ when $x = 2$

b) $\dfrac{dy}{dx} = 4x - 3, y = 6$ when $x = -1$

c) $\dfrac{dy}{dx} = 6x^2 - 4x, y = 24$ when $x = 3$

d) $\dfrac{dy}{dx} = 4 - 6x, y = -4$ when $x = -2$

e) $\dfrac{dy}{dx} = \dfrac{2}{x^2} - 1, x \ne 0; y = 5$ when $x = 1$

f) $\dfrac{dy}{dx} = -\dfrac{10}{x^3}, x \ne 0; y = 13$ when $x = \frac{1}{2}$

g) $\dfrac{dy}{dx} = \sqrt{x} - 5, x > 0; y = -18$ when $x = 9$

h) $\dfrac{dy}{dx} = x - \frac{1}{2}\sqrt{x}, x > 0; y = \frac{2}{3}$ when $x = 4$

10 Find y as a function of x given that $\dfrac{dy}{dx} = \dfrac{5}{x^2} - 4 \ (x \ne 0)$, and that $y = -12$ when $x = 5$.

11 A function $f(x)$ is such that $f'(x) = 3\sqrt{x} - 5, x \in \mathbb{R}, x \geqslant 0$. Given that $f(4) = 3$, find an expression for $f(x)$.

12 A function $f(x)$ is such that $f'(x) = 3\sqrt{x} - 5, x \in \mathbb{R}, x \geqslant 0$. Given that $f(4) = 3$, find an expression for $f(x)$.

13 A curve has an equation which satisfies $\dfrac{d^2y}{dx^2} = 6x - 4$. The point $P(2, 11)$ lies on the curve, and the gradient of the curve at the point P is 9. Determine the equation of the curve.

14 Given that $\dfrac{d^2y}{dx^2} = 6x + \dfrac{4}{x^3} \ (x \ne 0)$, and that $y = 1$ when $x = 1$, and that $y = 5$ when $x = 2$, find an expression for y in terms of x.

11.2 Area under a curve

You have already seen that, generally, the area under the curve
$y = f(x)$ between the limits $x = a$ and $x = b$ is given by

$$A = \int_a^b y \, dx \quad \text{or} \quad \int_a^b f(x) \, dx$$

See section 5.2.

Example 4

Find the area between the curve $y = x^2 + 4x$ and the x-axis from
a) $x = -2$ to $x = 0$ b) $x = -2$ to $x = 2$.

a) The required area is shown shaded in the diagram.
Let A be the required area, then

$$A = \int_{-2}^{0} (x^2 + 4x) \, dx$$

$$= \left[\frac{x^3}{3} + 2x^2 \right]_{-2}^{0}$$

$$= (0 + 0) - \left(\frac{-8}{3} + 8 \right)$$

$$= 0 - \frac{16}{3}$$

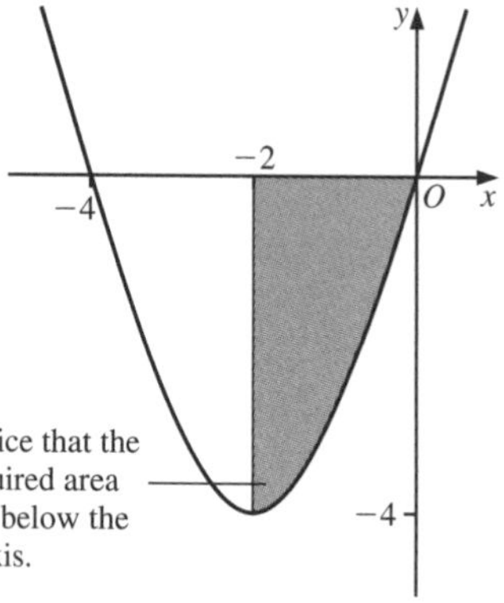

Notice that the
required area
lies below the
x-axis.

$$\therefore \quad A = -\frac{16}{3}$$

Remember: the constants of
integration cancel out in a
definite integral.

The minus signs tells you that the
area is below the x-axis.

Therefore, the required area is $\frac{16}{3}$.

b) The required area has two parts: one part below the
x-axis and one part above the x-axis.

Evaluating $\int_{-2}^{2} (x^2 + 4x) \, dx$ gives

$$\int_{-2}^{2} (x^2 + 4x) \, dx = \left[\frac{x^3}{3} + 2x^2 \right]_{-2}^{2}$$

$$= \left(\frac{8}{3} + 8 \right) - \left(-\frac{8}{3} + 8 \right)$$

$$= \frac{32}{3} - \frac{16}{3} = \frac{16}{3}$$

It is obvious that this cannot be the total shaded area,
since you know from part a) that the area between the
curve and the x-axis from $x = -2$ to $x = 0$ is $\frac{16}{3}$!

Calculating each of the integrals $\int_{-2}^{0} (x^2 + 4x) \, dx$
and $\int_{0}^{2} (x^2 + 4x) \, dx$ will explain the mystery.

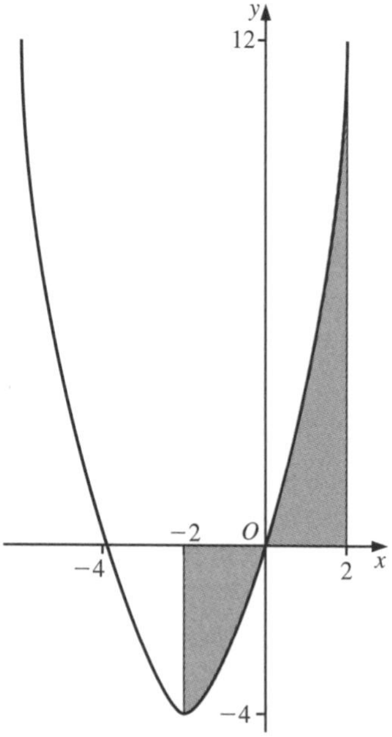

C2

You know from a) that

$$\int_{-2}^{0} (x^2 + 4x)\, dx = -\frac{16}{3}$$

and

$$\int_{0}^{2} (x^2 + 4x)\, dx = \left[\frac{x^3}{3} + 2x^2\right]_0^2 = \left(\frac{8}{3} + 8\right) - 0) = \frac{32}{3}$$

Therefore, the required area, A, is given by

$$A = \frac{16}{3} + \frac{32}{3} = 16$$

Notice that

$$\int_{-2}^{0} (x^2 + 4x)\, dx + \int_{0}^{2} (x^2 + 4x)\, dx = -\frac{16}{3} + \frac{32}{3} = \frac{16}{3}$$

$$\therefore \quad \int_{-2}^{0} (x^2 + 4x)\, dx + \int_{0}^{2} (x^2 + 4x)\, dx = \int_{-2}^{2} (x^2 + 4x)\, dx$$

This example illustrates the importance of drawing a sketch in order to identify whether part of the required area lies below the x-axis or not.

C2

Example 5

The sketch shows the curve given by $y = x^3 - 4x^2 + 3x$. Find the area between the curve and the x-axis from $x = 0$ to $x = 3$.

The required area is made up of two parts; A_1 and A_2, as shown.

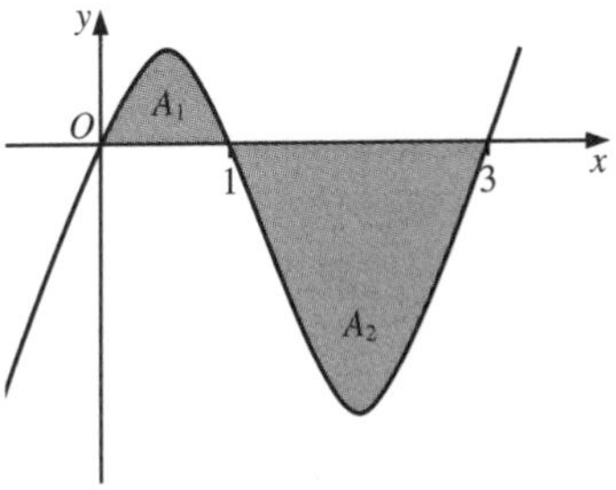

Calculating A_1 gives

$$\int_{0}^{1} (x^3 - 4x^2 + 3x)\, dx = \left[\frac{x^4}{4} - \frac{4x^3}{3} + \frac{3x^2}{2}\right]_0^1$$

$$= \left(\frac{1}{4} - \frac{4}{3} + \frac{3}{2}\right) - (0)$$

$$\therefore \quad A_1 = \frac{5}{12}$$

Calculating A_2 gives

$$\int_{1}^{3} (x^3 - 4x^2 + 3x)\, dx = \left[\frac{x^4}{4} - \frac{4x^3}{3} + \frac{3x^2}{2}\right]_1^3$$

$$= \left(\frac{81}{4} - 36 + \frac{27}{2}\right) - \left(\frac{1}{4} - \frac{4}{3} + \frac{3}{2}\right)$$

$$= -\frac{9}{4} - \frac{5}{12} = -\frac{8}{3}$$

$$\therefore \quad A_2 = \frac{8}{3}$$

The required area A is given by

$$A = A_1 + A_2 = \frac{5}{12} + \frac{8}{3} = \frac{37}{12}$$

Area between two curves

Consider two intersecting curves f(x) and g(x) as shown.

The shaded area, A, between the two curves is given by

$$A = \int_a^b g(x)\, dx - \int_a^b f(x)\, dx$$

$$\therefore \quad A = \int_a^b [g(x) - f(x)]\, dx$$

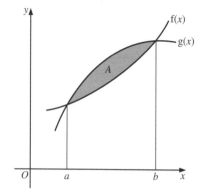

Example 6

Find the area enclosed between the curves $y = x^2 + 2x + 2$ and $y = -x^2 + 2x + 10$.

The x-coordinates of the points of intersection satisfy the equation

$$x^2 + 2x + 2 = -x^2 + 2x + 10$$

Simplifying gives

$$2x^2 - 8 = 0$$
$$\therefore \quad x^2 = 4$$
$$\therefore \quad x = \pm 2$$

> You must first find the points of intersection of the two curves.

The diagram shows the two curves.
The shaded area A is given by

$$A = \int_{-2}^{2} (-x^2 + 2x + 10)\, dx - \int_{-2}^{2} (x^2 + 2x + 2)\, dx$$

$$= \int_{-2}^{2} [(-x^2 + 2x + 10) - (x^2 + 2x + 2)]\, dx$$

$$= \int_{-2}^{2} (-2x^2 + 8)\, dx$$

$$= \left[-\frac{2x^3}{3} + 8x \right]_{-2}^{2} = \left(-\frac{16}{3} + 16 \right) - \left(\frac{16}{3} - 16 \right)$$

$$\therefore \quad A = \frac{32}{3} + \frac{32}{3} = \frac{64}{3}$$

The area enclosed between the two curves is $\frac{64}{3}$.

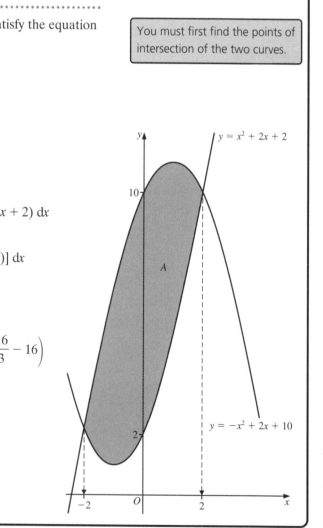

Exercise 11B

1 a) Sketch the curve with equation $y = x^2 + 6x$.

   b) Calculate the area between the curve and the x-axis from $x = -3$ to $x = 0$.

   c) Calculate the area between the curve and the x-axis from $x = 0$ to $x = 3$.

2 a) Sketch the curve with equation $y = x^2 - 4x$.

   b) Calculate the area between the curve and the x-axis from $x = 0$ to $x = 4$.

   c) Calculate the area between the curve and the x-axis from $x = 4$ to $x = 6$.

3 The sketch shows the graph with equation $y = \sqrt{x}$.

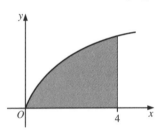

Calculate the area of the region bounded by the curve, the x-axis, and the line $x = 4$.

4 The sketch shows the graph with equation $y = \dfrac{5}{x^2}$ for positive values of x.

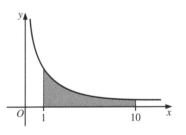

Calculate the area of the region bounded by the curve, the lines $x = 1$ and $x = 10$, and the x-axis.

5 a) Sketch the curve $y = x^3 - 2x^2$, showing where it cuts the x-axis.

   b) Hence find the area of the region bounded by the curve and the x-axis.

6 a) Sketch the curve with equation $y = \sqrt{x} - 3$, showing where it cuts the x-axis.

   b) Hence find the area of the region bounded by the curve and the x-axis.

C2

7   a) Sketch the curve $y = x(x + 2)(x - 1)$, showing where it cuts the x-axis.

b) Calculate the area of the region, above the x-axis, bounded by the curve and the x-axis.

c) Calculate the area of the region, below the x-axis, bounded by the curve and the x-axis.

8   a) Sketch the curve $y = x^3 + x^2 - 6x$, showing where it cuts the x-axis.

b) Calculate the area of the region, above the x-axis, bounded by the curve and the x-axis.

c) Calculate the area of the region, below the x-axis, bounded by the curve and the x-axis.

9   The line $y = 3x + 1$ meets the curve $y = x^2 + 3$ at the points P and Q.

a) Calculate the coordinates of P and Q.

b) Sketch the line and the curve on the same set of axes.

c) Calculate the area of the finite region bounded by the line and the curve.

10   The curve $y = x^2 - 2x + 3$ meets the line $y = 9 - x$ at the points A and B.

a) Find the coordinates of A and B.

b) Sketch the line and the curve on the same set of axes.

c) Calculate the area of the finite region bounded by the line and the curve.

11   The curve $y = x^2 + 16$ meets the line $y = x(12 - x)$ at the points C and D.

a) Find the coordinates of C and D.

b) Sketch the two curves on the same set of axes.

c) Calculate the area bounded by the two curves.

12   a) Sketch, on the same diagram, the curves $y = x^2 - 5x$ and $y = 3 - x^2$, and find their points of intersection.

b) Find the area of the region bounded by the two curves.

13   a) On the same diagram sketch the graphs of the line $y = \frac{1}{3}x$ and the curve $y = \sqrt{x}$ for positive values of x, and find the coordinates of their points of intersection.

b) Find the area of the region bounded by the line and the curve.

14   Find the area enclosed between the curves $y = 2x^2 - 7$ and $y = 5 - x^2$.

15   Find the area enclosed between the curves $y = (x - 1)^2$ and $y = 8 - (x - 1)^2$.

16   Calculate the area bounded by the y-axis, the line $y = 8$ and the curve $y = x^3$.

17   Calculate the area bounded by the curve $y = \dfrac{16}{x^2}$, the line $x = 4$ and the line $y = 16$.

18 The curve $y = x^2 - 2x$ cuts the x-axis at the points O and P, and meets the line $y = 2x$ at the point Q, as in the diagram.
a) Calculate the coordinates of P and Q.
b) Find the area of the shaded region.

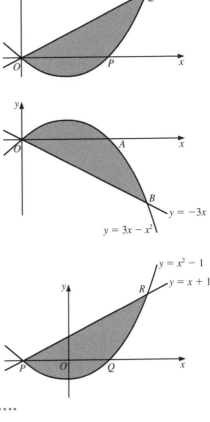

19 The curve $y = 3x - x^2$ cuts the x-axis at the points O and A, and meets the line $y = -3x$ at the point B, as in the diagram.
a) Calculate the coordinates of A and B.
b) Find the area of the shaded region.

C2

20 The curve $y = x^2 - 1$ cuts the x-axis at the points P and Q, and meets the line $y = x + 1$ at the points P and R, as in the diagram.
a) Calculate the coordinates of P, Q and R.
b) Find the area of the shaded region.

11.3 The trapezium rule

Suppose you want to find the area under the curve $y = x^2 + 1$ between $x = 0$ and $x = 2$.

One way would be to find $\int_0^2 (x^2 + 1)\, dx$. However, integration may not be an easy option with a more complex function. Instead you can use numerical techniques to find areas under curves.

One way of finding an approximation of the area shown is to fit trapeziums under the curve.

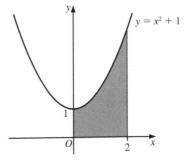

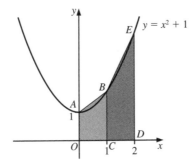

The lines $x = 1$ and $x = 2$ are called **ordinates**. In this case, two trapeziums or strips approximate the area.

The lengths of the parallel sides of each trapezium are found by finding the y value corresponding to each ordinate.

A is the point $(0, 1)$, B is $(1, 2)$ and E is $(2, 5)$.

You can estimate the required area by finding the areas of both trapeziums and adding them together. So:

Area of $OABC = \frac{1}{2}(1 + 2) = \frac{3}{2}$
Area of $BCDE = \frac{1}{2}(2 + 5) = \frac{7}{2}$

The total area is 5.

From the sketch you can see that this will be an overestimate of the actual area, because of the shape of the curve.

The actual area is given by

$$\int_0^2 x^2 + 1 \, dx = \left[\frac{x^3}{3} + x\right]_0^2$$
$$= \frac{8}{3} + 2 = 4\frac{2}{3}$$

You can achieve a better approximation by dividing the required area into smaller trapeziums as shown.

The table of values in this case is:

x	0	0.5	1	1.5	2
y	1	1.25	2	3.25	5

An estimate of the area is given by

$$A \approx \frac{0.5}{2}(1 + 1.25) + \frac{0.5}{2}(1.25 + 2) + \frac{0.5}{2}(2 + 3.25) + \frac{0.5}{2}(3.25 + 5)$$

$$= \frac{0.5}{2}(1 + 1.25 + 1.25 + 2 + 2 + 3.25 + 3.25 + 5)$$

Notice that the 'middle' ordinates generate lengths that are used twice in the calculation. The end ordinates only generate lengths that are used once. This can be written as:

$$A \approx \frac{0.5}{2}[1 + 2(1.25 + 2 + 3.25) + 5]$$

$$= 4.75$$

This is a better approximation to the actual area $\left(4\frac{2}{3}\right)$ than the one obtained using just two strips.

A table of values for the function is useful:

x	0	1	2
y	1	2	5

Add the areas of all the trapeziums.

For a large number of ordinates a computer is needed to do all of the calculations.
You only need to be able to do the calculations for five ordinates.

A general expression for the area between the curve $y = f(x)$, the ordinates a and b and the x-axis is:

$$A \approx \frac{h}{2}[y_0 + 2(y_1 + y_2 + \ldots + y_{n-1}) + y_n]$$

where $h = \dfrac{b - a}{n}$ and $y_i = f(a + ih)$ is the value of the function at each ordinate.

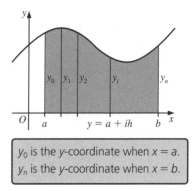

y_0 is the y-coordinate when $x = a$.
y_n is the y-coordinate when $x = b$.

This is called the **trapezium** rule.

Example 7

Using the trapezium rule with five ordinates, find an estimate for the area under the curve $y = 2x^2 + 3$ between $x = 1$ and $x = 3$.

$$h = \frac{3 - 1}{5 - 1} = \frac{1}{2}$$

Therefore,

$$A \approx \frac{0.5}{2}[y_0 + 2(y_1 + y_2 + y_3) + y_4]$$

$$\therefore \quad A \approx 0.25[5 + 2(7.5 + 11 + 15.5) + 21] = 23.5$$

An estimate of the area is 23.5.

$x = 1.0$	$y_0 = 5$
$x = 1.5$	$y_1 = 7.5$
$x = 2.0$	$y_2 = 11$
$x = 2.5$	$y_3 = 15.5$
$x = 3.0$	$y_4 = 21$

C2

Example 8

Using the trapezium rule with five ordinates, find an estimate for the area under the curve $y = \sin x$ between $x = 0$ and $x = \dfrac{\pi}{2}$.

State whether the estimate is an over-estimate or under-estimate of the actual area.

Five ordinates is four trapeziums. Therefore

$$h = \left(\frac{\frac{\pi}{2} - 0}{4} \right) = \frac{\pi}{8}$$

The table of values giving the lengths of the parallel sides of each trapezium is:

x	0	$\frac{\pi}{8}$	$\frac{\pi}{4}$	$\frac{3\pi}{8}$	$\frac{\pi}{2}$
y	0	0.383	0.707	0.924	1

Therefore:

$$A \approx \frac{\frac{\pi}{8}}{2} \left[0 + 2(0.383 + 0.707 + 0.924) + 1 \right]$$

$$= \frac{\pi}{16}(5.028)$$

$$= 0.987$$

The sketch shows that this estimate of the area is an under-estimate because all the trapeziums are below the curve.

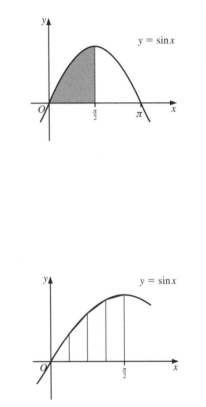

Exercise 11C

1   Using the trapezium rule with three ordinates, find an estimate for the area under the curve $y = x^2 - 3x$ from $x = 4$ to $x = 8$.

> You may be able to use a graphics calculator to check your estimates.

2   Using the trapezium rule with five ordinates, find an estimate for the area under the curve $y = 3x^2 + 2x$ from $x = 1$ to $x = 5$.

> Note that some questions refer to **ordinates**, and other questions refer to **strips**.

3   Using the trapezium rule with **three strips** find an estimate for the area under the curve $y = x^3$ from $x = 0$ to $x = 6$.

4   Using the trapezium rule with four strips find an approximate value for $\int_1^5 2x^3 - 1 \, dx$.

5 a) Sketch the curve $y = \dfrac{1}{x}$ for $x > 0$.

 b) Use the trapezium rule with four ordinates to find an
  approximate value for $\displaystyle\int_1^{10} \dfrac{1}{x}\, dx$.

 c) Use your sketch to explain why the value calculated in (b) is
  an over-estimate of the true value.

6 a) Sketch the curve $y = \sin x$ for $0 \leqslant x \leqslant \pi$.

 b) Use the trapezium rule with four strips to find an estimate
  for the area under the curve $y = \sin x$ from $x = 0$ to $x = \pi$.

 c) Use your sketch to explain why the value calculated in b) is
  an under-estimate of the true value.

7 a) Use the trapezium rule with three strips to find an
  approximate value for $\displaystyle\int_0^{12} x^2\, dx$.

 b) Now find an approximate value for $\displaystyle\int_0^{12} x^2\, dx$ by using the
  trapezium rule with six strips.

 c) Use a sketch to explain which of your two approximations
  above is closest to the true value of the integral.

C2

8 a) Copy and complete this table, giving values correct to three
  decimal places:

x	1	2	3	4	5
$\sqrt{1+x^2}$					

 b) Plot the graph of $y = \sqrt{1 + x^2}$, for $0 \leqslant x \leqslant 5$.

 c) Use the trapezium rule with four strips to find an
  approximate value for $\displaystyle\int_1^5 \sqrt{1 + x^2}\, dx$.

9 Use the trapezium rule with six strips to find an approximate
 value for $\displaystyle\int_4^{16} \dfrac{1}{1 + \sqrt{x}}\, dx$.

10 Find an approximate value for $\displaystyle\int_0^1 \sqrt{1 - x^3}\, dx$ using the trapezium
 rule with six ordinates.

11 Use the trapezium rule with four strips to find an approximate
 value for $\displaystyle\int_1^9 \sqrt{\log x}\, dx$.

12 Find an approximate value for $\displaystyle\int_0^{\frac{\pi}{3}} \dfrac{1}{1 + \tan x}\, dx$ using the
 trapezium rule with five ordinates.

Summary

You should know how to ...	Check out
1 Integrate ax^n for any rational number n.	**1** Find a) $\int 3x^{\frac{1}{2}} \, dx$ b) $\int_1^4 3x^{\frac{1}{2}} \, dx$
2 Integrate expressions containing sums and differences of the form ax^n.	**2** Find a) $\int \frac{1}{x^2} + x - 1 \, dx$ b) $\int_1^3 \frac{1}{x^2} + x - 1 \, dx$
3 Use integration in the techniques of Chapter 5.	**3** Find the area between the curve $y = \frac{1}{\sqrt{x}} + x^2 - 2$ and the x-axis, between $x = 0.5$ and $x = 1$.
4 Use the trapezium rule to estimate the area between a curve and the x-axis.	**4** Use the trapezium rule with four strips to estimate a) $\int_1^3 \frac{2}{x} \, dx$ b) $\int_0^{\frac{\pi}{2}} \sin x \, dx$
5 Determine whether an estimate made using the trapezium rule over- or under-estimate the area.	**5** Explain why the estimates in question 4 are over- or under-estimates of the true values.

C2

Revision exercise 11

1 The diagram shows the graphs of $y = x^{\frac{3}{2}}$, $0 \leqslant x \leqslant 4$, and a straight line joining the origin to the point P which has coordinates $(4, 8)$.

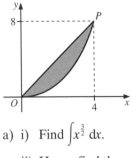

a) i) Find $\int x^{\frac{3}{2}} \, dx$.

   ii) Hence find the value of $\int_0^4 x^{\frac{3}{2}} \, dx$.

b) Calculate the area of the shaded region.

(AQA, 2003)

2 a) Express $\dfrac{x^5+1}{x^2}$ in the form $x^p + x^q$ where p and q are integers.

b) Hence, find $\displaystyle\int_1^2 \left(\dfrac{x^5+1}{x^2}\right) dx.$ *(AQA, 2002)*

3 a) Write $x^2\sqrt{x}$ in the form x^k, where k is a fraction.

b) The gradient of a curve at point (x, y) is given by $\dfrac{dy}{dx} = 7x^2\sqrt{x}$.

Use integration to find the equation of the curve, given that
the curve passes through the point $(1, 1)$.   *(AQA, 2002)*

4 A table of values for the function $f(x)$ is as shown.

x	0	3	6	9	12
$f(x)$	3	4	3	4	1

Use the trapezium rule, with four strips, to estimate the value of

$\displaystyle\int_0^{12} f(x)\, dx.$ *(AQA/NEAB, 2000)*

C2

5 The diagram shows the area under part of the quadrant of a circle of

radius 8 units. Angle AOB is $\dfrac{\pi}{7}$. The point B has coordinates

(3.471, 7.208), to 3 decimal places.

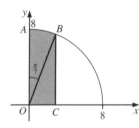

a) Find an exact expression for the area of sector AOB.

b) Hence, showing all your working, and without using calculus,
confirm that the shaded area is 26.87 square units to 2 decimal
places.

c) The equation of the quadrant of the circle is $y = \sqrt{(64 - x^2)}$. Use
the trapezium rule with 3 strips to estimate the shaded area, giving
your answer to 2 decimal places. Calculate the percentage error in
this estimation.   *(AQA/NEAB, 1999)*

6 Given that $y = x^2 - x^{-2}$

a) find the value of $\dfrac{dy}{dx}$ at the point where $x = 2$

b) find $\displaystyle\int y\, dx.$ *(AQA, 2001)*

7 a) Find $\int x^{\frac{1}{2}}\,dx$.

   b) Hence find the value of $\int_0^2 x^{\frac{1}{2}}\,dx$ giving your answer in the form $p\sqrt{2}$,
      where p is a rational number.   *(AQA, 2004)*

8 The function f is defined for $x \geqslant 0$ by $f(x) = x^{\frac{1}{2}} + 2$.

   a) i) Find $f'(x)$.
      ii) Hence find the gradient of the curve $y = f(x)$ at the point for
          which $x = 4$.

   b) i) Find $\int f(x)\,dx$.
      ii) Hence show that $\int_0^4 f(x)\,dx = \dfrac{40}{3}$.

   c) The diagram shows a symmetrical shaded region A bounded by:

      ✦ parts of the coordinate axes
      ✦ the curve $y = f(x)$ and its reflection in the line $y = x$ for
        $0 \leqslant x \leqslant 4$.

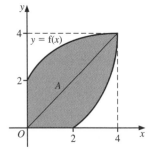

      Calculate the area of A.   *(AQA, 2003)*

9 A curve has equation $y = \dfrac{x^4}{4} + \dfrac{32}{x^2}$ and is sketched in the diagram.

   a) i) Find $\dfrac{dy}{dx}$.

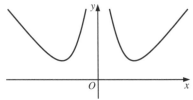

      ii) Hence find the gradient of the curve at the point
          where $x = 1$.
      iii) Show that the stationary points of the curve occur
          where $x^6 = 64$.
      iv) Hence find the x-coordinates of the stationary points.

   b) i) Find $\int \dfrac{x^4}{4} + \dfrac{32}{x^2}\,dx$.

      ii) Hence find the area of the region bounded by the curve,
          the lines $x = 1, x = 2$ and the x-axis.   *(AQA, 2002)*

C2

10 The curve with equation $y = 2x + \dfrac{27}{x^2} - 7$ is defined for $x > 0$ and is sketched below.

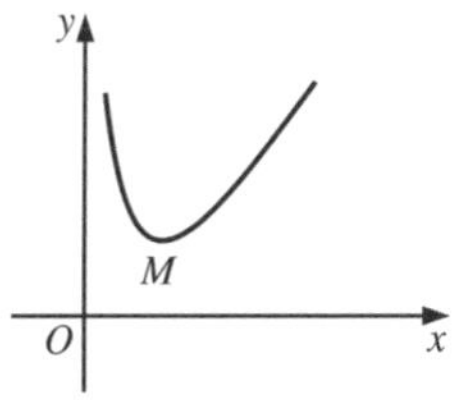

a) i) Find $\dfrac{dy}{dx}$.

ii) The curve has a minimum M. Find the x-coordinate of M.

b) i) Find $\displaystyle\int \left(2x + \dfrac{27}{x^2} - 7\right) dx$.

ii) Hence determine the area of the region bounded by the curve, the lines $x = 1, x = 2$ and the x-axis. (AQA, 2003)

11 The function f has domain $x \geqslant 2$ and is defined by $f(x) = \dfrac{2x - 3}{x}$

Find the derivative $f'(x)$ and deduce that f is an increasing function. (AQA/AEB, 1997)

12 Show that $\displaystyle\int_1^4 x^{\frac{3}{2}} \, dx = \dfrac{62}{5}$. (AQA, 2002)

13 The diagram shows a sketch of the curve $y = 14 - x^2 - \dfrac{9}{x^2}$ and the line $y = 4$.

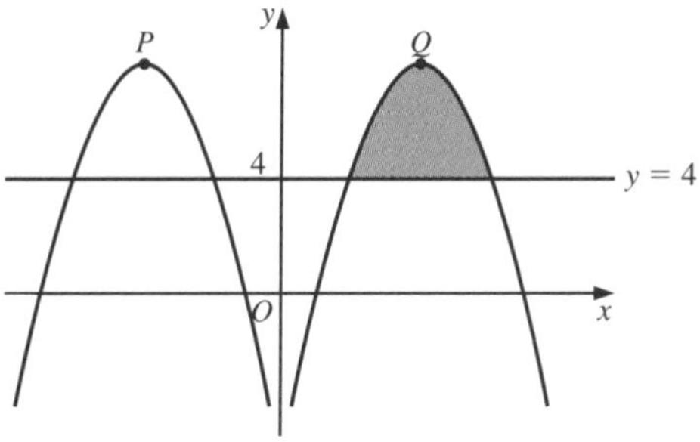

a) Find the coordinates of the two stationary points P and Q on the curve.

b) i) Show that the curve intersects the line $y = 4$ when $(x^2 - 9)(x^2 - 1) = 0$.

ii) Hence find the coordinates of the four points where the curve intersects the line $y = 4$.

iii) Show that the shaded region has area $5\frac{1}{3}$. (AQA, 2002)

C2 Practice Paper

90 minutes   *75 marks*   *You may use a calculator*

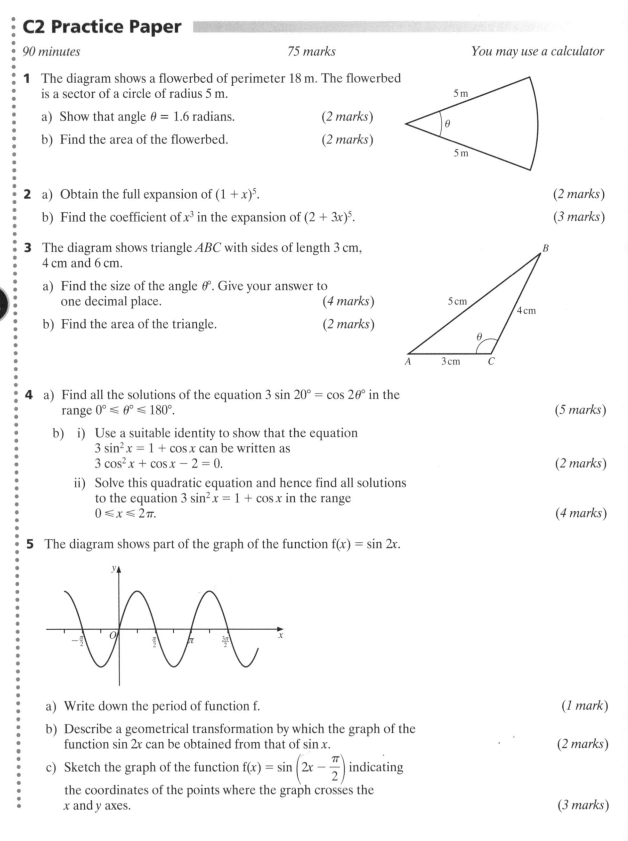

1 The diagram shows a flowerbed of perimeter 18 m. The flowerbed is a sector of a circle of radius 5 m.

   a) Show that angle $\theta = 1.6$ radians.   *(2 marks)*

   b) Find the area of the flowerbed.   *(2 marks)*

2 a) Obtain the full expansion of $(1 + x)^5$.   *(2 marks)*

   b) Find the coefficient of x^3 in the expansion of $(2 + 3x)^5$.   *(3 marks)*

3 The diagram shows triangle ABC with sides of length 3 cm, 4 cm and 6 cm.

   a) Find the size of the angle $\theta°$. Give your answer to one decimal place.   *(4 marks)*

   b) Find the area of the triangle.   *(2 marks)*

4 a) Find all the solutions of the equation $3 \sin 20° = \cos 2\theta°$ in the range $0° \leqslant \theta° \leqslant 180°$.   *(5 marks)*

   b) i) Use a suitable identity to show that the equation
      $3 \sin^2 x = 1 + \cos x$ can be written as
      $3 \cos^2 x + \cos x - 2 = 0$.   *(2 marks)*

     ii) Solve this quadratic equation and hence find all solutions
      to the equation $3 \sin^2 x = 1 + \cos x$ in the range
      $0 \leqslant x \leqslant 2\pi$.   *(4 marks)*

5 The diagram shows part of the graph of the function $f(x) = \sin 2x$.

   a) Write down the period of function f.   *(1 mark)*

   b) Describe a geometrical transformation by which the graph of the
      function $\sin 2x$ can be obtained from that of $\sin x$.   *(2 marks)*

   c) Sketch the graph of the function $f(x) = \sin\left(2x - \dfrac{\pi}{2}\right)$ indicating
      the coordinates of the points where the graph crosses the
      x and y axes.   *(3 marks)*

6 The diagram shows a series of rods joined together.

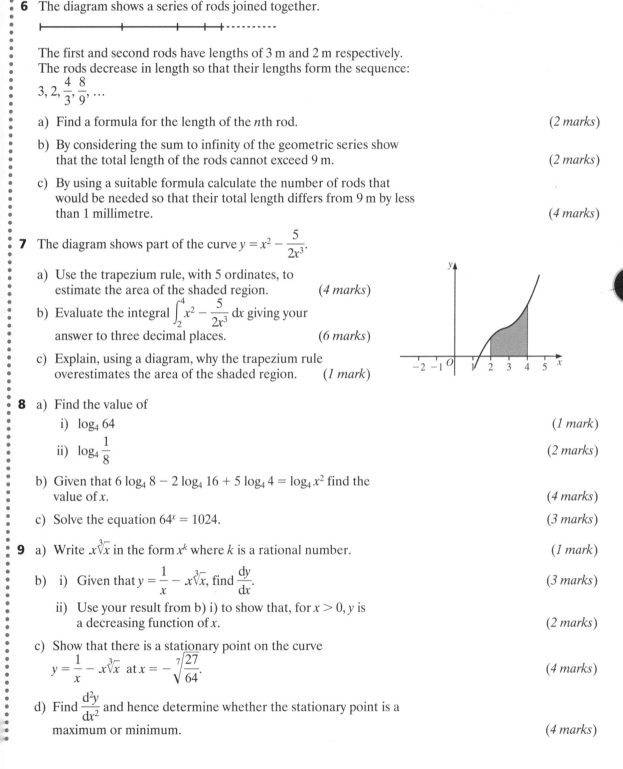

The first and second rods have lengths of 3 m and 2 m respectively.
The rods decrease in length so that their lengths form the sequence:

$3, 2, \dfrac{4}{3}, \dfrac{8}{9}, \ldots$

a) Find a formula for the length of the nth rod.   (*2 marks*)

b) By considering the sum to infinity of the geometric series show
   that the total length of the rods cannot exceed 9 m.   (*2 marks*)

c) By using a suitable formula calculate the number of rods that
   would be needed so that their total length differs from 9 m by less
   than 1 millimetre.   (*4 marks*)

7 The diagram shows part of the curve $y = x^2 - \dfrac{5}{2x^3}$.

a) Use the trapezium rule, with 5 ordinates, to
   estimate the area of the shaded region.   (*4 marks*)

b) Evaluate the integral $\displaystyle\int_2^4 x^2 - \dfrac{5}{2x^3}\, dx$ giving your
   answer to three decimal places.   (*6 marks*)

c) Explain, using a diagram, why the trapezium rule
   overestimates the area of the shaded region.   (*1 mark*)

8 a) Find the value of

   i) $\log_4 64$ (*1 mark*)

   ii) $\log_4 \dfrac{1}{8}$ (*2 marks*)

   b) Given that $6 \log_4 8 - 2 \log_4 16 + 5 \log_4 4 = \log_4 x^2$ find the
      value of x.   (*4 marks*)

   c) Solve the equation $64^x = 1024$.   (*3 marks*)

9 a) Write $x\sqrt[3]{x}$ in the form x^k where k is a rational number.   (*1 mark*)

   b) i) Given that $y = \dfrac{1}{x} - x\sqrt[3]{x}$, find $\dfrac{dy}{dx}$.   (*3 marks*)

   ii) Use your result from b) i) to show that, for $x > 0, y$ is
      a decreasing function of x.   (*2 marks*)

   c) Show that there is a stationary point on the curve
      $y = \dfrac{1}{x} - x\sqrt[3]{x}$ at $x = -\sqrt[7]{\dfrac{27}{64}}$.   (*4 marks*)

   d) Find $\dfrac{d^2y}{dx^2}$ and hence determine whether the stationary point is a
      maximum or minimum.   (*4 marks*)

GCSE algebra review

R1 Linear equations

This chapter is to help you revise the algebra that you have learned at GCSE level.

A linear equation can be expressed in the form $ax + b = 0$.

Each of these equations is linear:

$$x + 4 = 9 \qquad 3(x + 2) - 7 = x + 1 \qquad \frac{x}{3} + 7 = 4(x - 2)$$

Whatever you do to the left-hand side (LHS) of an equation must be done to the right-hand side (RHS). For example, the equation $x - 4 = 7$ can be manipulated so that x (the unknown) is the only term on the LHS.

$$x - 4 = 7$$

Add 4 to both sides to obtain:

$$x - 4 + 4 = 7 + 4$$
$$x + 0 = 11$$
$$\therefore \qquad x = 11$$

The solution is $x = 11$.

Example 1

Solve the equation $3x - 7 = x + 3$.

$$3x - 7 = x + 3$$

Add 7 to both sides to obtain:

$$3x - 7 + 7 = x + 3 + 7$$
$$\therefore \quad 3x = x + 10$$

To get all the x terms on the LHS subtract x from both sides.

$$3x - x = x + 10 - x$$
$$\therefore \quad 2x = 10$$

Dividing both sides by 2 gives:

$$x = 5$$

The solution is $x = 5$.

You can check that your solution works:
$$3x - 7 = x + 3$$
$$\text{LHS} = 3(5) - 7 = 8$$
$$\text{RHS} = 5 + 3 = 8$$
So $x = 5$ works.

Linear equations may contain brackets.

Example 2

Solve the equation $4(x + 1) - 3(x - 5) = 17$.

$$4(x + 1) - 3(x - 5) = 17$$
$$4x + 4 - 3x + 15 = 17$$
$$x + 19 = 17$$
$$x + 19 - 19 = 17 - 19$$
$$\therefore \quad x = -2$$

The solution is $x = -2$.

> Expand the brackets and simplify.

Linear equations may contain fractions. You should remove any fractions before proceeding.

Example 3

Solve the equation $\dfrac{x + 5}{2} = \dfrac{3x + 11}{5}$.

$$\frac{x + 5}{2} = \frac{3x + 11}{5}$$
$$\therefore \quad 10\left(\frac{x + 5}{2}\right) = 10\left(\frac{3x + 11}{5}\right)$$

> The lowest common multiple of 2 and 5 is 10, so multiply throughout by 10.

Simplifying the fractions gives:
$$5(x + 5) = 2(3x + 11)$$

Expanding the brackets gives:
$$5x + 25 = 6x + 22$$

Rearrange to obtain all the x terms on the LHS:
$$5x - 6x = 22 - 25$$
$$-x = -3$$
$$\therefore \quad x = 3$$

The solution is $x = 3$.

Alternatively, you could use the technique of **cross-multiplication**.

$$\frac{x + 5}{2} = \frac{3x + 11}{5}$$

Cross-multiplying gives:
$$5(x + 5) = 2(3x + 11)$$

Expanding and simplifying gives:
$$5x + 25 = 6x + 22$$
$$5x - 6x = 22 - 25$$
$$\therefore \qquad x = 3$$

The solution is $x = 3$, as before.

> **Remember**:
> To cross-multiply
> $$\frac{a}{b} = \frac{c}{d}$$
> multiply:
> $$\frac{a}{b} \bowtie \frac{c}{d}$$
> $$ad = bc$$

Exercise A

In each of these questions, solve the equations to find x.

1 a) $3x + 2 = 20$ b) $5x - 3 = 32$ c) $16 + 7x = 2$

d) $4 + 3x = 19$ e) $6 - x = 4$ f) $2x - 3 = 8$

g) $3x + 2 = x + 8$ h) $2x - 3 = 6x + 5$ i) $3x + 5 = 7x - 8$

j) $6x + 9 = 8 - 4x$ k) $2 - 5x = 8 - 3x$ l) $2x + 7 = 3 - 10x$

2 a) $2(x - 3) + 5(x - 1) = 3$

b) $3(5 - x) - 4(3x - 2) = 27$

c) $2(4x - 1) - 3(x - 2) = 14$

d) $3(x - 8) + 2(4x - 1) = 3$

e) $6(x + 4) + 5(2x - 1) = 7$

f) $3(2x + 5) - 4(x - 3) = 0$

g) $3(x - 1) - 4(x - 2) - 6(2x + 3) = 0$

h) $4(5 - x) - 2(x - 3) - 6(2x - 1) = 4$

i) $3(x + 5) + 2(x + 1) - 3x = 22$

j) $3(2x - 5) - 4(x - 2) = 5(x - 8)$

k) $7(x - 4) + 3(x - 6) = 6x - 12$

l) $4(2x + 1) + 6(9x - 2) = 3(5x - 4) + 4$

3 a) $\dfrac{x + 2}{3} = \dfrac{2x + 1}{5}$ b) $\dfrac{5x - 3}{4} = \dfrac{4x - 3}{3}$

c) $\dfrac{3x + 1}{4} = \dfrac{2 - x}{3}$ d) $\dfrac{2x + 3}{5} = \dfrac{4 + 3x}{3}$

Sometimes the unknown x may appear in the denominator. If you cross-multiply, you will remove the fractions.

Example 4

Solve the equation $\dfrac{2}{x + 1} = \dfrac{3}{5}$.

$$\dfrac{2}{x + 1} = \dfrac{3}{5}$$

Cross-multiply and expand the bracket to obtain:

$$2 \times 5 = 3(x + 1)$$
$$\therefore \quad 10 = 3x + 3$$

Rearranging gives:

$$3x = 7$$
$$\therefore \quad x = \tfrac{7}{3}$$

The solution is $x = \tfrac{7}{3}$.

You should aim to remove numerical fractions from equations as well.

Example 5

Solve the equation $\frac{1}{3}(5x - 4) + \frac{1}{7}(x + 2) = 13 - x$.

Since the lowest common multiple of 3 and 7 is 21, multiply throughout by 21:

$$21 \times \tfrac{1}{3}(5x - 4) + 21 \times \tfrac{1}{7}(x + 2) = 21(13 - x)$$

Simplifying gives:

$$7(5x - 4) + 3(x + 2) = 21(13 - x)$$
$$35x - 28 + 3x + 6 = 273 - 21x$$
$$59x = 295$$
$$\therefore \quad x = 5$$

The solution is $x = 5$.

In the next example, terms in x^2 appear in the working. However, these terms cancel and the equation reduces to a linear equation.

Example 6

Solve the equation $\dfrac{6x + 1}{2x - 5} = \dfrac{3x - 2}{x + 1}$.

Cross-multiply and expand the brackets:

$$(6x + 1)(x + 1) = (3x - 2)(2x - 5)$$
$$\therefore \quad 6x^2 + 7x + 1 = 6x^2 - 19x + 10$$

Rearranging gives

$$26x = 9$$
$$\therefore \quad x = \tfrac{9}{26}$$

The solution is $x = \tfrac{9}{26}$.

Exercise B

In each of these questions, solve the equations to find x.

1 a) $\dfrac{3}{x + 1} = \dfrac{4}{x}$

b) $\dfrac{2}{3x - 5} = \dfrac{5}{2x + 3}$

c) $\dfrac{6}{x + 8} = \dfrac{5}{3x + 4}$

d) $\dfrac{7}{x - 1} = \dfrac{3}{x + 2}$

e) $\dfrac{2}{x + 3} = \dfrac{4}{5}$

f) $\dfrac{5}{x - 1} = \dfrac{2}{3}$

g) $\dfrac{6}{2x - 3} = \dfrac{1}{3}$

h) $\dfrac{5}{2x - 3} = \dfrac{3}{8}$

2 a) $\frac{1}{2}(2x-1)+\frac{1}{4}(x-2)=4$
b) $\frac{1}{3}(x-1)-\frac{1}{4}(2x-3)=1$
c) $\frac{1}{5}(2x-1)-\frac{1}{4}(3x-4)=0$
d) $\frac{2}{3}(x-1)-\frac{1}{5}(x-3)=x+1$
e) $\frac{2}{5}(2-x)-\frac{1}{4}(3-5x)=x-4$
f) $\frac{1}{3}(x-1)-\frac{1}{6}(3x-5)=2x+3$
g) $\frac{1}{2}(x-1)-\frac{2}{3}(x-4)=\frac{1}{6}(3x-1)$
h) $\frac{1}{5}(x-2)+\frac{1}{3}(5x-4)=\frac{1}{2}x$
i) $\frac{3}{4}(2x-1)-\frac{1}{2}(x-3)=\frac{1}{3}(4x-1)$
j) $\frac{1}{3}(x-4)-\frac{1}{18}(2x-3)=\frac{1}{9}(5-x)$
k) $\frac{2}{3}x+\frac{1}{2}(3-8x)=\frac{1}{6}-4x$
l) $\frac{1}{2}(x+1)+\frac{1}{3}(x+2)=\frac{1}{4}(x+3)+\frac{1}{5}(x+4)$

3 a) $\dfrac{x+3}{x-2}=\dfrac{x+4}{x-3}$ b) $\dfrac{x-6}{x+4}=\dfrac{x-2}{x+3}$

c) $\dfrac{2x+3}{x+2}=\dfrac{4x}{2x+5}$ d) $\dfrac{6x+5}{2x-1}=\dfrac{3x+4}{x-3}$

e) $\dfrac{x-3}{3x-2}=\dfrac{x-1}{3x-5}$ f) $\dfrac{x-4}{x+5}=\dfrac{x+3}{x-6}$

g) $\dfrac{2x+5}{x+4}=\dfrac{2x-1}{x-1}$ h) $\dfrac{4x+3}{x-2}=\dfrac{8x+1}{2x-3}$

i) $\dfrac{3x+1}{2x-3}=\dfrac{6x+1}{4x-5}$ j) $\dfrac{4-x}{2x+3}=\dfrac{x-1}{3-2x}$

k) $\dfrac{3-2x}{2-3x}=\dfrac{5-6x}{1-9x}$ l) $\dfrac{5-6x}{7+3x}=\dfrac{2(1-x)}{x}$

R2 Linear functions

The function $y=mx+c$, where m and c are constants, is a linear function of x. It contains no power of x above degree 1. The following are some examples of linear functions:

◆ $y=5x-2$
◆ $y=\frac{1}{2}x+3$
◆ $\frac{1}{3}y=\frac{1}{4}x-1$

In those cases where fractions occur it is common practice to rearrange the linear function into the form $ax+by=c$ or $ax+by+c=0$, where a, b and c are constants.

For example, the linear function

$$y=\tfrac{1}{2}x+3$$

can be rearranged by multiplying throughout by 2, giving

$$2y=x+6$$

or $2y-x=6$

which is in the required form.

In the case of $\frac{1}{3}y = \frac{1}{4}x - 1$ multiplying throughout by 12 gives

$$4y = 3x - 12$$
$$4y - 3x = -12 \quad \text{or} \quad 4y - 3x + 12 = 0$$

Example 7

Determine which of the following functions are linear:

a) $y = 3 + 5x$ b) $2y - 6x = 7$

c) $y = x + x^2 - 1$ d) $3y + x = 2x - 1$

a) This can be written as $y = 5x + 3$, which is of the form $y = mx + c$ and is hence a linear function of x.

b) Rearranging gives

$$2y - 6x = 7$$
$$2y = 6x + 7$$
$$y = 3x + \frac{7}{2}$$

   This is in the form $y = mx + c$ and is hence a linear function of x.

c) The function $y = x + x^2 - 1$ contains powers of x greater than 1 and is in fact quadratic.

   This is not a linear function.

d) Rearranging gives

$$3y - x = 2x - 1$$
$$3y = x - 1$$
$$y = \frac{1}{3}x + \frac{1}{3}$$

   This is in the form $y = mx + c$ and is hence a linear function of x.

Plotting a linear function against x will always give a straight line. To plot a straight line you only need two points that the line passes through.

Example 8

Draw the graph of $y = 2x - 3$.

Consider the values 0 and 2 for x, which gives the values in the table.

x	0	2
y	-3	1

Plotting the points and drawing the line gives the graph shown.

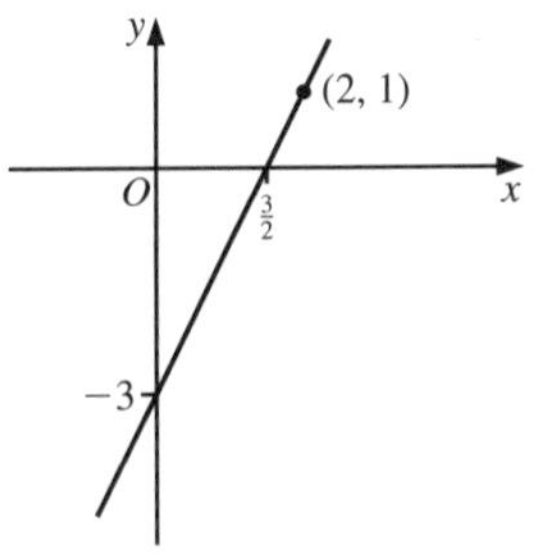

Example 9

Draw the graph of $2y + 3x = 1$.

Consider the values 0 and 2 for x, which gives

x	0	2
y	$\frac{1}{2}$	$-\frac{5}{2}$

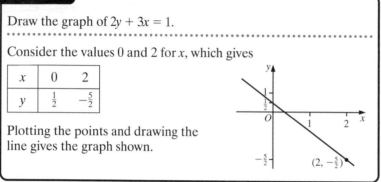

Plotting the points and drawing the
line gives the graph shown.

Exercise C

1   Determine which of the following are linear functions of x:
   a) $y = 5 - 7x$
   b) $y - 8 = 0$
   c) $3y - x = 0$
   d) $2y - 7x = x + y$
   e) $2y + x^2 = x - 1$
   f) $x^2 + 4y = x^2 + x - 7$

2   Draw the graph of each of the following linear functions:
   a) $y = 4x$
   b) $y = 2x - 1$
   c) $2y - 3 = x$
   d) $3y + 5x = 1$
   e) $5y - 7 = 2x + 3$
   f) $7x = y - 3$

R3   Linear inequalities

An inequality is a comparison between two mathematical expressions.

less than	is written as $<$
less than or equal to	is written as $\leqslant$
greater than	is written as $>$
greater than or equal to	is written as $\geqslant$

A **linear inequality** is a comparison between two linear expressions.
For example,

$$3x + 7 > x - 8 \qquad a < 3b + 2 \qquad 5x - 7y \leqslant 4$$

Inequalities can be solved using methods similar to those used for
solving equations.

Example 10

Simplify the inequality $3x + 7 \geqslant x + 2$.

$3x + 7 \geqslant x + 2$

Subtracting 7 from both sides gives:

$3x + 7 - 7 \geqslant x + 2 - 7$

$\therefore \quad 3x \geqslant x - 5$

Subtracting x from both sides gives:

$3x - x \geqslant x - 5 - x$

$2x \geqslant -5$

$\therefore \quad x \geqslant -\frac{5}{2}$

This result tells you that provided $x \geqslant -\frac{5}{2}$, the original inequality will be satisfied.

You can illustrate inequalities graphically. Just sketch the graphs of $y = 3x + 7$ and $y = x + 2$.

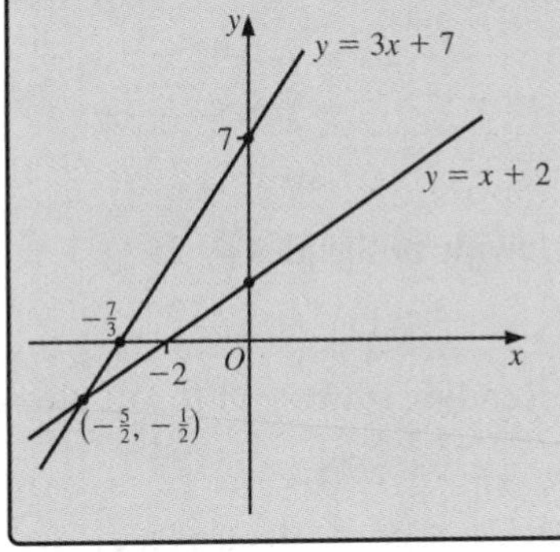

Inequalities can contain brackets.

Example 11

Simplify the inequality $4(3x + 1) - 3(x + 2) < 3x + 1$.

$4(3x + 1) - 3(x + 2) < 3x + 1$

Expand the brackets:

$12x + 4 - 3x - 6 < 3x + 1$

Simplifying and rearranging give:

$9x - 2 < 3x + 1$

$6x < 3$

$x < \frac{3}{6}$

$\therefore \quad x < \frac{1}{2}$

You can write this inequality as $x < \frac{1}{2}$.

You need to take care when you multiply or divide by a negative number.

$7 > 5$ is true.

Multiply both sides by -1:

$-7 > -5$ is false.

Reverse the inequality: $-7 < -5$ is true.

When you multiply or divide an inequality by a negative number you must reverse the inequality sign.

Example 12

Simplify the inequality $3x + 7 \geqslant 5x - 3$.

The x terms can be rearranged so that they are all on the RHS and therefore positive.

$$3x + 7 \geqslant 5x - 3$$
$$7 + 3 \geqslant 5x - 3x$$
$$\therefore \quad 10 \geqslant 2x$$

Divide both sides by 2:

$$5 \geqslant x$$

Reading from right to left gives:

$$x \leqslant 5$$

Alternatively, the x terms can be rearranged so that they are all on the LHS:

$$-2x \geqslant -10$$

Multiplying both sides by -1 gives:

$$2x \leqslant 10$$

Dividing both sides by 2 gives:

$$x \leqslant 5$$

You can illustrate this solution graphically:

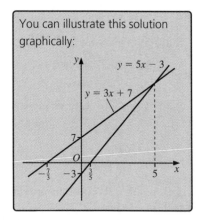

Remember to reverse the inequality.
$\geqslant$ becomes $\leqslant$

Exercise D

1 Solve each of these linear inequalities. In each case illustrate the solution graphically.

a) $3x + 5 > x + 13$

b) $2x - 3 \leqslant 5x + 9$

c) $4x - 7 \geqslant 2x + 4$

d) $5x - 8 > x + 7$

e) $2x - 1 < x + 4$

f) $7x - 3 \geqslant 2x - 1$

2 Solve each of these linear inequalities.

a) $6 - 5x < 2 - 3x$

b) $3 - x \geqslant 9 + 6x$

c) $7x - 2 \geqslant 4x + 3$

d) $9 - 8x > 4$

e) $2 - 3x < 6x + 20$

f) $3x - 2 \geqslant 5x - 9$

3 Remove the brackets and hence solve these linear inequalities.

a) $2(x + 3) - 3(x - 2) > 8$

b) $6(2x - 1) + 5(x + 1) < 33$

c) $5(x - 3) < 6(x - 4)$

d) $3(x + 4) \geqslant 6(x + 2)$

e) $3(x - 2) - 2(4 - 3x) > 5$

f) $7(1 - x) + 3(4 - 5x) \leqslant 41$

g) $3(2 - x) > 5(3 + 2x)$

h) $5(2 - x) - 2(3 - 6x) + 2(x - 1) > 0$

i) $2(3x - 1) - 2(x - 1) - x + 4 > 0$

j) $3(6x - 5) - 10(x - 4) \geqslant 3(x - 1)$

k) $5x - 2 + 3(2x - 7) < 2(5x - 3)$

l) $2(x - 3) - 3(5x - 2) \leqslant 6(3 - 2x)$

4 Solve these linear inequalities containing fractions.

a) $\frac{1}{2}x + 2 < 7$

b) $\frac{1}{6}(x - 1) \geqslant \frac{1}{3}(x - 4)$

c) $\frac{1}{2}(x + 3) \leqslant \frac{1}{3}(x - 5)$

d) $\frac{1}{7}(2x + 5) > \frac{1}{8}(x + 3)$

e) $\dfrac{x - 2}{4} < \dfrac{2x - 3}{3}$

f) $\dfrac{4 - x}{2} \geqslant \dfrac{2 - x}{3}$

....

R4 Simultaneous linear equations

Consider the equation $x + y = 9$.

The diagram shows its graph. Each point on the line is a solution of the equation. Examples are: $x = 0, y = 9; x = 4, y = 5; x = 0.25, y = 8.75$

You cannot solve the equation uniquely unless you are given further information, or another equation.

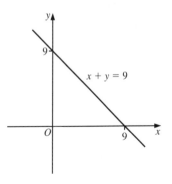

Suppose the second equation is

$$2x + y = 13$$

The diagram shows both graphs on the same axes.
$x + y = 9$ and $2x + y = 13$ are **simultaneous linear equations**.

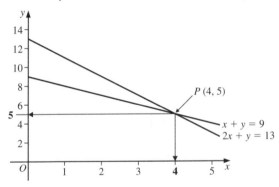

The point (4, 5) lies on both graphs. In other words, $x = 4, y = 5$ is the solution of the simultaneous linear equations.

You can solve a pair of simultaneous linear equations graphically by:

✦ drawing their graphs on the same axes
✦ finding their point of intersection.

There are two common algebraic methods for solving simultaneous linear equations.

Elimination

This method involves eliminating either the x terms or the y terms by adding or subtracting the two equations.

Example 13

Solve the simultaneous equations

$$2x + y = 7$$
$$2x - y = 5$$

Number the equations:

$$2x + y = 7 \qquad\qquad [1]$$
$$2x - y = 5 \qquad\qquad [2]$$

Subtract [2] from [1];

$$2y = 2 \qquad\qquad [1] - [2]$$
$$\therefore \quad y = 1$$

Substitute $y = 1$ into [1] to obtain x:

$$2x + 1 = 7$$
$$2x = 6$$
$$\therefore \quad x = 3$$

The solution is $x = 3, y = 1$.

> You could alternatively substitute $y = 1$ into [2].

In some cases, the coefficients of the x terms or the y terms may not be the same. You need to multiply the equations by a suitable constant so that the coefficients of either x terms or y are the same. This process is called **balancing the coefficients**.

Example 14

Solve the simultaneous equations:

$$5x - 7y = 27 \qquad\qquad [1]$$
$$2x + 3y = 5 \qquad\qquad [2]$$

To balance the coefficients of the y terms, multiply equation [1] by 3 and multiply equation [2] by 7. This gives:

$$15x - 21y = 81 \qquad\qquad [3]$$
$$14x + 21y = 35 \qquad\qquad [4]$$

> Note that the y terms match up.

Adding [3] and [4] gives:

$$29x = 116$$
$$\therefore \quad x = 4$$

Substituting $x = 4$ into [2] to find the corresponding y value gives:

$$2(4) + 3y = 5$$
$$8 + 3y = 5$$
$$3y = -3$$
$$\therefore \quad y = \frac{-3}{3} = -1$$

The solution is $x = 4, y = -1$.

Alternatively, you can balance the coefficients of the x terms by multiplying equation [1] by 2 and multiplying equation [2] by 5. This gives:

$$10x - 14y = 54 \qquad\qquad [5]$$
$$10x + 15y = 25 \qquad\qquad [6]$$

Subtracting [6] from [5] gives:

$$-29y = 29$$
$$\therefore \quad y = -1$$

Substituting $y = -1$ into [2] to find the corresponding x value gives:

$$2x + 3(-1) = 5$$
$$\therefore \quad x = 4$$

The solution is $x = 4, y = -1$, as before.

> To solve a pair of simultaneous equations, you need to find x and y.

> You can check the solution by substituting into [1]:
> $$5(4) - 7(1) = 20 + 7$$
> $$= 27$$

> Note that x has been eliminated.

Substitution

This method involves rearranging one of the equations so that you have either

✦ y in terms of x, in which case you then substitute this expression for y into the second equation,

or

✦ x in terms of y, in which case you substitute this expression for x into the second equation.

> The choice usually depends on which gives the simpler expression after rearranging.

Example 15

Solve the simultaneous equations

$$3x + 4y - 27 = 0 \qquad\qquad [1]$$
$$5x + y - 11 = 0 \qquad\qquad [2]$$

Rearranging [2] for y gives:

$$y = 11 - 5x \qquad\qquad [3]$$

Substituting [3] into [1] gives:

$$3x + 4(11 - 5x) - 27 = 0$$
$$\therefore \quad 3x + 44 - 20x - 27 = 0$$
$$\therefore \quad -17x = -17$$
$$\therefore \quad x = 1$$

Substituting $x = 1$ into [3] to find the corresponding y value gives:

$$y = 11 - 5(1)$$
$$\therefore \quad y = 6$$

The solution is $x = 1, y = 6$.

Exercise E

Solve each pair of simultaneous equations. Use the elimination method.

1 a) $2x - 3y = 7$ b) $3x - y = 1$ c) $2x - 7y = 1$
          $2x + 3y = 1$ $5x + y = 7$ $2x + 3y = 11$

   d) $3x - 4y = 5$ e) $5x + 2y = 7$ f) $x - 2y = 5$
          $6x - 4y = 2$ $2x + y = 2$ $3x + y = 8$

   g) $2x + 3y = 1$ h) $3x - 2y = 5$ i) $3x + 5y = 1$
          $3x + y = 5$ $2x + y = 8$ $2x + 3y = 0$

   j) $5x + 4y = 1$ k) $6x - 5y = 12$ l) $3x + 2y = 3$
          $7x + 5y = 2$ $5x - 4y = 11$ $x - 6y = 11$

2 Solve each pair of simultaneous equations. Use either the
elimination or substitution method, but show your working
clearly.

   a) $2x + y - 10 = 0$ b) $5x - 4y + 1 = 0$ c) $4x - 3y + 1 = 0$
          $3x - 2y - 8 = 0$ $3x + y - 13 = 0$ $3x - 4y + 6 = 0$

   d) $5x - 7y + 3 = 0$ e) $7x - 3y - 8 = 0$ f) $2x - 5y + 4 = 0$
          $3x + 2y + 8 = 0$ $5x + 7y + 8 = 0$ $3x - 5y + 1 = 0$

   g) $x - y - 1 = 0$ h) $3x + 2y - 2 = 0$ i) $2x + 2y + 1 = 0$
          $5x - 2y - 3 = 0$ $x - 6y + 1 = 0$ $3x + 5y + 4 = 0$

   j) $5x + 2y - 10 = 0$ k) $3x - 7y - 3 = 0$ l) $2x + 3y - 2 = 0$
          $3x - 7y - 6 = 0$ $6x - 11y - 9 = 0$ $4x + 9y - 3 = 0$

3 Solve each pair of simultaneous equations. Use the substitution
method, and in each case illustrate your solution graphically.

   a) $y = x + 3$ b) $y = x - 4$ c) $y = 5 - 2x$
          $y = 2x + 1$ $y = 3x - 16$ $y = x + 8$

   d) $y = 4 - x$ e) $y = x - 3$ f) $y = 2x - 10$
          $y = 2x + 10$ $y = 6x + 2$ $y = \frac{1}{3}x$

   g) $7x + 3y = 6$ h) $6x + y + 8 = 0$ i) $2x + 3y - 3 = 0$
          $5x + 4y = 8$ $5x - 4y + 26 = 0$ $3x - 2y + 15 = 0$

Answers

Answers are given only for questions with a numerical or algebraic solution.

Chapter 1
Check in

1 a) yes b) no (contains x^2) c) no $\left(\text{can be written } y = \dfrac{1}{x}\right)$ d) yes e) yes f) no (contains square root)

3 a) $3x - 6$ b) $-1 - 2x$ c) $2x - 9$ d) $x^2 - 1$ e) $6x^2 + 13x + 6$ f) $4 - 5x - 6x^2$

4 a) $3(x - 4)$ b) $x(x + 5)$ c) $3x(1 - 2x)$ d) $(x + 3)(x - 2)$ e) $(2x + 3)(2x - 3)$ f) $(3x - 1)(x + 4)$

5 a) $x = 5$ b) $x = -2$ c) $x = 2$ d) $x = 2$ e) $x = 12$ f) $x = -15$

6 a) $x = 4, y = 2$ b) $x = 2, y = -1$ c) $x = \dfrac{29}{13}, y = \dfrac{18}{13}$ d) $x = -1, y = -1$ **7** a) $x < 4$ b) $x > -1.5$ c) $x < 3$ d) $x < -2$

Exercise 1A

1 a) $2\sqrt{3}$ b) $5\sqrt{2}$ c) $4\sqrt{7}$ d) $11\sqrt{3}$ e) $16\sqrt{5}$ f) $2\sqrt{2}$ g) $2\sqrt{2}$ h) $9\sqrt{5}$

2 a) $\dfrac{3\sqrt{2}}{2}$ b) $\dfrac{5\sqrt{3}}{3}$ c) $\dfrac{\sqrt{6}}{3}$ d) $\dfrac{\sqrt{14}}{2}$ e) $2\sqrt{35}$ f) $\dfrac{\sqrt{30}}{4}$ g) $\dfrac{\sqrt{6}}{3}$ h) $\dfrac{3\sqrt{10}}{5}$

3 a) $2 + \sqrt{3}$ b) $\dfrac{3 - \sqrt{5}}{4}$ c) $\dfrac{5 + \sqrt{7}}{9}$ d) $\dfrac{6 - \sqrt{3}}{11}$ e) $3 + 2\sqrt{2}$ f) $\dfrac{13 - 2\sqrt{2}}{23}$ g) $-17 - 8\sqrt{5}$ h) $\dfrac{6 - \sqrt{6}}{2}$

4 $\sqrt{2}$

Exercise 1B

1 a) $3x^2 - 12x + 12$ b) $4x^2 + 4x + 6$ c) $3 - 4x - x^2$ d) $2x^2 + 2x + 25$ e) $24 - 8x$ f) $13x^2 + 13$ g) $2x^2 + 4x + 7$

1 h) $3x^2 - 4x + 10$ i) $9x^2 - 4x + 44$ **2** a) $(0, 5), y$-axis b) $(0, -1), y$-axis c) $(0, -12), y$-axis d) $(0, 9), y$-axis

2 e) $(2, 0), x = 2$ f) $(-3, 0), x = -3$ g) $(5, 0), x = 5$ h) $(1, 3), x = 1$ i) $(3, 5), x = 3$

Exercise 1C

2 b) $-4, 4$ **3** b) $2, 3$ **4** b) $-1, 7$ **5** b) $-1, 2\frac{2}{3}$

Exercise 1D

1 a) $2, 3$ b) $-1, 4$ c) $2, 5$ d) $-3, -2$ e) $2, 4$ f) $-1, 6$ g) ± 3 h) $-4, 2$ i) $-3, 4$ j) $4, 5$ k) $0, 4$ l) $-1, 8$

2 a) $-2, -\frac{1}{2}$ b) $\frac{1}{3}, 2$ c) $-1, \frac{5}{2}$ d) $-3, \frac{1}{5}$ e) $-1, -\frac{1}{4}$ f) $\frac{1}{3}, \frac{1}{2}$ g) $-\frac{2}{3}, 4$ h) $-3, \frac{5}{2}$ i) $\pm\frac{3}{4}$ j) $-\frac{5}{3}, 2$ k) $-3, \frac{2}{5}$ l) $\frac{1}{4}, \frac{3}{2}$

3 $5 \, \text{cm} \times 12 \, \text{cm}$ **4** $\frac{3}{4}$ **5** b) $x^2 - 6x + 9 = 0, x = 3$ **6** 120 **7** 10

Exercise 1E

1 a) $(x + 2)^2 + 2$ b) $(x - 3)^2 + 4$ c) $(x - 5)^2 + 15$ d) $\left(x - \frac{1}{2}\right)^2 - 5\frac{1}{4}$ e) $\left(x - 2\frac{1}{2}\right)^2 + 2\frac{3}{4}$ f) $(x - 10)^2 - 97$

2 a) $2 \pm \sqrt{5}$ b) $-3 \pm \sqrt{7}$ c) $1 \pm \sqrt{2}$ d) $4 \pm \sqrt{19}$ e) $-\dfrac{1}{2} \pm \dfrac{\sqrt{5}}{2}$ f) $-\dfrac{3}{2} \pm \dfrac{\sqrt{5}}{2}$ g) $\dfrac{5}{2} \pm \dfrac{\sqrt{33}}{2}$ h) $\dfrac{1}{2} \pm \dfrac{\sqrt{13}}{2}$ i) $-\dfrac{5}{2} \pm \dfrac{\sqrt{21}}{2}$

2 j) $-6 \pm \sqrt{31}$ k) $\dfrac{9}{2} \pm \dfrac{\sqrt{41}}{2}$ l) $\dfrac{1}{4} \pm \dfrac{\sqrt{5}}{4}$

Exercise 1F

1 a) $2(x + 2)^2 - 21$ b) $3(x - 1)^2 - 1$ c) $9 - (x + 2)^2$ d) $7 - 2(x - 1)^2$ e) $2\left(x - 1\frac{1}{2}\right)^2 + \frac{1}{2}$ f) $28 - 5(x + 1)^2$

2 a) $\dfrac{3}{4} \pm \dfrac{\sqrt{33}}{4}$ b) $1 \pm \dfrac{1}{3}\sqrt{6}$ c) $-\dfrac{1}{2} \pm \dfrac{1}{2}\sqrt{6}$ d) $-\dfrac{5}{6} \pm \dfrac{\sqrt{37}}{6}$ e) $-\dfrac{1}{10} \pm \dfrac{\sqrt{61}}{10}$ f) $\dfrac{3}{4} \pm \dfrac{\sqrt{17}}{4}$ g) $\dfrac{1}{4} \pm \dfrac{\sqrt{17}}{4}$ h) $-\dfrac{3}{8} \pm \dfrac{\sqrt{41}}{8}$

2 i) $1 \pm \dfrac{\sqrt{14}}{7}$ j) $-\dfrac{1}{3} \pm \dfrac{1}{6}\sqrt{22}$ k) $2 \pm \dfrac{1}{5}\sqrt{15}$ l) $-\dfrac{9}{2} \pm \dfrac{\sqrt{39}}{2}$ **4** b) $100 \, \text{m}^2$ **5** $x(40 - 2x) \, \text{m}^2$

6 Split figure into two rectangles, x by $(20 - x)$ and x by $(20 - 2x)$, so area is $40x - 3x^2$; max area $= \dfrac{400}{3} \, \text{m}^2$

Exercise 1G

1 a) $-6, -1$ b) $-5, 2$ c) $3, 4$ d) $-5, 4$ e) $3, 6$ f) $-6, 1$ g) $\frac{1}{2}, 2$ h) $-\frac{1}{3}, 4$ i) $\frac{1}{2}, -1\frac{1}{2}$ j) $-1, -\frac{2}{3}$ k) $2, 2\frac{1}{2}$ l) $-\frac{1}{5}, 2$

2 a) $\dfrac{-3 \pm \sqrt{13}}{2}$ b) $\dfrac{-1 \pm \sqrt{13}}{2}$ c) $\dfrac{5 \pm \sqrt{13}}{2}$ d) $\dfrac{1 \pm \sqrt{17}}{2}$ e) $\dfrac{-5 \pm \sqrt{13}}{2}$ f) $\dfrac{3 \pm \sqrt{29}}{2}$ g) $\dfrac{-3 \pm \sqrt{41}}{4}$ h) $\dfrac{-1 \pm \sqrt{37}}{6}$

2 i) $\dfrac{-5 \pm \sqrt{137}}{8}$ j) $\dfrac{7 \pm \sqrt{17}}{4}$ k) $\dfrac{9 \pm \sqrt{129}}{12}$ l) $\dfrac{1 \pm \sqrt{61}}{10}$ **3** a) 0 b) 2 c) 1 d) 2 e) 1 f) 0   **4** -71 **5** -16

10 4 or 16   **11** $-\frac{2}{9}$ or 2

Exercise 1H

1 a) $-5, 0$ b) $2, 6$ c) $-2, 8$ d) $2 \pm \sqrt{2}$ e) $-2, \frac{1}{3}$ f) $\dfrac{3 \pm \sqrt{73}}{4}$

2 a) $0, \frac{2}{3}$ b) $-3, 5$ c) $-5, 3$ d) $-2 \pm \sqrt{5}$ e) $-\frac{1}{2}, \frac{2}{3}$ f) $\dfrac{3 \pm 2\sqrt{6}}{5}$ **3** $-1, 2$ **4** $3, 5\frac{1}{2}$ **5** $y = 2x^2 - 11x + 12$

6 $(x + 2)^2 + 3$

Exercise 1I

1 a) $x < 3$ or $x > 5$ b) $-4 < x < 3$ c) $-3 \leqslant x \leqslant -1$ d) $-\frac{3}{2} < x < 1$ e) $x \leqslant \frac{1}{2}$ or $x \geqslant \frac{2}{3}$ f) $x < -3$ or $x > 1$

2 a) $x < -2$ or $x > 4$ b) $-3 \leqslant x \leqslant 5$ c) $-4 < x < -3$ d) $x \leqslant -\frac{5}{2}$ or $x \geqslant 1$ e) $-\frac{6}{5} \leqslant x \leqslant -1$ f) $x = 4$

3 a) $x \leqslant -5$ or $x \geqslant 2$ b) $3 < x < 7$ c) $x < 1$ or $x > 4$ d) $3 \leqslant x \leqslant 8$ e) $x < -3$ or $x > \frac{1}{2}$ f) $\frac{1}{2} < x < \frac{4}{5}$ **4** $x < 3$ or $x \geqslant 5$

Exercise 1J

1 a) $(2, 2), (5, 11)$ b) $\left(\frac{1}{2}, 3\right), (3, 13)$ c) $\left(-\frac{1}{3}, 3\right), (4, 16)$ d) $(-3, 37), \left(-\frac{5}{2}, \frac{63}{2}\right)$ e) $\left(\frac{1}{2}, -\frac{5}{2}\right), (2, -1)$ f) $(-4, 11), \left(\frac{1}{2}, 2\right)$

1 g) $(2, 3), (3, 2)$ h) $\left(-6, -\frac{1}{3}\right), \left(\frac{1}{2}, 4\right)$ **2** a) $(-1, -2)$ b) The line is a tangent to the curve.

Exercise 1K

1 $(6, 2), (-2, 10); (6, 2)$ **2** $12\,\text{cm} \times 4\,\text{cm}$ **3** $(10, 26), (48, 7), (10, 26)$ **4** $(2, 4), (4, 2)$

Check out

1 a) 15 b) $\sqrt{5} + \sqrt{3}$ **3** a) $(x - 3)^2 + 2$; 2, at $x = 3$ b) $2(x + 3)^2 - 5$; -5, at $x = -3$

4 a) 2 b) 1 c) 2 d) 0   **5** a) $-5, \frac{3}{2}$ b) $0.85, -2.35$ c) $-0.37, 3.37$ **6** a) $x = -\frac{1}{2}, y = -2$; $x = 2, y = 3$ b) $x = \frac{7}{4}, y = \frac{3}{4}$

7 a) $x > \frac{5}{2}, x < -1$ b) $-\frac{3}{2} \leqslant x \leqslant \frac{3}{2}$

Revision exercise 1

1 a) $a = 2, b = -9$ b) $x < -5, x > 1$ **2** $(3, -1)$ or $(1, 1)$ **3** a) $x = -8 \pm \frac{3}{2}\sqrt{2}$ b) i) $m = 8, n = -9$

3 b) ii) minimum value $= -9$ **4** a) $16 + 9\sqrt{3}$ b) $8 + 2\sqrt{3}$ **5** a) i) $3\sqrt{5}$ ii) $4\sqrt{5}$ b) $7\sqrt{5}$

6 a) $(x + 4)^2 - 5$ b) $(-4, -5)$ **7** a) i) $x = \dfrac{-8 \pm 2\sqrt{2}}{4}$ ii) $x > -2 + \dfrac{\sqrt{2}}{2}$ and $x < -2 - \dfrac{\sqrt{2}}{2}$

7 b) $2(x + 2)^2 - 1$ c) i) -1 ii) -2 **8** a) $y < -3$ b) $x > 2$ **9** $\left(\frac{3}{2}, -\frac{1}{4}\right), (-1, 1)$ **10** b) $x = \dfrac{2 \pm 3\sqrt{2}}{7}$

10 c) i) $x < 0, x > \frac{3}{7}$ ii) $\dfrac{2 - 3\sqrt{2}}{7} < x < \dfrac{2 + 3\sqrt{2}}{7}$

Chapter 2

Check in

2 a) $(x + 3)^2 - \frac{17}{4}$ b) $2\left(x + \frac{7}{4}\right)^2 - \frac{137}{8}$ c) $-4(x + 1)^2 + 24$

3 a) $-3, 4$ b) $\dfrac{3 \pm \sqrt{5}}{2}$ c) $\dfrac{3 \pm \sqrt{7}}{2}$

4 a) $x = 2, y = 2; x = 5, y = 11$ b) $x = \frac{1}{2}, y = 3\,x = 3, y = 8$ c) $x = -\frac{1}{3}, y = 3; x = 4, y = 16$

Exercise 2A

1 a) 3 b) 2 c) 1 d) 12 e) 2 f) 4   **2** a) 14 b) 25 c) -4 d) 70 e) -1 f) 47   **3** a) $3x^3 + x^2 + 2x - 2$

3 b) $4x^3 - 2x^2 - x - 5$ c) $x^3 + x^2 + x - 1$ d) $2x^3 + 2x^2 + 4x$ e) $9x^4 - 2x^3 - x^2 + 13x - 20$ f) $9x^5 + 2x^4 + 23x^2 - 20$

4 a) $2x^3 + 3x^2 - 8x + 3$ b) $x^3 - 5x^2 + 11x - 10$ c) $5x^3 - 22x^2 + 5x + 12$ d) $2x^3 - x^2 + 5x + 3$ e) $6x^3 + 11x^2 - 13x + 2$
4 f) $8x^3 - 22x^2 + 29x - 6$ **5** $6x^4 - x^3 - 18x^2 + 43x - 30$ **6** $8a^3 + 36a^2b + 54ab^2 + 27b^3$

Exercise 2B

1 a) $(x - 3)(x - 1)(x + 3)$ b) $(x + 1)(x + 2)(x + 3)$ c) $(x - 2)(x^2 + 2)$ d) $(x - 4)(x - 1)(x + 1)$ e) $(x - 3)(x - 1)(x + 2)$
1 f) $x(x - 7)(x + 3)$ g) $(x - 2)^2(x - 1)$ h) $(x - 3)^3$ i) $(x - 2)(x + 3)(x + 5)$ j) $(x^2 + 4)(x + 1)$ k) $(x + 1)^2(x - 3)$
1 l) $(x - 1)(x + 1)(x + 7)$ **2** a) $(x - 3)(x - 2)(x + 2)$ c) $-2, 2, 3$ **3** a) $(x - 4)(x - 3)(x + 2)$ c) $-2, 3, 4$
4 a) $(x - 2)(x^2 + x + 1)$ c) 2 **5** a) $-4, 1, 2$ b) 2 **3** c) $-2, -1, 3$ d) $-1, 2$ e) $-5, -3, 1$ f) $1, \dfrac{-3 \pm \sqrt{29}}{2}$
6 $(x - 3)(x - 1)(x + 4)$, $-4, 1, 3$ **7** $(x + 1)^2(x - 5)$, $-1, 5$ **8** a) $(x - 2)2x + 1)(x + 1)$ c) $-1, -\frac{1}{2}, 2$
9 a) $(5x - 1)(x + 1)(x + 2)$ c) $x < -2, -1 < x < \frac{1}{5}$

Exercise 2C

1 a) $x + 4, -3$ b) $x - 5, 8$ c) $2x + 1, -6$ d) $2x - 5, 8$ e) $6x - 7, 9$ f) $6x + 11, 38$
2 a) $x^2 + 5x + 8, 17$ b) $x^2 + 2x - 12, 39$ c) $2x^2 + 5x + 16, 65$ d) $2x^2 + 5x + 7, 0$ e) $2x^2 + 3x + 8, 4$ f) $4x^2 - 15x + 46, -136$

Exercise 2D

1 a) 10 b) 24 c) 1 d) 5 e) -4 f) -69 **2** 4 **3** 8 **4** -2 **5** 1 **6** -20 **7** $a = 5$ rem 13
8 $b = -52$ rem -56 **9** $a = -13, b = 5$ **10** $c = 1, d = 7$

Exercise 2E

1 a) $x - 3, 1$ b) $x + 5, -13$ c) $x^2 + x + 7, 14$ d) $x^2 + x + 6, 45$ e) $x^2 + 2x - 1, 25$ f) $x^2 - 2x + 6, -8$
2 $a = 1, b = 1, c = -4, d = 4$ **3** $a = 1, b = -1, c = -4, d = 12$ **4** $2x^3 - 3x^2 + 3x - 4, 14$ **5** $a = 3, b = -1$

Exercise 2F

4 $y = \frac{1}{2}(x + 1)(x - 2)(x - 4)$

Exercise 2G

1 a) $(x - 3)^2 + 4$ b) $\begin{pmatrix} 3 \\ 4 \end{pmatrix}$ **2** a) $(x - 4)^2 + 4$ b) $\begin{pmatrix} 4 \\ 4 \end{pmatrix}$ **3** a) $(x + 2)^2 + 8$ b) $\begin{pmatrix} -2 \\ 8 \end{pmatrix}$

Exercise 2H

2 a) $(x - 4)^2 + (y - 5)^2 = 9$ b) $(x - 6)^2 + (y - 7)^2 = 64$ c) $(x - 2)^2 + (y + 1)^2 = 16$ d) $(x + 3)^2 + (y - 4)^2 = 4$
2 e) $(x - 5)^2 + y^2 = 9$ f) $(x + 6)^2 + (y + 9)^2 = 121$ **3** $(x - 2)^2 + (y + 3)^2 = 25, (2, -3), 5$

Check out

1 a) quadratic b) other (reciprocal) c) linear d) cubic e) quadratic f) other (sine wave) g) linear h) cubic
1 i) other (exponential) j) other (quartic) k) cubic l) linear   **2** a) ii) $(x - 2)(x - 3)(x + 1)$ b) $a = 1, b = 1$
3 a) -24 b) -4 **4** centre $(2, -3)$, radius $2\sqrt{3}$ **5** a) i) $y = x^2 - 6x + 13$ ii) translation $\begin{pmatrix} 3 \\ 4 \end{pmatrix}$
5 b) i) $(x - 2)^2 + (y - 5)^2 = 25$ ii) translation $\begin{pmatrix} 2 \\ 5 \end{pmatrix}$

Revision exercise 2

1 a) $p(-2) = 0$ b) $(x + 2)(x - 1)^2$ c) ii) $x < -2$ **2** $a = -3, b = 0$ **3** b) $p = -2, q = -5$
4 a) i) $f(x) = (x + 3)^2 + 2$ ii) $x = -3$ b) $x < -2, x > -4$
5 a) $x = 4 \pm \sqrt{19}$ c) $x \leqslant 4 - \sqrt{19}, 4 + \sqrt{19} \leqslant x \leqslant 8.5$ **6** a) $f(1) = 0, f(-1) = -4$ b) $(x - 1)(x + 2)(x + 3)$
7 a) $p(1) = 0$ b) $(x - 1)(2x - 3)(x + 2)$ **8** a) $(x + 2)$ is a factor   b) $f(x) = (x + 2)(5x^2 + 14x + 1)$ c) $x = -\frac{7}{5} \pm \frac{2}{5}\sqrt{11}, 2$
9 $p = -3$

Chapter 3

Check in

2 a) 2 b) $\frac{1}{2}$ c) infinite d) -1 e) 0 f) -6 **3** a) 10 b) 7.62 (3 s.f.) c) 6.24 (3 s.f.) d) 5.74 (3 s.f.)

4 a) 90° (angle in semi-circle) b) 90° (perpendicular bisector of chord) c) tangent **5** a) -1 b) -2 c) 7 d) -4

6 a) $2x - y - 7 = 0$ b) $x + 6y - 12 = 0$ c) $3x - 5y + 15 = 0$ d) $y = -3x + 6$ e) $y = \frac{2}{3}x + \frac{16}{5}$ f) $y = -\frac{1}{2}x$

Exercise 3A

1 a) 5 b) 13 c) 10 d) 17 e) 20 f) $4\sqrt{2}$ g) $\sqrt{29}$ h) 10 i) $5\sqrt{5}$ j) $3\sqrt{5}$ k) $2\sqrt{10}$ l) $3\sqrt{2}$ **2** $\sqrt{7^2 + 1^2} = \sqrt{5^2 + 5^2}$

3 4 **4** $AB = 3\sqrt{2}, BC = 3\sqrt{2}, AC = 6; AC^2 = AB^2 + BC^2$, so ABC is right-angled

5 Sides have length 13, 13 and $7\sqrt{2}$, so triangle is isosceles **6** Sides have length $\sqrt{409}, \sqrt{272}, \sqrt{65}$; triangle is not right-angled

7 Sides have length $4\sqrt{2}, 2\sqrt{10}, 2\sqrt{10}$; triangle is isosceles **8** $AB = 5, BC = 10, AC = \sqrt{125}$; area $= \frac{1}{2} \times 5 \times 10 = 25$

9 -5 or 9 **10** 3

Exercise 3B

1 a) $(5, 3)$ b) $(5, 6)$ c) $(1, 2)$ d) $(4, 2)$ e) $\left(2\frac{1}{2}, -4\right)$ f) $(-5, -5)$ g) $(5, 0)$ h) $\left(5\frac{1}{2}, \frac{1}{2}\right)$ i) $(0, 0)$ j) $(4, -5)$ k) $\left(3\frac{1}{2}, 2\right)$

1 l) $\left(3\frac{1}{2}, \frac{1}{2}\right)$ **2** $(10, 7)$ **3** $(9, -1)$ **4** $(-3, -2)$ **5** $\left(-\frac{1}{2}, -2\frac{1}{2}\right)$ **8** a) $P(4, 3), Q(8, 4), R(9, 3), S(5, 2)$

Exercise 3C

1 a) 2 b) 3 c) $\frac{1}{2}$ d) $\frac{3}{4}$ e) $-\frac{1}{4}$ f) $\frac{4}{7}$ g) $\frac{1}{5}$ h) 0 i) 3 j) $-\frac{8}{7}$ k) $-\frac{11}{4}$ l) infinity **2** c) It is a parallelogram. **3** 3

Exercise 3D

3 $m_{AB} = 12, m_{BC} = -\frac{5}{2}, m_{CA} = \frac{2}{5}; m_{BC} \times m_{CA} = -1$ **4** 1 **5** 3, 11 **6** $-2, 5$ **7** 20

Exercise 3E

1 a) 5 b) 3 c) -4 d) 7 e) 5 f) $\frac{1}{4}$ g) $\frac{5}{2}$ h) $-\frac{2}{7}$ i) $-\frac{5}{2}$ j) $-\frac{5}{4}$ k) $-\frac{3}{2}$ l) $-\frac{3}{5}$ **2** a) $y = 2x - 7$ b) $y = -2x + 9$

2 c) $4y - x = 18$ **3** a) $y = 3x - 9$ b) $y = \frac{1}{3}x - 4$ c) $2y + 5x = 5$ **4** a) $y = 2x - 1$ b) $y = \frac{1}{2}x - 1$ c) $y = -9x + 15$

4 d) $y = 4x + 4$ e) $y = -12x + 43$ f) $y = 9$ **5** a) $y = -2x + 12$ b) $y = -x + 6$ c) $2y + x + 3 = 0$ d) $4y + 2x = 11$

5 e) $2y - 8x + 1 = 0$ f) $y = -7x - 2$ **6** $y = -2x + 9, 20\frac{1}{4}$ **7** $16y - 6x + 13 = 0, 3y + 8x - 66 = 0$

9 a) $y = -3x + 25, y = -3x + 5$ b) $104\frac{1}{6}$ c) $4\frac{1}{6}$

Exercise 3F

1 a) $x^2 + y^2 - 2x - 4y - 4 = 0$ b) $x^2 + y^2 - 6x - 2y - 6 = 0$ c) $x^2 + y^2 + 4x - 6y + 12 = 0$ d) $x^2 + y^2 - 2x + 6y - 15 = 0$

1 e) $x^2 + y^2 + 8x = 0$ f) $x^2 + y^2 - 4x + 8y - 29 = 0$ g) $x^2 + y^2 + 6x - 10y - 2 = 0$ h) $x^2 + y^2 - 8x + 2y + 8 = 0$

2 a) $(0, 0), 4$ b) $(0, 0), 9$ c) $(-3, 2), 1$ d) $(2, 0), 2$ e) $(0, -3), 5$ f) $(3, -4), 6$ g) $(-7, 5), 9$ h) $(6, 6), 8$ l) $(-8, -6), 10$

2 j) $(1, -1), 2$ k) $(7, -8), 12$ l) $\left(0, \frac{5}{2}\right), \frac{3}{2}$ **3** a) $x^2 + y^2 - 10x - 8y + 16 = 0$ b) $x^2 + y^2 - 2x + 14y - 119 = 0$

3 c) $x^2 + y^2 - 10x - 14y + 25 = 0$ d) $x^2 + y^2 + 4x + 6y + 9 = 0$ **4** $x^2 + y^2 - 12x - 16y + 75 = 0$

5 $x^2 + y^2 - 2x - 8y + 7 = 0$ **6** $x^2 + y^2 - 10y = 0, x^2 + y^2 - 12x - 10y + 36 = 0$

Exercise 3G

1 b) $m_{AB} = \frac{1}{7}, m_{BC} = -7$ **2** b) $x + y + 8 = 0$ c) $(-11, 3)$ **3** b) $(-4, 2)$ c) $7y - x = 18$ d) $7y + 49x = 18$

4 b) $(4, 3)$ c) $x + 2y = 10$ d) $(6 - 2\sqrt{5}, 2 + \sqrt{5})$

Exercise 3H

1 a) $y = x$ b) $y = 2x + 3$ c) $x + y + 7 = 0$ d) $y = -2x$ e) $x + y = 7$ f) $4y + 3x = 0$ **2** a) $3y = 5x + 1$ b) $y = x - 5$

2 c) $y = 4$ d) $y = -x - 2$ e) $7y - 3x = 36$ f) $y = x - 5$ **3** a) $(3, 0), (7, 0)$ b) $x + 2y = 3, x - 2y = 7$

4 a) $(0, 3), (0, 5)$ b) $y = 3x + 5, 3x + y = 3$ **5** a) $2y + x = 6$ b) $A(6, 0), B(0, 3)$ c) 9 **6** b) $(-1, 3)$ c) $2y + 5x = 22$

7 b) $(3, 9)$ **8** 5 **9** a) $\sqrt{17}$

Exercise 3I

1 a) $(3, 4), (5, 2)$ b) $(-1, -5), (0, 2)$ c) $(3, 8), (4, 7)$ d) $(-4, -5), (-1, 10)$
4 a) 2 b) 0 c) 2 d) 2 e) 0 f) 0   **5** $5y + 2x = -28, 5x + 2y = 21$

Check out

1 a) $(3, 3)$ b) $(1\frac{1}{2}, \frac{1}{2})$ c) $(-1, 0)$ **2** a) $2\sqrt{5}$ b) $5\sqrt{2}$ c) $6\sqrt{2}$ **3** a) $-\frac{1}{2}$ b) 1 c) -1
4 a) i) $y = -\frac{1}{2}x + \frac{7}{2}$ ii) $x + 2y - 9 = 0$ b) i) $y = x - 1$ ii) $x - y - 1 = 0$ c) i) $y = -x - 1$ ii) $x + y + 1 = 0$
5 a) $y = 3x - 5$ b) $y = -2x - 1$ or $2x + y + 1 = 0$ c) $2y = -x + 7$ d) $3y = 2x + 8$ **6** b) $3y = -2x + 14$ c) $2y = 3x - 8$
7 a) $P(3, 0), Q(-2, 5)$ b) no intersection

Revision exercise 3

1 a) $A(-3, 0), B(0, 6)$ b) $M\left(-\frac{3}{2}, 3\right)$ c) $y = -\frac{1}{2}x + \frac{9}{4}$ **2** a) i) -3 ii) $r = 3, s = 4$ b) i) $M(2, -2)$ ii) $\frac{1}{3}$ iii) $p = -1$
3 a) i) $\frac{3}{4}$ ii) $4y = 3x - 19$ b) i) $4x + 3y = 17$ ii) $X(5, -1)$ **4** a) radius 7, centre $(-2, 7)$ c) $CT = 4$
5 $x = 2, y = 3$. The line is a tangent to the circle as there is only one solution to the simultaneous equations.
6 a) $x + 7y - 50 = 0$ c) ii) centre of circle is mid-point of OB $\left(7\frac{1}{2}, 2\frac{1}{2}\right)$ iii) radius $= \frac{5}{2}\sqrt{10}$
7 b) centre $(3, 4)$, radius 4 c) $y = \frac{4}{3}x$ d) $3x + 4y = 5$ **8** $y = -20x + 70$ **9** a) $\frac{3}{2}, y = \frac{3}{2}x$
10 a) $\frac{5}{3}$ b) ii) $3x + 5y = 2$ c) $(7, 3)$ **11** a) i) 4 ii) $\frac{5}{2}$ b) $5y + 2x + 3 = 0$ c) $p = 5$ **12** a) $y = -x + 5$ b) $y = x - 1$
12 c) $(3, 2)$ d) $(x - 5)^2 + (y - 4)^2 = 8$ **13** a) centre $(-1, 3)$, radius $= \sqrt{10}$ b) $y = -3x + 10$
14 a) centre $(2, -4)$, radius $\sqrt{10}$ c) $P(5, -3), Q(1, -1)$

Chapter 4
Check in

1 gradient $\frac{1}{2}$, y-intercept -2 b) gradient $-\frac{2}{3}$, y-intercept 2 c) gradient $\frac{4}{3}$, y-intercept 4 d) gradient 2, y-intercept -2

2 a) 1 b) $-\frac{1}{3}$ c) $\frac{1}{2}$ d) $-\frac{1}{8}$ **3** a) $y = 3x - 5$ b) $y = -2x - 1$ c) $y = -\frac{x}{2} + \frac{9}{2}$ d) $y = \frac{1}{3}x - \frac{17}{3}$

4 a) 3 b) -5 c) 1 d) 4   **5** a) $x = 6$ b) $x = 1$ c) $x = 3, x = -1$ d) $x = -1 \pm \sqrt{3}$

6 a) $(2x - 5)(x - 3)$ b) $(3 + x)(1 - 3x)$ c) $x^2(3 - 2x)$ d) $x(2x - 1)(x + 4)$

Exercise 4A

1 a)

x	-3	-2	-1	-0.5	0	0.5	1	2	3
y	9	4	1	0.25	0	0.25	1	4	9

1 c) 4 d) -2
2 a)

x	0	0.5	1	1.5	2	2.5	3
$\frac{1}{4}x^3$	0	0.03125	0.25	0.84375	2	3.90625	6.75

2 c) 0.75 d) 3

Exercise 4B

1 a) $5x^4$ b) $9x^8$ c) $7x^6$ d) $12x^{11}$ e) $20x^{19}$ f) $8x^7$ g) $14x^{13}$ h) $11x^{10}$ i) $3x^2$ j) $17x^{16}$ k) $100x^{99}$ l) 1
2 a) $14x$ b) $18x^8$ c) $15x^4$ d) $12x^2$ e) $56x^6$ f) $28x^3$ g) $-15x^2$ h) $24x$ i) $36x^3$ j) $-28x^6$ k) 6 l) $45x^2$
3 a) 6 b) 3 c) 80 d) 40 e) -5 f) 144 g) 120 h) 224 i) 12 j) -42 k) -70 l) 400   **4** $(-2, -8), (2, 8)$

Exercise 4C

1 a) $2x + 5$ b) $6x - 7$ c) $-5 - 2x$ d) $7 - 10x$ e) $3x^2 - 6x$ f) $-1 + 4x - 3x^2$ g) $6x^2 - 5$ h) $12x^2 - 6x + 7$
1 i) $-12x - 12x^2$ j) $4x^3 - 4x + 6$ **2** a) $2x - 6$ b) $10x - 2$ c) $-7 - 2x$ d) $1 - 10x$
2 e) $3x^2 + 4$ f) $3x^2 + 14x - 3$ g) $-3 - 3x^2$ h) $5 - 2x - 3x^2$ i) $6x^2 + 8x - 3$ j) $16x^3 - 6x + 7$
3 a) 1 b) 8 c) -12 d) -8 e) -9 f) -5 g) 8 h) -101 **4** a) $(-3, -34), (3, 32)$ b) $(0, 0), \left(-\frac{3}{2}, -\frac{27}{16}\right)$
5 $y = 4x^4 - 12x^2 + 9$, so $\dfrac{dy}{dx} = 16x^3 - 24x = 8x(2x^2 - 3)$

Exercise 4D

1 a) $2t + 3$　b) $7\,\text{m s}^{-1}$　**2** a) $6t^2 + 5$　b) $59\,\text{m s}^{-1}$　**3** a) $6t - 15t^2$　b) $6 - 30t$　**4** a) $1 + 3t^2$　b) $6t$

5 a) $6t - 2$　b) $34\,\text{m s}^{-2}$　**6** a) $3t^2 - 6t + 6$　b) $6\,\text{m s}^{-2}$　**7** a) $2t - 8$　b) 4　**8** a) $1, 3$　b) $9, 5$　**9** $27\,\text{m s}^{-1}$

Exercise 4E

1 a) $y = 6x - 9$　b) $y = 24x - 36$　c) $y = -8x + 7$　d) $y = 5x + 16$　e) $y = 4x - 2$　f) $x + y = 2$

2 a) $x + 3y = 4$　b) $x - 6y + 31 = 0$　c) $x + 14y = 114$　d) $x + 8y + 49 = 0$　e) $x - 5y - 28 = 0$　f) $x = 2y$　**3** $y = 8x - 7$

4 $y = -18x + 34$　**5** $x - 6y - 52 = 0$　**6** a) $(0, 1)$　b) $y = -3x + 1$　**7** a) $(2, 0)$　b) $x + 12y - 2 = 0$

8 a) $(1, 0), (4, 0)$　b) $y = -3x + 3, y = 3x - 12$　c) $\left(\frac{5}{2}, -\frac{9}{2}\right)$　**9** a) $(-3, 9), (3, 9)$　b) $y = -6x - 9, y = 6x - 9$　c) $(0, -9)$

10 a) $(-2, 0), (3, 0)$　b) $x - 5y + 2 = 0, x + 5y - 3 = 0$　c) $\left(\frac{1}{2}, \frac{1}{2}\right)$　**11** $\left(-\frac{1}{3}, -\frac{16}{3}\right)$　**12** a) $-2, 4$　b) $y = 15x + 38, y = 15x - 70$

Exercise 4F

1 a) $(2, -1)$　b) $(-3, -4)$　c) $(0, 6)$　d) $\left(\frac{5}{2}, -\frac{13}{4}\right)$　e) $\left(\frac{3}{4}, -\frac{1}{8}\right)$　f) $(-1, 4), (1, 0)$　g) $(-2, 40), (6, -216)$　h) $(1, 11), (-3, -21)$

1 i) $(0, 5), (2, 9)$　j) $(-3, 115), (3, -101)$　k) $(1, 0), (2, 1)$　l) $(1, -11), (3, -203)$　**2** a) -8　b) 6　c) $6x$　d) $6x + 4$

2 e) $30x - 6$　f) $-24x$　g) $12x^2 + 6$　h) $6x - 30x^2$　i) $40x^3 + 42x$　j) $6x - 20x^3 - 42x^5$　k) $-54x - 60x^4$　l) $56x^6 + 60x^4 - 12x^2$

3 a) $(1, 4)$ min　b) $(-2, -2)$ min　c) $\left(\frac{1}{2}, \frac{13}{4}\right)$ max　d) $(3, -1)$ min　e) $\left(-\frac{5}{4}, -\frac{147}{8}\right)$ min　f) $(5, 0)$ min

3 g) $(2, -40)$ min, $(-6, 216)$ max　h) $\left(\frac{1}{3}, \frac{40}{27}\right)$ max, $(3, -8)$ min　**4** a) $(3, 3)$ min　b) $(5, -4)$ min　c) $(-1, 5)$ max, $(1, 1)$ min

4 d) $(-2, -27)$ min, $(4, 81)$ max　e) $(1, 1)$ max, $(2, 0)$ min　f) $(1, -4)$ min, $(3, 0)$ max

Exercise 4G

1 $20, £10\,000$　**2** $4000, £20\,800$　**3** $55\,\text{mph}$　**4** $600\,\text{miles}$　**5** $1.5\,\text{s}, 11.25\,\text{m}$　**6** a) $(40 - 2x)\,\text{m}$　b) $10, 200\,\text{m}^2$

7 a) surface area $= x^2 + 4xh = 48$, so $h = \dfrac{48 - x^2}{4x}$　b) volume $= x^2 h = \dfrac{x^2(48 - x^2)}{4x} = 12x - \dfrac{x^3}{4}$　c) $\dfrac{dV}{dx} = 12 - \frac{3}{4}x^2$

7 d) $x = 4\,\text{m}, V = 32\,\text{m}^3$　**8** a) surface area $= 4x^2 + 6xl = 75$, so $l = \dfrac{75 - 4x^2}{6x}$　b) Volume $= 2x^2 l = \dfrac{2x^2(75 - 4x^2)}{6x} = 25x - \frac{4}{3}x^3$

8 c) $\dfrac{dV}{dx} = 25 - 4x^2$　d) $x = 2.5\,\text{m}, V = 41\frac{2}{3}\,\text{m}^3$　**9** $\frac{5}{3}$

Exercise 4H

1 a) increase $x > 4$, decrease $x < 4$　b) increase $x < -1$, decrease $x > -1$　c) increase $x < -1$ and $x > 3$, decrease $-1 < x < 3$

1 d) increase $x < 1$ and $x > 6$, decrease $1 < x < 6$　e) increase $-3 < x < 2$, decrease $x < -3$ and $x > 2$

1 f) increase $-3 < x < -2$ and $x > 2$, decrease $x < -3$ and $-2 < x < 2$

Check out

1 $3x^2 - 6x + 4$　**2** -7　**3** $12\,\text{cm}^3\,\text{s}^{-1}$, the rate at which volume is increasing at $t = 2$　**4** a) i) $y = x - 4$　ii) $y = -x$

4 b) i) $y = 7x + 16$　ii) $7y = -x + 62$　**5** a) $\left(-\frac{2}{3}, 12\frac{22}{27}\right), (4, -38)$　b) $(0, 4), (\sqrt{2}, 0), (-\sqrt{2}, 0)$

6 a) max, min　b) max, min, min　**7** a) i) $f'(2) = -16, f'(-2) = 24$　ii) decreasing at $x = 2$, increasing at $x = -2$

7 b) min $(0, 4)$, max $(\sqrt{2}, 0)$, max $(-\sqrt{2}, 0)$

Revision exercise 4

1 a) $f'(x) = 18x^2 - 6x - 60$　b) $x = -\frac{5}{3}, x = 2$　c) $f(2) = 1; f(x) = 0$ has 1 root　**2** $y = 2x + 6$

3 $\dfrac{dy}{dx} = 12x(x + 1)^2$; stationary values at $x = 0, x = -1$　**4** a) $y = -px + q$　b) $p > 0$, so gradient of tangent at $(0, q)$ is negative

5 minimum $\left(\frac{2}{3}, -\frac{1}{3}\right)$; range $f(x) \geqslant -\frac{1}{3}$　**6** a) $f(x) = 0$ at $x = 2$ and $x = \frac{11}{5}$　b) stationary point at $(2.1, 0.05)$

6 c) $k = -5, a = -2.1, b = 0.05$　**7** a) $\dfrac{dh}{dt} = 6t - 3t^2$　b) -3.75　c) $0 < t < 2$　**8** a) i) $h = 120 - 6x$　ii) $A = 600x - 24x^2$

8 b) i) $x = 12.5$　ii) max　**9** a) $V = x^2 h, A = 4xh + x^2$　b) i) $V = 750x - \frac{1}{4}x^3$　ii) $x = 10\sqrt{10}$　iii) $V_{max} = 5000\sqrt{10}$

10 a) $3x^2 + 6x + 3$　b) 30　**11** $9x^2 + 2x + 1, x = 0, -\frac{2}{9}$　**12** a) $\dfrac{dV}{dx} = 2400 - 280x + 6x^2; x = 35.4, 11.3$

12 c) $11.3\,\text{cm} \times 37.4\,\text{cm} \times 28.7\,\text{cm}$　**13** a) $117 + 114t - 3t^2$　b) i) 39　ii) max　c) i) 2009　ii) $P = 0$, all birds gone!

Chapter 5

Check in
1 a) $6x$ b) $3x^2$ c) -5 d) 0 **2** a) $12x^2 - 7$ b) $-4x$ c) $6x - 20x^4$ d) $x - x^3$ **3** a) 9 b) -10 c) 12 d) 4
4 a) $(0,0),(4,0)$ b) $\left(\frac{3}{2},0\right),(-5,0),(0,-15)$ c) $(0,0),\left(-\frac{1}{2},0\right)$ d) $(-1,0),(0,4)$; touches x-axis at $(2,0)$

Exercise 5A
The constant of integration is omitted in the answers to questions 1 to 3.
1 a) $\frac{1}{4}x^4$ b) $\frac{1}{5}x^5$ c) x^3 d) $2x^6$ e) $-2x^2$ f) $3x^5$ g) $\frac{1}{2}x^4$ h) $3x$ i) $\frac{1}{12}x^6$ j) $\frac{1}{6}x^4$ k) $-\frac{1}{9}x^3$ l) $\frac{2}{3}x$ **2** a) $x^3 + 7x$ b) $x^4 - x^2$
2 c) $2x - x^6$ d) $2x^2 - 2x^3$ e) $5x - 4x^2$ f) $\frac{1}{2}x^2 - \frac{1}{4}x^4$ g) $x + \frac{1}{2}x^2 + \frac{1}{3}x^3$ h) $2x - \frac{5}{2}x^2 + \frac{8}{3}x^3$ i) $2x^2 - x^4 + x^7$ j) $\frac{3}{2}x^2 - \frac{1}{2}x^4 + \frac{1}{3}x^9$
3 a) $\frac{1}{3}x^3 - 2x^2$ b) $\frac{2}{3}x^3 - \frac{3}{2}x^2$ c) $x^3 + 3x^2$ d) $5x^3 - 5x^2$ e) $\frac{1}{4}x^4 + \frac{1}{3}x^3$ f) $x^5 - \frac{1}{2}x^4$ g) $4x^3 - \frac{5}{2}x^4$ h) $\frac{1}{3}x^3 + \frac{3}{2}x^2 + 2x$
4 a) $5x^2 + 3x - 2$ b) $x^3 - 2x^2 + 3$ c) $3x^2 - 4x^3 - 15$ d) $\dfrac{15x^2}{2} - 4x - \dfrac{19}{2}$ e) $x^4 + x^2 + 1$ f) $2 + x - 5x^2$ g) $x^6 - \dfrac{2x^3}{3} + \dfrac{4}{3}$
4 h) $12 - 2x - 2x^2$ **5** $y = x^3 + 4x + 2$ **6** $y = x^4 - 3x^2 + 4$ **7** $y = 4x^4 + x^2 + x + 2$ **8** $y = x^3 - 2x^2 + 5x + 1$
9 $y = x^4 - 3x^2 + 3$ **10** $a = 3, b = -5, c = 4$

Exercise 5B
1 9 **2** 32 **3** 42 **4** 10 **5** 96 **6** 12 **7** 24 **8** 40 **9** $63\frac{3}{4}$ **10** -3 **11** $49\frac{1}{2}$ **12** $\frac{1}{3}$

Exercise 5C
1 a) $4\frac{2}{3}$ b) $16\frac{1}{2}$ c) 20 d) $20\frac{5}{6}$ e) 15 f) $\frac{4}{3}$ g) 4 h) $53\frac{2}{5}$ **2** a) $70\frac{1}{2}$ b) $19\frac{1}{2}$ c) $18\frac{1}{4}$ d) 4 e) $11\frac{1}{3}$ f) 14 **3** 50
4 $85\frac{1}{3}$ **5** $\frac{1}{6}$ **6** $2\frac{2}{3}$ **7** $6\frac{3}{4}$ **8** b) $\frac{7}{12}$ c) $11\frac{1}{4}$ **9** b) $\frac{13}{60}$ c) $2\frac{14}{15}$

Check out
1 a) $x^3 - \frac{3}{2}x^2 - 5x + c$ b) $x^4 - 3x^2 + 3x + c$ **2** a) $8\frac{2}{3}$ b) 62

Revision exercise 5
1 a) $y = (x - 3)^2 + 5$ b) $12\frac{2}{3}$ **2** a) $\frac{1}{4}x^4 - 2x^2 + c$ b) 0
2 c) The area above the x-axis between $x = -2$ and $x = 0$ is the same as the area below the x-axis between $x = 0$ and $x = 2$.
3 a) $w = 40, k = \frac{1}{40}$ b) $266\frac{2}{3}$ cm^2, 0.16 m^3 **4** a) i) $3x^2 - 6x + 3$ ii) $3(x - 1)^2$ b) i) $\frac{1}{4}x^4 - x^3 + \frac{3}{2}x^2 + c$
5 a) 16 b) i) -12 ii) $y = -12x + 24$, Q is $(0, 24)$ c) 8 **6** a) $f(3) = -2, f(4) = 0$ b) $f(x) = (x - 1)(x - 2)(x - 4)$
5 c) i) $3x^2 - 14x + 14$ ii) $f'(3) = -1$, so f is decreasing iii) $\frac{1}{4}x^4 - \frac{7}{3}x^3 + 7x^2 - 8x + c$ iv) 0.416 or $\frac{5}{12}$ **7** a) $6x - y - 6 = 0$
7 b) $\frac{1}{4}$ **8** a) 6.75 b) $2y = x + 11.5$ or $4y = 2x + 23$ **9** a) $x^4 - \frac{1}{3}x^3 + c$ b) $12\frac{2}{3}$ **10** a) 4 b) $2\sqrt{2}$
11 a) i) $1 - 8x^3$ ii) $\frac{3}{8}$ b) i) $\frac{1}{2}x^2 - \frac{2}{5}x + c$ ii) $\frac{9}{80}$ $(= 0.1125)$ **12** a) i) $3x^2 - 12x + 9$ ii) $(1, 20), (3, 16)$ b) i) $47\frac{1}{4}$ ii) $20\frac{1}{4}$

C1 Practice Paper
1 a) $4\sqrt{13}$ b) $2 + \sqrt{13}$ c) $x = -2 \pm \frac{1}{2}\sqrt{26}$ **2** $A\left(\frac{1}{2}, 2\frac{1}{2}\right), B(-5, -3)$ **3** a) $f(-2) = 0$ b) $x^2 + 2x + 5$
3 c) discriminant $= -16$; $x^2 + 2x + 5 = 0$ has no solution and $x^2 + 2x + 5$ has no factors
4 a) $(x - 3)^2 - 2$ c) line of symmetry $x = 3$ d) $y = x^2$ is translated by $\begin{pmatrix} 3 \\ -2 \end{pmatrix}$ **5** a) $\frac{3}{2}$ b) $3x - 2y + 5 = 0$ c) $2y = 3x - 12$
5 d) 5 **6** a) $(-4, 3)$ b) $y = -2x - 5$ c) $(x + 3)^2 + (y - 1)^2 = 10$ **7** a) i) $6x^2 - 6x$ ii) $P(1, -1)$
7 b) i) 6 ii) minimum at $x = 1$ c) i) $\frac{1}{2}x^4 - x^3 + c$ ii) $\frac{27}{32}$ **8** a) i) $f'(x) = 7 - 2x$ ii) Profits are increasing for $0 < x < 3\frac{1}{2}$
8 a) iii) £12 250 b) $1 \leqslant x \leqslant 6$; they should make at least 1000 and at most 6000 widgets.

Chapter 6

Check in
2 a) 9 b) 11 c) -9 d) 9 e) $27, 4x^2$ f) -9 g) -11 h) 9 i) 7 j) $18, -8x - 1$

Exercise 6A

1 a) translation $\begin{pmatrix} 0 \\ 3 \end{pmatrix}$ **b)** translation $\begin{pmatrix} 4 \\ 0 \end{pmatrix}$ **c)** stretch parallel to the y-axis by a scale factor 2 **d)** reflection in the x-axis

1 e) translation $\begin{pmatrix} -2 \\ 0 \end{pmatrix}$ **f)** stretch parallel to the y-axis by a scale factor $\frac{1}{3}$. **2 a)** reflection in the x-axis **b)** translation $\begin{pmatrix} 0 \\ 1 \end{pmatrix}$

2 c) stretch parallel to the y-axis by a scale factor of 2 **d)** translation $\begin{pmatrix} 4 \\ 0 \end{pmatrix}$ **e)** translation $\begin{pmatrix} 0 \\ -6 \end{pmatrix}$ **f)** translation $\begin{pmatrix} -2 \\ 0 \end{pmatrix}$

3 a) stretch parallel to the y-axis by a scale factor of 4 **b)** translation $\begin{pmatrix} 2 \\ 0 \end{pmatrix}$ **c)** translation $\begin{pmatrix} 0 \\ 3 \end{pmatrix}$ **d)** reflection in the x-axis

3 e) translation $\begin{pmatrix} -1 \\ 0 \end{pmatrix}$ **f)** stretch parallel to the y-axis by a scale factor $\frac{1}{2}$.

4 a) translation $\begin{pmatrix} -3 \\ 0 \end{pmatrix}$ **b)** reflection in the y-axis **c)** reflection in the x-axis **d)** stretch parallel to the x-axis by a factor of $\frac{1}{3}$

4 e) stretch parallel to the x-axis by a factor of 2. **f)** translation $\begin{pmatrix} 0 \\ -5 \end{pmatrix}$

Check out

1 a) i) translation $\begin{pmatrix} 0 \\ 2 \end{pmatrix}$ **b) i)** stretch parallel to y-axis, scale factor 3 **c)** stretch parallel to x-axis, scale factor 2

2 a) ii) $y = -x^2 - 2$ **b) i)** $y = \dfrac{1}{x-3}$ **ii)** $y = \dfrac{3}{x}$ **iii)** $y = \dfrac{3}{x}$ **iv)** $y = -\dfrac{1}{x}$ **c) i)** $f(x-5) = 2^{x-5}$ **ii)** $5f(x) = 5 \times 2^x$

2 c) iii) $f(5x) = 2^{5x}$ **iv)** $-2f(x) = -2 \times 2^x$

Revision exercise 6

1 $f(x+3) = \dfrac{1}{(x+3)^2 + 1}$ **4** $f(x+3) = \dfrac{1}{(x+3)^2}$

5 a) translation $\begin{pmatrix} -2 \\ 0 \end{pmatrix}$ **b)** stretch parallel to x-axis, scale factor $\frac{1}{3}$, stretch parallel to y-axis, scale factor 4

6 translation $\begin{pmatrix} -1 \\ 0 \end{pmatrix}$, stretch parallel to y-axis, scale factor 3 **7 b)** stretch parallel to x-axis, scale factor $\frac{1}{3}$

Chapter 7
Check in

1 a) The difference between terms is 2, then 3, then 4 and so on, increasing by one each time. Sequence continues 22, 29, ...

1 b) The terms are $2^2 - 1$, $3^2 - 1$, $4^2 - 1$, and so on, one less than the square numbers, starting at 4. Sequence continues 48, 63.

1 c) The difference between terms is 3. 3 is subtracted each time to get the next term. Sequence continues -8, -11, ...

2 a) ii) 231 **b) i)** 28 **ii)** 128 **iii)** All members end in 3 or 8. $5n - 2 = 333 \Rightarrow 5n = 335 \Rightarrow n = 67$

Exercise 7A

1 a) 3, 5, 7, 9, 11, 13; divergent **b)** 1, 4, 7, 10, 13, 16; divergent **c)** 3, 1, −1, −3, −5, −7; divergent **d)** 4, 7, 12, 19, 28, 39; divergent

1 e) $1, \frac{1}{2}, \frac{1}{3}, \frac{1}{4}, \frac{1}{5}, \frac{1}{6}$; convergent $\to 0$ **f)** $\frac{1}{2}, \frac{2}{3}, \frac{3}{4}, \frac{4}{5}, \frac{5}{6}, \frac{6}{7}$; convergent $\to 1$ **g)** $\frac{1}{2}, \frac{1}{5}, \frac{1}{10}, \frac{1}{17}, \frac{1}{26}, \frac{1}{37}$; convergent $\to 0$

1 h) $3\frac{1}{2}, 3\frac{1}{6}, 3\frac{1}{12}, 3\frac{1}{20}, 3\frac{1}{30}, 3\frac{1}{42}$; convergent $\to 3$ **i)** 6, 24, 60, 120, 210, 336; divergent **j)** 2, 4, 8, 16, 32, 64; divergent

1 k) −1, 2, −3, 4, −5, 6; divergent **l)** $1, -\frac{1}{4}, \frac{1}{9}, -\frac{1}{16}, \frac{1}{25}, -\frac{1}{36}$; convergent $\to 0$ **2 a)** $4n$ **b)** $2n + 3$ **c)** $5n - 1$ **d)** $3n + 5$

2 e) $\dfrac{1}{n+1}$ **f)** $\dfrac{1}{3n}$ **g)** $\dfrac{2}{3n+2}$ **h)** $\dfrac{n}{n+1}$ **i)** $\dfrac{n+1}{3n-2}$ **j)** $\dfrac{2n+1}{6n-1}$ **k)** $\dfrac{13-n}{5n+2}$ **l)** $\dfrac{7-3n}{7n-2}$ **3 a)** 2^n **b)** 5×2^n **c)** $5 \times 2^{n-1}$

3 d) $4 \times 3^{n-1}$ **e)** $2 \times (-3)^{n-1}$ **f)** $\left(-\frac{1}{2}\right)^{n-1}$ **g)** n^2 **h)** $\dfrac{n}{(n+1)^2}$ **i)** $(-1)^n n(n+1)$ **j)** $\dfrac{n+1}{n(n+2)}$ **k)** $(-1)^n \dfrac{n-1}{5n-6}$ **l)** n^n

4 a) 5, 7, 9, 11, 13, 15; divergent **b)** 3, 9, 15, 21, 27, 33; divergent **c)** 2, 5, 8, 11, 14, 17; divergent

4 d) 3, 7, 15, 31, 63, 127; divergent **e)** 3, −1, 11, −25, 83, −241; divergent **f)** 5, 5, 5, 5, 5, 5; convergent $\to 5$

4 g) $7, \frac{1}{7}, 7, \frac{1}{7}, 7, \frac{1}{7}$; periodic **h)** $1, 2, \frac{1}{2}, 8, \frac{1}{32}, 2048$; divergent **i)** 2, 1, −2, 1, −2, 1; periodic after the first term

5 a) $-2, 3, 5\frac{1}{2}, 6\frac{3}{4}, 7\frac{3}{8}$ **b)** 8 **6 a)** $6, 3, 4, 3\frac{2}{3}, 3\frac{7}{9}$ **b)** $3\frac{3}{4}$ **7 a)** $22, 6, 2, 1, \frac{3}{4}$ **b)** $\frac{2}{3}$ **8 a)** $4, 2\frac{1}{2}, 3\frac{2}{5}, 2\frac{13}{17}, 3\frac{8}{47}$ **b)** 3

Exercise 7B

1 a) $1^2 + 2^2 + 3^2 + 4^2 + 5^2$ b) $2 + 5 + 8 + 11 + 14 + 17$ c) $5 + 11 + 21 + 35$ d) $1 \times 2 + 2 \times 3 + 3 \times 4 + 4 \times 5 + 5 \times 6$

1 e) $3^3 + 4^3 + 5^3 + 6^3$ f) $5 \times 2 + 6 \times 3 + 7 \times 4 + 8 \times 5 + 9 \times 6 + 10 \times 7$ g) $1^2 + 3^2 + 5^2 + 7^2 + 9^2 + 11^2$

1 h) $1 + \frac{1}{2} + \frac{1}{3} + \dots + \frac{1}{n}$ i) $4^4 + 5^5 + 6^6 + 7^7 + 8^8$ j) $1 - \frac{1}{2} + \frac{1}{3} - \frac{1}{4} + \frac{1}{5} - \frac{1}{6} + \frac{1}{7}$ k) $2 + 0 + 18 + 50 + 0 + 98 + 0 + 162 + 0$

1 l) $3 + 3 + 3 + 3 + 3$ **2** a) $\sum_{r=1}^{5} r$ b) $\sum_{r=1}^{7} r^3$ c) $\sum_{r=1}^{7} (3r + 4)$ d) $\sum_{r=3}^{20} \frac{1}{r}$ e) $\sum_{r=5}^{18} r(r+1)$ f) $\sum_{r=3}^{n} r^4$ g) $\sum_{r=1}^{7} (-1)^{r-1} r$

2 h) $\sum_{r=1}^{9} (-2)^{r+1}$ i) $\sum_{r=5}^{n} \frac{r}{r^2 - 1}$ j) $\sum_{r=1}^{n} \frac{r}{(r+1)(r+2)}$ k) $\sum_{r=1}^{15} (-1)^{r+1} (2r-1)(3r+1)$ l) $\sum_{r=1}^{6} \frac{3r-1}{3^r}$

Exercise 7C

1 a) 3 b) -11 c) not d) not e) 0.1 f) $\frac{3}{10}$ g) not h) not **2** a) 37 b) 65 c) -25 d) -61 e) 3.8 f) $85 - 4n$

2 g) -7.1 h) 51 **3** a) 11 b) 21 c) 100 d) 44 e) 8 f) 19 g) 30 h) 28

Exercise 7D

1 a) 55 b) 725 c) 837 d) 390 e) -580 f) $\frac{n}{2}(3n + 11)$ g) -2775 h) $592\frac{1}{2}$ **2** a) 5050 b) 234 c) 225 d) 650

2 e) -187 f) 35.4 g) 120 h) 96 **4** 7, 1590 **5** $-14, 9, 265$ **6** $10, -3, -133$ **7** $-9, 210$ **8** 5, 1 **9** 3, 5, 7

10 4.5, 5.5, 13.5 **11** 10 **12** $x = 3$, sum $= 152$ **14** $n = 15$

Exercise 7E

1 a) 3 b) -2 c) not d) not e) 1.2 f) not g) not h) $\frac{1}{2}$ **2** a) 1024 b) 729 c) 640 d) $51\frac{33}{128}$ e) $-4\frac{20}{27}$ f) $\frac{2}{625}$

2 g) $\frac{1}{2048}$ h) $-\frac{1}{243}$ **3** a) 5 b) 9 c) 7 d) 11 e) 6 f) 6 g) 7 h) 10 **4** 5, 3 **5** $-4, 3$ **6** $\pm\frac{1}{2}, \pm 384$

7 $\pm 11, \pm 77$

Exercise 7F

1 a) 3069 b) -1023 c) 2049 d) 1275 e) 1638 f) 1 111 111 g) $1\frac{364}{729}$ h) $18\frac{17}{36}$ **2** a) 765 b) 2186 c) -728 d) 301

2 e) $53\frac{25}{27}$ f) $39\frac{11}{16}$ g) $\frac{1365}{4096}$ h) $\frac{182}{729}$ **3** 5115 **4** 8200 **5** $\frac{1}{7}$ **6** $\frac{1}{11}$ **7** $\frac{1}{29}, -\frac{5}{29}, \frac{25}{29}$ **8** $-3, -2$

9 $5 + 15 + 45 + 135 + 405$

Exercise 7G

1 a) 2 b) $\frac{3}{2}$ c) $\frac{1}{4}$ d) $\frac{4}{5}$ e) $\frac{1}{72}$ f) $\frac{1}{8}$ g) $\frac{9}{70}$ h) $\frac{49}{170}$ i) 6 j) $-\frac{1}{2}$ k) $\frac{1}{1-a}$ l) $\frac{9x^2}{1-3x}$ **2** a) $\frac{5}{9}$ b) $\frac{8}{9}$ c) $\frac{8}{11}$ d) $\frac{34}{333}$ e) $\frac{22}{9}$

2 f) $\frac{443}{135}$ **3** 12 **4** $\frac{8}{3}$ **5** $\frac{9}{10}$ **6** $-\frac{1}{2}$ **7** $\frac{1}{2}$ **8** 18, 6, 2; 9, 6, 4

Exercise 7H

1 a) 10 b) 15 c) 36 d) 6 e) 1 f) 66 g) 35 h) 100 **2** a) $1 + 4x + 6x^2 + 4x^3 + x^4$ b) $1 + 5x + 10x^2 + 10x^3 + 5x^4 + x^5$

2 c) $1 + 12x + 54x^2 + 108x^3 + 81x^4$ d) $1 - 3x + 3x^2 - x^3$ e) $1 - 8x + 24x^2 - 32x^3 + 16x^4$ f) $1 - 15x + 75x^2 - 125x^3$

2 g) $1 + 2x + \frac{3}{2}x^2 + \frac{1}{2}x^3 + \frac{1}{16}x^4$ h) $1 - \frac{2}{5}x + \frac{1}{25}x^2$ **3** a) 35 b) 36 c) 80 d) 700 e) -540 f) -42 g) 96 h) 80 i) $\frac{3}{4}$

Exercise 7I

1 a) $8 + 12x + 6x^2 + x^3$ b) $81 + 108x + 54x^2 + 12x^3 + x^4$ c) $216 - 540x + 450x^2 - 125x^3$ d) $16 + 16x + 6x^2 + x^3 + \frac{1}{16}x^4$

1 e) $27x^3 + 54x^2y + 36xy^2 + 8y^3$ f) $32x^5 - 80x^4y + 80x^3y^2 - 40x^2y^3 + 10xy^4 - y^5$ g) $8x^3 + 60x^2y + 150xy^2 + 125y^3$

1 h) $81x^4 - 432x^3y + 864x^2y^2 - 768xy^3 + 256y^4$ **2** a) 1080 b) 44 800 c) 6048 d) 8960 e) -224 f) 20 000 g) $\frac{5}{2}$

2 h) $-\frac{8}{15}$ **3** a) $1 - 15x + 90x^2 - 270x^3$ b) $1 + 20x + 180x^2 + 960x^3 + \dots$ c) $1 - 35x + 525x^2 - 4375x^3 + \dots$

3 d) $32 - 24x + 720x^2 - 1080x^3 + \dots$ e) $1024 - 1280x + 640x^2 - 160x^3 + \dots$ f) $64 + 576x + 2160x^2 + 4320x^3 + \dots$

3 g) $1 + 3x + 4x^2 + \frac{28}{9}x^3 + \dots$ h) $4096 + 1536x + 240x^2 + 20x^3 + \dots$ **4** a) $2 + 11x + 25x^2 + \dots$ b) $5 + 29x + 69x^2 + \dots$

4 c) $5 - 66x + 364x^2$ d) $486 + 2997x + 7344x^2$ e) $5 - 90x + 674x^2$ f) $567 - 756x - 216x^2$ g) $2 + 15x + 55x^2$

4 h) $32 + 112x + 192x^2$ **5** a) $1 + 4x^3 + 6x^6 + 4x^9 + x^{12}$ b) $1 + 9x^2 + 27x^4 + 27x^6$ c) $27 - 54x^3 + 36x^6 - 8x^9$

5 d) $1 + 2x + 3x^2 + 2x^3 + x^4$ e) $4 + 12x + 5x^2 - 6x^3 + x^4$ f) $4 + 4x - 15x^2 - 8x^3 + 16x^4$ **6** a) -810 b) 960 c) 240 d) 54

6 e) 216 f) 490 g) 1350 h) 2 949 120 **7** a) i) $1 + 4x + 6x^2$ ii) $1 - 8x + 24x^2$ b) $(1+x)(1-2x); 1 - 4x - 2x^2$

8 a) i) $1 + 18x + 135x^2$ ii) $1 - 24x + 240x^2$ b) $(1+3x)(1-4x); 1 - 6x - 57x^2$

Check out

1 2, 3, 5, 9, 17   **2** a) $u_n = 3_n + 2$ b) $u_n = \dfrac{5}{2^{n-1}}$ **3** a) i) 65   ii) 735   b) i) 0.00488   ii) 9.995

4 a) 1.185 ...   b) 17.688   c) 18   **5** a) $1 + 4x + 6x^2 + 4x^3 + x^4$ b) $1 - \frac{5}{2}x + \frac{10}{4}x^2 - \frac{10}{8}x^3 + \frac{5}{16}x^4 - \dfrac{x^5}{32}$ c) $27 + 54x + 36x^2 + 8x^3$

Revision exercise 7

1 b) 48   c) 96   **2** a) $a + 9d = 14$ b) $a = -13, d = 3$ **3** a) 0.9   b) $10 \times 0.9^{n-1}$ c) ~92.8   d) 100

4 a) 392   b) i) $u_1 = 47, u_2 = 44, u_3 = 41, u_4 = 38$ **5** $1200r, 1200r^2$ **6** a) $a = 8, d = 4$ b) 5300

7 a) ii) $r = -\frac{1}{2}$ b) $24(-\frac{1}{2})^{2k-1}$ **8** $a = -3, d = 2.5$ **9** a) 18   **10** $a = -5.6, d = 3.8$ **11** b) 546.75

12 $1 + 4x + 7x^2 + 7x^3$ **13** $1 + 5x + 10x^2 + 10x^3 + 5x^4 + 1; 76 - 44\sqrt{3}$ **14** a) £98 (nearest penny)   b) £1501.79

Chapter 8

Check in

1 a) 0.6018   b) 0.9925   c) 1.7321   **2** a) 30°   b) 72.5°   c) 45°   **3** a) 26.6°   b) 75.5°   c) 19.5°

4 a) 6.6   b) 3.5   c) 15.7   **5** a) 0.5, −0.866, −0.577   b) −0.866, 0.5, −1.732   c) 0.643, −0.766, −0.839   d) 0.5, 0.866, 0.577

5 e) −0.707, 0.707, −1

Exercise 8A

1 a) $x = 8.96, y = 8.65$ b) $x = 6.60, \theta = 39.9$ c) $x = 10.6, y = 9.13$ d) $x = 8.01, \theta = 27.3$

1 e) $x = 7.67, \theta = 60.1$ or $x = 1.69, \theta = 120$ f) $x = 7.62, y = 7.25$ g) $x = 7.18, \theta = 38.7, y = 4.80$

1 h) $x = 3.80, \theta = 69.1$ or $x = 1.23, \theta = 110.9$ i) $x = 3.80, y = 10.0$ j) $x = 13.8, y = 11.7$

1 k) $x = 5.50, \theta = 103$ or $x = 8.38, \theta = 77.2$ l) $x = 5.84, \theta = 20.7$

Exercise 8B

1 a) 109.5°   b) 13.8   c) 3.91   d) 52.2°   e) 2.33   f) 8.94   g) 2.18   h) 7.43   i) 5.68   j) 53.6°   k) 163.2°   l) 4.18

Exercise 8C

1 a) 6.19 cm   b) 82.0°   **2** a) 74.8°   b) 49.3°   **3** a) 146.8°   b) 3.33 cm   **4** 3.93 cm or 9.93 cm

5 b) 48 km   c) 320.1°   **6** 1139 m at 345.8°   **7** b) 94.3 m at 328°   c) 154.0 m at 144.9°   **8** a) 4.14 km   b) 2.93 km

9 a) $\sqrt{89}$ cm   b) $\sqrt{61}$ cm   c) 10 cm   d) 62.6°

Exercise 8D

1 a) 12 cm²   b) 126 cm²   c) 24 cm²   d) 30 cm²   e) 20.2 cm²   f) 91.4 cm²   g) 18.4 cm²   h) 32.1 cm²   i) 13.6 cm²

1 j) 89.3 cm²   k) 1160 cm²   l) 14.4 cm²   **2** 26.7 cm²   **3** 13.8 m²   **4** a) 38.2°   b) 17.3 cm²   **5** a) 41.6°   b) 17.9 cm²

6 a) 64.6 mm²   b) 93.1 mm²   c) £2.52

Exercise 8E

1 a) $\dfrac{\pi}{6}$ rad   b) $\dfrac{\pi}{2}$ rad   c) $\dfrac{2\pi}{3}$ rad   d) $\dfrac{\pi}{18}$ rad   e) $\dfrac{4\pi}{9}$ rad   f) $\dfrac{5\pi}{3}$ rad   g) $\dfrac{\pi}{5}$ rad   h) $\dfrac{4\pi}{3}$ rad   i) $\dfrac{2\pi}{5}$ rad   j) 2π rad

1 k) $\dfrac{19\pi}{10}$ rad   l) $\dfrac{\pi}{180}$ rad   **2** a) 180°   b) 45°   c) 540°   d) 30°   e) 144°   f) 15°   g) 300°   h) 180°   i) 75°   j) 2°   k) 270°

2 l) 210°   **3** a) 229.2°   b) 11.5°   c) 246.4°   d) 28.6°   e) 40.1°   f) 171.9°   g) 297.9°   h) 120.3°   i) 286.5°   j) 2.3°

3 k) 916.7°   l) 57.3°   **4** a) $\dfrac{3\pi}{2}$ cm   b) $\dfrac{15\pi}{4}$ cm²   **5** a) 6π cm   b) 27π cm²   **6** a) $\left(12 + \dfrac{5\pi}{2}\right)$ cm   b) $\dfrac{15\pi}{2}$ cm²

7 a) $\left(14 + \dfrac{5\pi}{2}\right)$ cm   b) $\dfrac{35\pi}{4}$ cm²   **8** a) $\dfrac{4\pi}{3}$ cm   b) $\dfrac{16\pi}{3}$ cm²   **9** a) $(24 + 3\pi)$ cm   b) 18π cm²   **10** $\dfrac{25}{4}(\pi - 2)$ cm²

11 $\dfrac{25}{3}(2\pi - 3\sqrt{3})$ cm²   **12** a) $36(\pi - 2)$ cm²   b) $6(\pi + 2\sqrt{2})$ cm   **13** a) 1.30 cm²   b) 9.97 cm   **14** a) 17.0 cm²   b) 24.5 cm

15 a) $16\sqrt{3}\,\text{cm}^2$ b) $\dfrac{32\pi}{3}\,\text{cm}^2$ c) $(32\pi - 48\sqrt{3})\,\text{cm}^2$ **16** a) $\dfrac{9\pi}{4}\,\text{m}^2$ b) $9\,\text{m}^2$ c) $\dfrac{9}{2}(\pi - 2)\,\text{m}^2$ d) $\dfrac{3\sqrt{2}\pi}{4}\,\text{m}$ e) $6(\sqrt{2} - 1)\,\text{m}$

16 f) $\dfrac{3}{2}\left[\sqrt{2}(\pi + 4) - 4\right]\text{m}$

Exercise 8F

1 a) $-\sin 30°$ b) $-\cos 50°$ c) $-\tan 20°$ d) $-\sin 50°$ e) $-\tan 60°$ f) $\cos 70°$ g) $\tan 80°$ h) $-\sin 54°$ i) $-\tan 7°$

1 j) $-\cos 72°$ k) $\sin 54°$ l) $-\cos 59°$ **2** a) $\cos 60°$ b) $-\sin 60°$ c) $\tan 30°$ d) $-\sin 50°$ e) $\tan 26°$ f) $-\cos 80°$

2 g) $-\sin 65°$ h) $-\cos 21°$ i) $-\tan 33°$ j) $\cos 29°$ k) $-\tan 85°$ l) $\sin 10°$ **3** a) $\sin\left(\dfrac{\pi}{3}\right)$ b) $-\cos\left(\dfrac{\pi}{6}\right)$ c) $-\tan\left(\dfrac{\pi}{8}\right)$

3 d) $-\tan\left(\dfrac{\pi}{5}\right)$ e) $-\cos\left(\dfrac{\pi}{3}\right)$ f) $-\sin\left(\dfrac{2\pi}{9}\right)$ g) $-\cos\left(\dfrac{\pi}{13}\right)$ h) $\tan\left(\dfrac{\pi}{4}\right)$ i) $\cos\left(\dfrac{6\pi}{19}\right)$ j) $-\sin\left(\dfrac{\pi}{5}\right)$ k) $-\tan\left(\dfrac{2\pi}{7}\right)$ l) $\sin\left(\dfrac{\pi}{2}\right)$

Exercise 8H

1 $32 + 8\sqrt{3}$ **2** $56 + 7\sqrt{2}$ **3** $12 + 4\sqrt{2} + 4\sqrt{3}$ **4** $12 + 6\sqrt{2} + 6\sqrt{6}$

Exercise 8I

1 a) $17.5°, 162.5°$ b) $45.6°, 314.4°$ c) $63.4°, 243.4°$ d) $120°, 240°$ e) $200.5°, 339.5°$ f) $98.1°, 278.1°$ g) $66.4°, 293.6°$

1 h) $270°$ **2** a) $0.93, 2.21$ b) $1.37, 4.91$ c) $1.25, 4.39$ d) $2.21, 4.07$ e) $3.99, 5.44$ f) $1.74, 4.88$ g) $0.45, 5.83$

2 h) $0.30, 2.84$ **3** a) $93.1°, 166.9°$ b) $58.5°, 261.5°$ c) $126.0°, 306.0°$ d) $254.4°, 345.6°$ e) $74.1°, 254.1°$ f) $29.5°, 238.5°$

3 g) $229.2°, 280.8°$ h) $97.8°, 277.8°$ **4** a) $\pm 0.89, \pm 2.26$ b) $\pm 1.25, \pm 1.89$ c) $\pm 0.46, \pm 2.68$ d) $0, \pm 3.14, 0.52, 2.62$

4 e) $\pm 1.23, \pm 1.57$ f) $0, \pm 1.37, \pm 3.14$ g) $0, -1.33, 1.82, \pm 3.14$ h) $0.34, 2.80, 0.52, 2.62$

Exercise 8J

1 a) $0.32, 1.25$ b) $0.59, 1.64, 2.68$ c) $0.58, 2.56$ d) $0.31, 0.74, 2.40, 2.83$ **2** a) $1.3^c, 4.4^c$ b) $1.0^c, 4.2^c$ c) $2.4^c, 5.5^c$

2 d) $0.6^c, 3.7^c$ e) $1.1^c, 4.2^c$ f) $2.6^c, 5.7^c$ g) $1.4^c, 4.5^c$ h) $0.4^c, 3.6^c$ **3** a) $-150°, -30°, 19.5°, 160.5°$

3 b) $0°, \pm 60°$ c) $\pm 109.5°, \pm 120°$ d) $30°, 150°$ e) $90°, 30°, 150°$ f) $\pm 109.5°$ g) $\pm 41.4°, \pm 60°$ h) $41.8°, 138.2°$

4 a) $(2x - 1)(3x + 1)(x + 1)$ b) $-160.5°, -19.5°, -90°, 30°, 150°$

Check out

1 a) $a = 4.0\,\text{cm}, b = 7.4\,\text{cm}$ b) $\hat{Q} = 111.95°, \hat{R} = 28.0°$ **2** a) $13.8\,\text{cm}^2$ b) $9.2\,\text{m}^2$ **3** a) i) 0.733^c ii) 3.787^c

3 b) i) $\dfrac{2\pi}{3}$ ii) $\dfrac{7\pi}{4}$ c) i) $42.97°$ ii) $143.24°$ d) i) $30°$ ii) $135°$ **4** a) i) $7.2\,\text{cm}$ ii) $21.6\,\text{cm}^2$ b) i) 1.25^c ii) $40\,\text{m}^2$

5 a) $y = 3\sin x$ b) $y = \sin 2x$ c) $y = -2\cos x$ d) $y = \tan x$ e) $y = \cos(x + 60°)$ f) $y = \tan(x + 30°)$

7 a) $x = 15°, 75°$ b) $x = 3.1°, 66.1°, 126.1°$ c) $x = 270°$ d) $x = \dfrac{\pi}{9}, \dfrac{5\pi}{9}, \dfrac{7\pi}{9}$

Revision exercise 8

1 a) $\sqrt{10}, \sqrt{125}, \sqrt{125}$ b) 17.5 c) $(x - 3)^2 + (y - 2)^2 = \frac{49}{5}$ **2** a) $\dfrac{2\pi}{3}$ b) 0.788 (3 s.f.)

3 a) perimeter of triangle $= 3x$, perimeter of sector $= 10$ b) ii) 1.209 iii) max.

4 a) i) $\dfrac{\pi}{3}\,\text{rad}$ ii) $2\pi\,\text{cm}$ iii) $9\sqrt{3}$ iv) $6\pi\,\text{cm}$ b) i) $6\pi\,\text{cm}$ ii) $25\,\text{cm}^2$

5 a) $y = \cos x$ transforms to $y = \cos 2x$ by a stretch, scale factor $\frac{1}{2}$, parallel to Ox. b) $y = \dfrac{\pi}{2}$

6 c) i) $\sin\theta = \frac{1}{2}$ or -1, but $\tan\theta$ undefined when $\sin\theta = -1$ ii) $\dfrac{\pi}{6}, \dfrac{5\pi}{6}$ iii) $\cos\theta = \dfrac{\sqrt{3}}{2}, \tan\theta = \dfrac{\sqrt{3}}{3}$

7 b) $\sin\theta = 0 \Rightarrow \theta = 0, \pi, 2\pi$ $\sin\theta = -\frac{1}{2} \Rightarrow \theta = \dfrac{7\pi}{6}, \dfrac{11\pi}{6}$ **8** a) i) $\sin^2 x = 1 - \cos^2 x$ b) $y = \frac{1}{4}, -2$ c) $75.5°, 284.5°$

9 a) $\tan 2x = 0.8$ b) $19.3°, 109.3°$ **10** $15\,\text{cm}$ **11** a) $4.5\,\text{cm}$ b) $6.75\,\text{cm}^2$ **12** a) 25θ b) $\dfrac{25}{2}\tan\theta$

14 a) ii) $\dfrac{5}{12}$ b) 0.395 rad c) ii) $32\,\text{cm}^2$ **15** $x = 40.5°, 92.8°, 160.5°$ **16** a) $\dfrac{1}{2}, \dfrac{\sqrt{3}}{2}, \dfrac{1}{\sqrt{3}}$ b) $\dfrac{\pi}{6}, \dfrac{5\pi}{6}, \dfrac{7\pi}{6}, \dfrac{11\pi}{6}$ **17** $x = \dfrac{\pi}{2}, \dfrac{7\pi}{6}$

18 $x = \dfrac{\pi}{12}, \dfrac{5\pi}{12}, \dfrac{9\pi}{12}, \dfrac{13\pi}{12}, \dfrac{17\pi}{12}, \dfrac{21\pi}{12}$ **19** a) 4:11 pm, 8:04 pm b) February, October c) $L = 6.125 - 2.25\cos\left(\dfrac{\pi(3+t)}{6}\right)$

Chapter 9

Check in

1 a) 16 b) 216 c) 1 d) $\frac{1}{5}$ e) $\frac{1}{16}$ **2** a) i) p^7 ii) q^2 iii) r^{12} iv) s^{-1} b) i) $24p^3q$ ii) $4x^2y$ iii) $\dfrac{y^2}{2x}$ iv) 1

Exercise 9A

1 a) x^9 b) p^2 c) $9k^6$ d) $y^{\frac{5}{6}}$ e) c^4 f) $\dfrac{3h^6}{2}$ g) $2d$ h) $16p^{-4}$ **2** a) ± 2 b) 3 c) ± 27 d) 32 e) 25 f) 343

2 g) $\pm\frac{1}{5}$ h) $\frac{4}{9}$ **3** a) $\frac{1}{7}$ b) $\frac{1}{9}$ c) $\pm\frac{1}{2}$ d) $\pm\frac{1}{125}$ e) $\frac{3}{2}$ f) $\frac{1}{9}$ g) $\pm\frac{2}{3}$ h) $\frac{2}{5}$ **4** a) 5 b) $\pm\frac{1}{7}$ c) -7 d) $\frac{9}{5}$ e) $\frac{1}{2}$ f) $\pm\frac{1}{5}$

4 g) $\pm\frac{1}{2}$ h) $\pm\frac{5}{3}$ **5** a) 9 b) 32 c) $\frac{4}{49}$ d) $\frac{1}{256}$ e) $\frac{1}{2}$ f) $\frac{1}{5}$ g) $\frac{1}{7}$ h) $\pm\frac{2}{3}$ **6** a) ± 27 b) 16 c) 16 d) $\pm\frac{1}{729}$ e) $\frac{1}{25}$

6 f) 81 g) $-\frac{1}{216}$ h) -32 **7** a) $-1, 8$ b) $\frac{1}{16}, 256$

Exercise 9B

1 a) $\log_2 32 = 5$ b) $\log_3 81 = 4$ c) $\log_4\left(\frac{1}{16}\right) = -2$ d) $\log_9 729 = 3$ e) $\log_6 36 = 2$ f) $\log_7\left(\frac{1}{343}\right) = -3$ g) $\log_{12} 1 = 0$

1 h) $\log_{10} 1\,000\,000 = 6$ i) $\log_2\left(\frac{1}{512}\right) = -9$ j) $\log_{16} 4 = \frac{1}{2}$ k) $\log_{10} 1000 = \frac{1}{3}$ l) $\log_{\frac{1}{2}}\left(\frac{1}{8}\right) = 3$ **2** a) 3 b) 5 c) 2 d) 3 e) 1

2 f) 2 g) -2 h) -4 i) -4 j) 0 k) 10 l) -5 **3** a) $\log a + \log b$ b) $\log a - \log b$ c) $2\log a + \log b$

3 d) $\frac{1}{2}\log a$ e) $-2\log a$ f) $\log a + \frac{1}{2}\log b$ g) $3\log a - \log b$ h) $2\log a - 3\log b$ i) $\frac{1}{2}\log a - \frac{1}{2}\log b$ j) $-\log a - 4\log b$

3 k) $-\frac{1}{2}\log a - \frac{1}{2}\log b$ l) $\frac{1}{3}\log a + \frac{1}{6}\log b$ **4** a) $\log 12$ b) $\log 14$ c) $\log 5$ d) $\log 6$ e) $\log 30$ f) $\log 2$ g) $\log 3$

4 h) $\log 10$ i) $\log 4$ j) $\log 5$ k) $\log\left(\dfrac{a^2}{bc}\right)$ l) $\log\left(\dfrac{a\sqrt{b}}{c^3}\right)$ **5** $x = 10\,000, y = 1000$

Exercise 9C

1 a) 2.32 b) 1.77 c) 1.52 d) 0.65 e) 3.86 f) 2.57 g) 0.71 h) 0.24   **2** a) 0.79 b) 0.70 c) 0.67 d) 2.91 e) 2.77

2 f) -1.02 g) 2.58 h) 0.22   **3** a) 1.22 b) -0.83 c) 0.76 d) -0.50 **4** a) -4.42 b) 5.78 c) 1.87 d) 0.28

5 a) $(2u - 1)(u - 5)$ b) $-1, 2.32$

Check out

1 a) i) $3^{\frac{5}{2}}$ ii) 3^{-3} b) i) $2^{-\frac{5}{2}}$ ii) $2^{\frac{3}{2}}$ c) i) $\frac{1}{4}$ ii) $\frac{1}{64}$ **2** a) 4 b) -3 c) -3 **3** a) $\log_a\left(\frac{1}{3}\right)$ b) $\log_2 8\sqrt{2}$

5 a) $x = 2.86$ b) $x = -0.63$

Revision exercise 9

1 a) i) $\sqrt{3} = 3^{\frac{1}{2}}$ ii) $3^{x - \frac{1}{2}}$ b) $-\frac{1}{2}$ **2** b) $2^{\frac{3}{2}}$ c) 2^3 **3** a) $t = \dfrac{\log p}{\log 0.98}$ b) 114 seconds (to nearest second)

4 4.17 (3 s.f.)   **5** $M = \dfrac{\log B}{\log 0.3981} + 1$ **6** $\log\left(\dfrac{x^4}{y}\right); y = x^4$ **7** a) $x = 3$ b) $2\log_2 3$ c) $2\log_2 3 + 3$

8 a) $\log_a 45$ b) i) 1 ii) $\sqrt{2}$ **9** a) $k^2 = 4x$ b) $y = 3^{\frac{3}{2}}(= 5.196)$ **10** b) i) 6 ii) 1.5 iii) -1.5

11 b) ii) $\log u = 97\log 2 - 93\log 3$ **12** $\log 24$ **13** 34 years   **14** b) 1992

Chapter 10

Check in

1 a) $6x, 6$ b) $3x^2 - 4, -1$ c) $6x^2 + 6x, 36$ **2** a) -4 b) -11 **3** a) $(0, -2)$ min.

3 b) $\left(\dfrac{2\sqrt{3}}{3}, -\dfrac{16\sqrt{3}}{9}\right)$ min., $\left(\dfrac{-2\sqrt{3}}{3}, \dfrac{16\sqrt{3}}{9}\right)$ max.

4 a) increasing b) decreasing c) increasing d) decreasing e) decreasing   **5** a) $x^{\frac{3}{2}}$ b) $x^{\frac{7}{2}}$ c) $x^{\frac{7}{3}}$ d) $x^{-\frac{7}{4}}$

5 e) $\dfrac{1}{x^{\frac{2}{3}}} - \dfrac{1}{x^3}$ f) $\dfrac{1}{x^{\frac{1}{2}}} + \dfrac{1}{x}$ g) $\dfrac{1}{x^{\frac{2}{3}}} - \dfrac{1}{x^{\frac{1}{2}}}$

Exercise 10A

1 a) $-2x^{-3}$ b) $-4x^{-5}$ c) $-6x^{-4}$ d) $-4x^{-2}$ e) $-\dfrac{3}{x^4}$ f) $\dfrac{2}{x^3}$ g) $-\dfrac{9}{x^4}$ h) $\dfrac{2}{x^2}$ i) $-\dfrac{3}{x^3}$ j) $-\dfrac{27}{2x^4}$ **2** a) $\frac{1}{2}x^{-\frac{1}{2}}$ b) $3x^{-\frac{2}{3}}$

2 c) $-\frac{2}{3}x^{-\frac{5}{3}}$ d) $2x^{-\frac{6}{5}}$ e) $\dfrac{7}{2\sqrt{x}}$ f) $\dfrac{1}{3\sqrt[3]{x^2}}$ g) $-\dfrac{2}{5\sqrt{x^3}}$ h) $\dfrac{3}{\sqrt[5]{x^6}}$ i) $\dfrac{5\sqrt{x^3}}{2}$ **3** a) $2x+2$ b) $6x-5$ c) $-12x^2$ d) $2x+2$

3 e) $7x^6+12x^3$ f) $4x^3-6x$ g) $10x+\dfrac{6}{x^4}$ h) $2x-8x^3$ i) $-\dfrac{3}{x^2}+12x^2$ **4** a) $\dfrac{1}{\sqrt{x}}$ b) $\dfrac{1}{2\sqrt{x}}-\dfrac{1}{x^2}$ c) $-8x^{-3}-3$

4 d) $x^{-\frac{2}{3}}+\frac{4}{3}x^{-\frac{4}{3}}$ e) $2x^{-\frac{1}{2}}+2$ f) $4x^{-\frac{1}{3}}-10x^{\frac{3}{2}}$ g) $-\dfrac{3}{\sqrt[3]{x^4}}+\dfrac{2}{\sqrt{x^5}}$ h) $-\dfrac{3}{\sqrt{x^3}}-\dfrac{2}{\sqrt{x}}$ i) $\dfrac{1}{2\sqrt{x}}-\dfrac{1}{2\sqrt{x^3}}$ **5** a) 4 b) $\dfrac{1}{\sqrt{x}}-\dfrac{5}{2x^2}$

5 c) $8x+7$ d) $\dfrac{5}{6\sqrt[6]{x}}$ e) $\dfrac{3}{\sqrt{x}}+\dfrac{3}{x^3}$ f) $-14x^{-8}+15x^{-4}+1$ g) $-\dfrac{1}{2\sqrt[6]{x^7}}+\dfrac{1}{2\sqrt{x^5}}$ h) $-\dfrac{10}{x^3}+\dfrac{2}{x^2}$ i) $12x^{\frac{1}{3}}$ j) $-8x^{-5}+8x^{-3}$

6 a) $3x(x+2)$ b) $12x^2-5x^4$ c) $\dfrac{5+3x}{2\sqrt{x}}\left[=\dfrac{5}{2}x^{-\frac{1}{2}}+\dfrac{3}{2}x^{\frac{1}{2}}\right]$ d) $\dfrac{3(7x^3-6x+1)}{\sqrt{x}}\left[=21x^{\frac{5}{2}}-18x^{\frac{1}{2}}+3x^{-\frac{1}{2}}\right]$

6 e) $\frac{1}{2}x^{-\frac{3}{4}}(9x^2-2)\left[=\frac{9}{2}x^{\frac{5}{4}}-x^{-\frac{3}{4}}\right]$ f) $2x-1$ g) $2(x+4)$ h) $4(x-3)$ i) $2(x+3)$ j) $4x-9$ **7** a) $\frac{1}{2}x^{-\frac{3}{2}}(x-1)\left[=\frac{1}{2}x^{\frac{1}{2}}-\frac{1}{2}x^{-\frac{3}{2}}\right]$

7 b) $\dfrac{x^2-7}{x^2}[=1-7x^{-2}]$ c) $-\dfrac{x+10}{x^3}[=-x^{-2}-10x^{-3}]$ d) $\dfrac{3x^2-2}{x^2}[=3-2x^{-2}]$ e) $\dfrac{2(3x^3+7)}{x^3}[=6+14x^{-3}]$ f) $-\dfrac{3}{5x^2}$

7 g) $\dfrac{\sqrt{x}(18-35x)}{6}\left[=3x^{\frac{1}{2}}-\dfrac{35}{6}x^{\frac{3}{2}}\right]$ h) $4x(x-1)(x-2)[=8x-12x^2+4x^3]$ i) $\dfrac{(x-5)(x+5)}{x^2}[=1-25x^{-2}]$

8 a) $3x^2(4x-1)$ b) $4x(2x-1)(x-1)[=8x^3-12x^2+4x]$ c) $\dfrac{3x^3-10}{x^3}[=3-10x^{-3}]$

8 d) $-\dfrac{2(x^2-13x+30)}{x^4}[=-2x^{-2}+26x^{-3}-60x^{-4}]$ e) $\dfrac{9x^2-1}{2x^2}\left[=\dfrac{9}{2}-\dfrac{1}{2}x^{-2}\right]$ f) $\dfrac{5x-3}{4\sqrt{x^3}}\left[=\dfrac{5}{4}x^{-\frac{1}{2}}-\dfrac{3}{4}x^{-\frac{3}{2}}\right]$

8 g) $\dfrac{2x^2+5}{9x^2}\left[=\dfrac{2}{9}+\dfrac{5}{9}x^{-2}\right]$ h) $\dfrac{7}{4}x^{-\frac{3}{2}}$

Exercise 10B

1 a) 6 b) 24 c) $\frac{1}{6}$ d) $-\frac{1}{9}$ e) 4 f) $\frac{1}{8}$ g) $\frac{2}{3}$ h) -1 i) -5 j) 3 k) $\frac{9}{4}$ l) 0   **2** a) $(-2,-8),(2,8)$ b) $(-1,3)$

2 c) $(2,17)$ d) $\left(-\frac{1}{2},-8\right),\left(\frac{1}{2},8\right)$ e) $(-2,4)$ f) $(-3,-34),(3,32)$ g) $(0,3),\left(\frac{2}{3},\frac{77}{27}\right)$ h) $\left(\frac{1}{4},\frac{71}{2}\right),(1,3)$ i) $\left(\frac{1}{4},\frac{11}{2}\right)$ j) $\left(\frac{1}{9},\frac{11}{9}\right)$

2 k) $(-2,-3),(2,1)$ l) $(-1,2)$ **3** $a=\frac{3}{4}, b=-5$ **4** $A=\frac{17}{18}, B=-\frac{13}{3}$ **5** $a=-45, c=24$ **6** $a=12, b=-18$

7 $A=2, B=4$ **8** a) $y=4x-1$ b) $y=6x-5$ c) $y=-x-6$ d) $y=-2x+16$ e) $y=-2x-1$ f) $2y-3x=12$

8 g) $y=x+1$ h) $y=5$

Exercise 10C

1 a) $y=-x$ b) $3y+x=8$ c) $2y-3x+5=0$ d) $y=-3x+33$ e) $2y+x=11$ f) $4y+x+14=0$ g) $54y+x=3$

1 h) $7y-x+27=0$ i) $3y+2x+1=0$ j) $8y-3x=1$ k) $x=-2$ l) $4y-4x=13$ **2** a) 1, 3 b) $y=2, y=6$

3 a) $-2,4$ b) $y=15x+38, y=15x-70$ **4** $9y-x+16=0, 9y-x=464$ **5** $6y-x+19=0$

6 a) $y=3x+1$ b) $\left(\frac{1}{5},\frac{8}{5}\right)$ **7** a) $y=6x-4$ b) $(-2,-16)$ **8** $(-4,-71)$ **9** a) $y=x+1$ b) $(1,2),(3,4)$

10 $(-2,1),(2,5)$ **11** $a=3, b=4$ **12** $c=-14, d=-20$ **13** $a=8, b=11$

Exercise 10D

1 a) $18x$ b) $2-120x^4$ c) $\dfrac{2}{x^3}$ d) $\dfrac{12}{x^4}$ e) $\dfrac{3}{4\sqrt{x^5}}+\dfrac{1}{4\sqrt{x^3}}$ f) $-\dfrac{2}{9\sqrt[3]{x^5}}-6x$ g) $10x(2x^2+3)$ h) $6(2x+1)$ i) $-\dfrac{2}{x^3}$ j) $\dfrac{15}{4\sqrt{x^5}}$

1 k) $\dfrac{6(2x-5)}{x^4}[=12x^{-3}-30x^{-4}]$ l) $-\dfrac{12+5x}{12\sqrt{x^5}}\left[=-x^{-\frac{5}{2}}-\dfrac{5}{12}x^{-\frac{3}{2}}\right]$ **2** a) $2ax+b, 2a$ b) $-\dfrac{a}{x^2}-\dfrac{2b}{x^3}, \dfrac{2a}{x^3}+\dfrac{6b}{x^4}$

2 c) $\dfrac{a}{2\sqrt{x}} - \dfrac{b}{2\sqrt{x^3}}, \dfrac{3b}{4\sqrt{x^5}} - \dfrac{a}{4\sqrt{x^3}}$ **d)** $2acx + ad + bc, 2ac$ **e)** $\dfrac{2ax+b}{c}, \dfrac{2a}{c}$

Exercise 10E

1 a) $(-1, -2)$ max, $(1, 2)$ min **b)** $\left(-\frac{1}{3}, -6\right)$ max, $\left(\frac{1}{3}, 6\right)$ min **c)** $(2, 12)$ min **d)** $(2, 3)$ min **e)** $\left(6, \frac{1}{12}\right)$ max **f)** $\left(3, -\frac{1}{27}\right)$ min

1 g) $\left(-\frac{1}{2}, -16\right)$ min, $\left(\frac{1}{2}, 16\right)$ max **h)** $\left(2, -\frac{3}{8}\right)$ min **i)** $(4, -4)$ min **j)** $(16, -32)$ min **k)** $(1, 2)$ min **l)** $\left(64, \frac{1}{2048}\right)$ max **2 c)** 2

3 c) 6 **4 c)** 6 **5 c)** $2, 18\,\mathrm{m}^3$ **6 c)** $3, 172.8\,\mathrm{cm}^3$ **7 a)** $\dfrac{36}{x^2}\,\mathrm{cm}$ **b)** $(40x^2)$ pence **c)** $\left(\dfrac{1080}{x}\right)$ pence

7 d) $\left(\dfrac{4320}{x} + 80x^2\right)$ pence **e)** 3 **f)** £21.60 **8 a)** $\left(\dfrac{5}{6x^2}\right)\mathrm{m}$ **b)** $£\left(\dfrac{80}{3x}\right)$ **c)** $£(45x^2)$ **d)** $\frac{2}{3}$ **e)** £60

Exercise 10F

1 a) Increase $x > 4$, decrease $x < 4$ **b)** Increase $x < -1$, decrease $x > -1$ **c)** Increase $x < -1$ and $x > 3$, decrease $-1 < x < 3$

1 d) Increase $-3 < x < 2$, decrease $x < -3$ and $x > 2$ **e)** Increase $-3 < x < -2$ and $x > 2$, decrease $x < -3$ and $-2 < x < 2$

1 f) Increase $x < -2$ and $x > 2$, decrease $-2 < x < 0$ and $0 < x < 2$

Check out

1 $2x^{-\frac{1}{2}}$ **2 a)** $4x - \dfrac{4}{x^3}$ **b)** $\frac{3}{2}x^{\frac{1}{2}} - \dfrac{4}{x^{\frac{1}{3}}}$ **3 a)** $(-1, 2)$ min, $(1, 2)$ min **b)** $4y = -15x + 33$

3 c) decreasing at $x = 1$, increasing at $x = 4$

Revision exercise 10

1 $\dfrac{dy}{dx} = 2x + \dfrac{54}{x^2}, \dfrac{d^2y}{dx^2} = 2 - \dfrac{108}{x^3}; (-3, 27)$ min **2 a)** $\dfrac{dy}{dx} = 1 - 8x^{-3}, \dfrac{d^2y}{dx^2} = \dfrac{24}{x^4}$ **b)** $(2, 3)$ **c)** min

3 a) i) $4\pi x - \dfrac{1000}{x^2}$ **iii)** $4\pi + \dfrac{2000}{x^3}$ **v)** $x = 4.3$, min **b)** $349\,\mathrm{cm}^2$

Chapter 11

Check in

1 a) $x^3 - 2x + c$ **b)** $\frac{3}{2}x^2 + \frac{1}{2}x^4 + c$ **c)** $\frac{4}{3}x^3 - \frac{1}{2}x^2 + 7x + c$ **2 a)** 22 **b)** -2 **c)** $\frac{148}{3}$ **3 a)** $-\frac{4}{3}$ **b)** $\frac{4}{3}$

Exercise 11A

The constant of integration is omitted in the answers to questions 1 to 7.

1 a) $-x^{-1}$ **b)** $-\frac{1}{3}x^{-3}$ **c)** $-x^{-2}$ **d)** $2x^{-3}$ **e)** $-\dfrac{1}{2x^2}$ **f)** $\dfrac{1}{4x^4}$ **g)** $-\dfrac{3}{x}$ **h)** $\dfrac{1}{x^2}$ **i)** $-\dfrac{2}{3x^6}$ **j)** $-\dfrac{1}{2x^3}$ **k)** $\dfrac{5}{3x}$ **l)** $-\dfrac{2}{9x^3}$

2 a) $\frac{3}{4}x^{\frac{4}{3}}$ **b)** $2x^{\frac{3}{2}}$ **c)** $3x^{\frac{1}{3}}$ **d)** $-5x^{\frac{4}{5}}$ **e)** $-2\sqrt{x^3}$ **f)** $\frac{4}{5}\sqrt[4]{x^5}$ **g)** $6\sqrt[3]{x^2}$ **h)** $-\frac{5}{2}\sqrt[5]{x^4}$ **i)** $\frac{6}{7}\sqrt{x}$ **j)** $\frac{9}{5}\sqrt[3]{x^2}$ **k)** $\frac{2}{5}\sqrt[5]{x^5}$ **l)** $2\sqrt{x^3}$

3 a) $\frac{1}{4}x^4 + x^2$ **b)** $x^3 - 2x^2$ **c)** $\frac{1}{4}x^4 - x$ **d)** $6x + \frac{1}{6}x^6$ **e)** $\frac{1}{3}x^3 - \frac{5}{2}x^2 + 3x$ **f)** $\frac{1}{9}x^9 + \frac{1}{6}x^6$ **g)** $\frac{1}{5}x^5 - \frac{3}{2}x^2 + 2x$ **h)** $\frac{1}{3}x^3 - \dfrac{1}{x}$

3 i) $x^5 + \dfrac{1}{x^2}$ **j)** $\frac{2}{7}x^7 - \dfrac{2}{x^4}$ **k)** $\frac{1}{3}x^3 + \dfrac{3}{x}$ **l)** $-\dfrac{5}{x} - 2x - \frac{1}{4}x^4$ **4 a)** $2\sqrt{x^3} - 4x$ **b)** $\frac{2}{3}\sqrt{x^3} + 2\sqrt{x}$ **c)** $\frac{9}{4}x^{\frac{4}{3}} - \frac{8}{5}x^{\frac{5}{4}}$ **d)** $10x^{\frac{1}{2}} + 3x^{\frac{2}{3}}$

4 e) $\frac{8}{3}\sqrt{x^3} + \dfrac{2}{3x}$ **f)** $\frac{3}{2}\sqrt[3]{x^4} - 12\sqrt{x}$ **g)** $6\sqrt[3]{x^2} - \frac{16}{3}\sqrt{x^3}$ **h)** $\frac{4}{5}\sqrt[4]{x^5} - \frac{4}{3}\sqrt[4]{x^3}$ **i)** $2\sqrt[3]{x^2} - \frac{7}{4}\sqrt[7]{x^8}$ **j)** $\frac{12}{5}x^{\frac{5}{6}} - 10x^{\frac{4}{5}}$

5 a) $\frac{3}{2}x^2 - \frac{1}{3}x^3$ **b)** $\frac{1}{4}x^4 + \frac{5}{3}x^3$ **c)** $\frac{1}{4}x^4 - \frac{5}{6}x^6$ **d)** $\frac{2}{5}\sqrt{x^5} + 2\sqrt{x^3}$ **e)** $\frac{6}{7}\sqrt{x^7} - \frac{6}{5}\sqrt{x^5} + 2\sqrt{x^3}$ **f)** $\frac{6}{7}x^{\frac{7}{3}} + \frac{9}{4}x^{\frac{4}{3}}$ **g)** $\frac{2}{3}x^3 + 10x^2 + 50x$

5 h) $\frac{1}{4}x^4 - \frac{2}{3}x^3 + \frac{1}{2}x^2$ **i)** $\frac{1}{2}x^2 + \frac{4}{3}\sqrt{x^3} - 15x$ **j)** $\frac{4}{3}x^{\frac{9}{4}} - \frac{24}{5}x^{\frac{5}{4}}$ **6 a)** $\frac{5}{3}x^3 - 5x^2$ **b)** $x^6 - \frac{1}{4}x^4$ **c)** $\frac{2}{7}\sqrt{x^7} + \frac{2}{3}\sqrt{x^3}$ **d)** $\frac{6}{5}x^{\frac{5}{3}} + \frac{9}{2}x^{\frac{2}{3}}$

6 e) $x - \dfrac{5}{x}$ **f)** $-\dfrac{1}{x} + \dfrac{2}{x^2}$ **g)** $3x - \dfrac{5}{x}$ **h)** $\frac{2}{3}x^3 - \frac{3}{4}x^2$ **i)** $2\sqrt{x^5} - 8\sqrt{x}$ **j)** $\frac{1}{5}x^5 - \frac{20}{9}x^{\frac{9}{2}} + \frac{25}{4}x^4$ **7 a)** $\dfrac{a}{2}x^2 + bx$ **b)** $\frac{2}{3}a\sqrt{x^3} + 2b\sqrt{x}$

7 c) $\frac{1}{3}acx^3 + \frac{1}{2}(ad + bc)x^2 + bdx$ **9 a)** $y = x^3 + x + 2$ **b)** $y = 2x^2 - 3x + 1$ **c)** $y = 2x^3 - 2x^2 - 12$ **d)** $y = 16 + 4x - 3x^2$

9 e) $y = 8 - \dfrac{2}{x} - x$ **f)** $y = \dfrac{5}{x^2} - 7$ **g)** $y = \frac{2}{3}\sqrt{x^3} - 5x + 9$ **h)** $y = \frac{1}{2}x^2 - \frac{1}{3}\sqrt{x^3} - \frac{14}{3}$

10 $y = -\dfrac{5}{x} - 11$ **11** $f(x) = 2\sqrt{x^3} - 5x + 7$ **12** $f(x) = 2\sqrt{x^3} - 5x + 7$ **13** $y = x^3 - 2x^2 + 5x + 1$ **14** $y = x^3 - 2x + \dfrac{2}{x}$

Exercise 11B

1 b) 18 c) 36   **2** b) $\frac{32}{3}$ c) $\frac{16}{3}$ **3** $\frac{16}{3}$ **4** $\frac{9}{2}$ **5** b) $\frac{4}{3}$ **6** b) 9   **7** b) $\frac{8}{3}$ c) $\frac{5}{12}$ **8** b) $15\frac{3}{4}$ c) $\frac{16}{3}$

9 a) $P(1,4), Q(2,7)$ c) $\frac{1}{6}$ **10** a) $A(-2,11), B(3,6)$ c) $20\frac{5}{6}$ **11** a) $C(2,20), D(4,32)$ c) $\frac{8}{3}$

12 a) $\left(-\frac{1}{2}, 2\frac{3}{4}\right), (3,-6)$ b) $14\frac{7}{24}$ **13** a) $(0,0), (9,3)$ b) $\frac{9}{2}$ **14** 32   **15** $21\frac{1}{3}$ **16** 12   **17** 36

18 a) $P(2,0), Q(4,8)$ b) $10\frac{2}{3}$ **19** a) $A(3,0), B(6,-18)$ b) 36   **20** a) $P(-1,0), Q(1,0), R(2,3)$ b) $\frac{9}{2}$

Exercise 11C

1 80   **2** 150   **3** 360   **4** 320   **5** b) 2.829   **6** b) 1.896   **7** a) 608   b) 584 c) second is better

8 a)

x	1	2	3	4	5
$\sqrt{1+x^2}$	1.414	2.236	3.162	4.123	5.099

c) 12.8

9 2.99   **10** 0.809   **11** 5.869   **12** 0.682

Check out

1 a) $2x^{\frac{3}{2}} + c$ b) 14   **2** a) $-\frac{1}{x} + \frac{1}{2}x^2 - x + c$ b) $2\frac{2}{3}$ **3** 0.123 (below x-axis)   **4** a) 2.23 (3 s.f.) b) 0.987 (3 s.f.)

Revision exercise 11

1 a) i) $\frac{2}{5}x^{\frac{5}{2}} + c$ ii) 12.8 b) 3.2   **2** a) $x^3 + \frac{1}{x^2}$ b) $4\frac{1}{4}$ **3** a) $x^{\frac{5}{2}}$ b) $y = 2x^{\frac{7}{2}} - 1$ **4** 39

5 a) $\frac{32\pi}{7}$ b) 26.871 ... c) $\sim 0.2\%$ **6** a) $4\frac{1}{4}$ b) $\frac{1}{3}x^3 + \frac{1}{x} + c$ **7** a) $\frac{2}{3}x^{\frac{3}{2}} + c$ b) $\frac{4}{3}\sqrt{2}$

8 a) i) $\frac{1}{2x^2}$ ii) $\frac{1}{4}$ b) i) $\frac{40}{3}$ **9** a) i) $x^3 - \frac{64}{x^3}$ ii) -63 iii) $x^6 = 64$ iv) $x = 2, -2$ b) i) 17.55

10 a) i) $2 - \frac{54}{x^3}$ ii) $x = 3$ b) i) 9.5   **11** $f'(x) = \frac{3}{x^2}$ **13** a) $P(-\sqrt{3},8), Q(+\sqrt{3}, 8)$ b) ii) $(-3,4), (-1,4), (1,4), (3,4)$

C2 Practice Paper

1 b) $20\,m^2$ **2** a) $1 + 5x + 10x^2 + 10x^3 + 5x^4 + x^5$ b) 1080   **3** a) $117.3°$ b) $5.3\,cm^2$ **4** a) $9.2°, 99.2°$

4 b) ii) $0.841, 5.44, 3.14$ **5** a) period is π b) stretch, scale factor $\frac{1}{2}$, parallel to Ox

6 a) $3\left(\frac{2}{3}\right)^{n-1}$ b) 9 c) 23   **7** a) 18.507 b) 18.432

7 c) Between $x = 2$ and $x = 4$ the curvature is concave so each trapezium is bigger than the actual area.

8 a) i) 3 ii) $-\frac{3}{2}$ b) 16 c) $x = \frac{5}{3}$ or 1.67   **9** a) $x^{\frac{4}{3}}$ b) i) $-\frac{1}{x^2} - \frac{4}{3}\sqrt[3]{x}$ or $-x^{-2} - \frac{4}{3}x^{\frac{1}{3}}$ c) -0.884 d) max

GCSE algebra review
Exercise A

1 a) 6 b) 7 c) -2 d) 5 e) 2 f) $\frac{11}{2}$ g) 3 h) -2 i) $\frac{13}{4}$ j) $-\frac{1}{10}$ k) -3 l) $-\frac{1}{3}$ **2** a) 2 b) $-\frac{4}{15}$ c) 2 d) $\frac{29}{11}$

2 e) $-\frac{3}{4}$ f) $-\frac{27}{2}$ g) -1 h) $\frac{14}{9}$ i) $\frac{5}{2}$ j) 11 k) $\frac{17}{2}$ l) 0   **3** a) 7 b) 3 c) $\frac{5}{13}$ d) $-\frac{11}{9}$

Exercise B

1 a) -4 b) $\frac{31}{11}$ c) $\frac{16}{13}$ d) $-\frac{17}{4}$ e) $-\frac{1}{2}$ f) $\frac{17}{2}$ g) $\frac{21}{2}$ h) $\frac{49}{6}$ **2** a) 4 b) $-\frac{7}{2}$ c) $\frac{16}{7}$ d) -2 e) 27 f) $-\frac{15}{13}$ g) $\frac{7}{2}$ h) $\frac{52}{41}$

2 i) $\frac{13}{4}$ j) $\frac{31}{6}$ k) -2 l) 1   **3** a) $-\frac{1}{2}$ b) -2 c) $-\frac{15}{8}$ d) $-\frac{11}{18}$ e) $\frac{13}{9}$ f) $\frac{1}{2}$ g) $-\frac{1}{4}$ h) $\frac{7}{9}$ i) $\frac{2}{5}$ j) $\frac{5}{4}$ k) $-\frac{7}{2}$ l) $\frac{14}{13}$

Exercise C

1 a), c), d) and f)

Exercise D

1 a) $x > 4$ b) $x \geqslant -4$ c) $x \geqslant \frac{11}{2}$ d) $x > \frac{15}{4}$ e) $x < 5$ f) $x \geqslant \frac{2}{5}$ **2** a) $x > 2$ b) $x \leqslant -\frac{6}{7}$ c) $x \geqslant \frac{5}{3}$ d) $x < \frac{5}{8}$ e) $x > -2$

2 f) $x \leqslant \frac{7}{2}$ **3** a) $x < 4$ b) $x < 2$ c) $x > 9$ d) $x \leqslant 0$ e) $x > \frac{19}{9}$ f) $x \geqslant -1$ g) $x < -\frac{9}{13}$ h) $x > -\frac{2}{9}$ i) $x < -\frac{4}{3}$ j) $x \geqslant -\frac{28}{5}$

3 k) $x < 17$ l) $x \geqslant -18$ **4** a) $x < 10$ b) $x \leqslant 7$ c) $x \leqslant -19$ d) $x > -\frac{19}{9}$ e) $x > \frac{6}{5}$ f) $x \leqslant 8$

Exercise E

1 a) $(2, -1)$ b) $(1, 2)$ c) $(4, 1)$ d) $(-1, -2)$ e) $(3, -4)$ f) $(3, -1)$ g) $(2, -1)$ h) $(3, 2)$ i) $(-3, 2)$ j) $(1, -1)$

1 k) $(7, 6)$ l) $\left(2, -\frac{3}{2}\right)$ **2** a) $(4, 2)$ b) $(3, 4)$ c) $(2, 3)$ d) $(-2, -1)$ e) $\left(\frac{1}{2}, -\frac{3}{2}\right)$ f) $(3, 2)$ g) $\left(\frac{1}{3}, -\frac{2}{3}\right)$ h) $\left(\frac{1}{2}, \frac{1}{4}\right)$

2 i) $\left(\frac{3}{4}, -\frac{5}{4}\right)$ j) $(2, 0)$ k) $\left(\frac{10}{3}, 1\right)$ l) $\left(\frac{3}{2}, -\frac{1}{3}\right)$ **3** a) $(2, 5)$ b) $(6, 2)$ c) $(-1, 7)$ d) $(-2, 6)$ e) $(-1, -4)$ f) $(6, 2)$

3 g) $(0, 2)$ h) $(-2, 4)$ i) $(-2, 3)$

Formulae

This section lists formulae which relate to the Core modules C1 and C2, and which candidates are expected to remember. These formulae will **not** be included in the AQA formulae book.

Quadratic equations

$ax^2 + bx + c = 0$ has roots $\dfrac{-b \pm \sqrt{b^2 - 4ac}}{2a}$

Circles

A circle, centre (a, b) and radius r, has equation $(x - a)^2 + (y - b)^2 = r^2$

Trigonometry

In the triangle ABC

$\dfrac{a}{\sin A} = \dfrac{b}{\sin B} = \dfrac{c}{\sin C}$

area $= \frac{1}{2}ab \sin C$

arc length of a circle, $l = r\theta$

area of a sector of a circle, $A = \frac{1}{2}r^2\theta$

$\tan \theta = \dfrac{\sin \theta}{\cos \theta}$

$\sin^2 \theta + \cos^2 \theta = 1$

Laws of logarithms

$\log_a x + \log_a y = \log_a (xy)$

$\log_a x + \log_a y = \log_a \left(\dfrac{x}{y}\right)$

$k \log_a x = \log_a (x^k)$

Differentiation

function	derivative
ax^n	nax^{n-1}, n is a rational number
$f(x) + g(x)$	$f'(x) + g'(x)$

Integration

function	integral
ax^n	$\dfrac{a}{n+1}x^{n+1} + c$, n is a rational number, $n \neq -1$
$f'(x) + g'(x)$	$f(x) + g(x)$

Area

Area under a curve $= \displaystyle\int_a^b y \, dx, y \geqslant 0$

Mathematical Notation

Set notation

$\in$	is an element of
$\notin$	is not an element of
$\{x_1, x_2, \ldots\}$	the set with elements $x_1, x_2, \ldots$
$\{x: \ldots\}$	the set of all x such that …
$n(A)$	the number of elements in set A
$\mathbb{N}$	the set of natural numbers, $\{1, 2, 3, \ldots\}$
$\mathbb{Z}$	the set of integers, $\{0, \pm 1, \pm 2, \pm 3, \ldots\}$
$\mathbb{Z}^+$	the set of positive integers, $\{1, 2, 3, \ldots\}$
$\mathbb{Q}$	the set of rational numbers, $\left\{\dfrac{p}{q}: p \in \mathbb{Z}, q \in \mathbb{Z}^+\right\}$
$\mathbb{Q}^+$	the set of positive rational numbers, $\{x \in \mathbb{Q}, x > 0\}$
$\mathbb{R}$	the set of real numbers
$\mathbb{R}^+$	the set of positive real numbers, $\{x \in \mathbb{R}, x > 0\}$
(x, y)	the ordered pair, x, y

Miscellaneous symbols

$=$	is equal to
$\neq$	is not equal to
$\equiv$	is identical to or is congruent to
$\approx$	is approximately equal to
$\propto$	is proportional to
$<$	is less than
$\leqslant, \not>$	is less than or equal to, is not greater than
$>$	is greater than
$\geqslant, \not<$	is greater than or equal to, is not less than
∞	infinity
$p \Rightarrow q$	p implies q (if p then q)
$p \Leftarrow q$	p is implied by q (if q then p)
$p \Leftrightarrow q$	p implies and is implied by q (p is equivalent to q)
$\exists$	there exists
$\forall$	for all

Operations

$a + b$	a plus b
$a - b$	a minus b
$a \times b, ab, a.b$	a multiplied by b
$a \div b, \dfrac{a}{b}, a/b$	a divided by b
$\displaystyle\sum_{i=1}^{n} a_i$	$a_1 + a_2 + \ldots + a_n$
$\sqrt{a}$	the positive square root of a

$n!$	n factorial
$\dbinom{n}{r}$	the binomial coefficient $\dfrac{n!}{r!(n-r)!}$ for $n \in \mathbb{Z}^+$

Functions

$f(x)$	the value of the function f at x
$f: A \rightarrow B$	f is a function under which each element of set A has an image in set B
$f: x \rightarrow y$	the function f maps the element x to the element y
f^{-1}	the inverse function of the function f
$\displaystyle\lim_{x \to a} f(x)$	the limit of $f(x)$ as x tends to a
$\dfrac{dy}{dx}$	the derivative of y with respect to x
$\dfrac{d^n y}{dx^n}$	the nth derivative of y with respect to x
$f'(x), f''(x), ..., f^{(n)}(x)$	first, second, ..., nth derivatives of $f(x)$ with respect to x
$\displaystyle\int y \, dx$	the indefinite integral of y with respect to x
$\displaystyle\int_a^b y \, dx$	the definite integral of y with respect to x between the limits $x = a$ and $x = b$

Exponential and logarithmic functions

e	base of natural logarithms
$e^x, \exp x$	exponential function of x
$\log_a x$	logarithm to the base a of x
$\ln x, \log_e x$	natural logarithm of x
$\log_{10} x$	logarithm of x to base 10

Circular functions

$\left.\begin{array}{l}\sin, \cos, \tan, \\ \operatorname{cosec}, \sec, \cot\end{array}\right\}$	the circular functions
$\left.\begin{array}{l}\sin^{-1}, \cos^{-1}, \tan^{-1}, \\ \operatorname{cosec}^{-1}, \sec^{-1}, \cot^{-1}\end{array}\right\}$	the inverse circular functions

Index

acute-angled triangles, 179, 183
addition, polynomials, 34
adjacent sides, 178
algebra, 1–32
    reviews, 278–90
algebraic division, 44–5
ambiguous case, 181
angles
    measures, 190
    multiple, 209–10
    in semi-circles, 74
area
    between curves, 264
    triangles, 108–9, 187–9
    under curves, 123–7, 262–7
arithmetic progressions (APs), 155–60
    general formula, 158–9
arithmetic series, 157
asymptotes, 196
axes, coordinate, 58
ax^n, integrating, 256–61

balancing the coefficients, 288
bases, 225
bearings, 186–7
binomial expansions, 169–74
brackets, expanding, 3

calculus, 92
    see also differentiation; integration
cartesian coordinates, 68
chords, 75
circles
    equation of, 51, 72–4
    intersections, 80–2
    normals to, 77–9
    properties, 74–6
    tangents, 77–9, 80
    translations, 51
coefficients, balancing, 288
common difference, 155
common ratio, 160
completing the square, 14–19
constant of integration, 118
constants, differentiating, 93
converging sequences, 149–51
coordinate axes, 58
coordinate geometry, 56–86
cosine functions, 195–200
    properties, 195
cosine ratios, 178, 200–3
cosine rule, 183–5
cross-multiplication, 279
cubics, 34
curves
    area between, 264
    area under, 123–7, 262–7
    gradients, 88–94, 240
    normals to, 100–3, 240–6

    sketching, 198–200
    tangents, 88–9, 100–3, 240–6
    translations, 48–52
cylinders, volume, 109

definite integrals, 122–3, 262
degrees, 190
denominators, rationalising, 3
derivatives
    first, 91
    general expression, 92–3
    notation, 92
    second, 106, 246–7
derived expressions, 91
Descartes, René (1596–1650), 68
difference of two squares, 10
differentiation, 87–116, 235–55
    constants, 93
    distance–time graphs, 97–8
    linear functions, 93
    polynomials, 95–7
    reversing, 118–21
    see also derivatives
discriminant, 21
distance, between two points, 58–61
distance–time graphs, differentiating, 97–8
division, algebraic, 44–5

elimination, 288–9
equation solving, logarithms, 229–30
equations
    linear, 278–82
    trigonometric, 203–12
    see also quadratic equations; simultaneous equations
equivalent fractions, 3
expansions, binomial, 169–74
exponential functions, 138
    graphs, 230–1

factor theorem, 36–9, 41
factorials, 170
factorising, quadratic functions, 9–12, 96
factors, 39
    quadratic, 9–14
    scale, 140
first derivatives, 91
fractional indices, 221–4
fractions
    equivalent, 3
    rationalising, 4
functions
    decreasing, 111–13, 253–4
    difference, 236–9
    exponential, 138, 230–1
    graphs of, 46–8
    increasing, 111–13, 253–4
    reflections, 139–40
    stretches, 140–4
    sum, 236–9
    transformations, 134–47
    translations, 135–8
    trigonometric, 195–200
    see also linear functions; quadratic functions